W12 £3.50

AHDB LIBRARY
☎ 02476 478839
BARCODE 4326   PO N ✓
PRICE: £ ✓   DATE: ✓
CLASS.NO. 613.2 mcc.

MEDICAL RESEARCH COUNCIL

Special Report Series No. 297

(Third revised edition of Special Report No. 235)

The Composition
of Foods

R. A. McCANCE and E. M. WIDDOWSON

LONDON: HER MAJESTY'S STATIONERY OFFICE 1960

© *Crown copyright* 1960

HER MAJESTY'S STATIONERY OFFICE

Goverment Bookshops

49 High Holborn, London WC1V 6HB
13a Castle Street, Edinburgh EH2 3AR
41 The Hayes, Cardiff CF1 1JW
Brazennose Street, Manchester M60 8AS
Wine Street, Bristol BS1 2BQ
258 Broad Street, Birmingham B1 2HE
80 Chichester Street, Belfast BT1 4JY

Government publications are also available through booksellers

First published 1960
Third impression 1973

ISBN 0 11 450005 3 *

Universal Decimal Classification
613.2.543

Printed in England for Her Majesty's Stationery Office
by UDO (Litho) Ltd., London.

Preface

The nutritional and dietetic treatment of disease, as well as research into problems of human nutrition, demands an exact knowledge of the chemical composition of food. Research in this field was first supported by the Council in 1925, when Professor McCance was awarded a grant for a study, in the first instance, of the amount of carbohydrate in foods used in the treatment of diabetes. It was recognized at the time that the project was likely to have wide practical applications, and the Council have continued to support similar and related studies by Professor McCance and his colleagues, first at King's College Hospital and subsequently at the Department of Experimental Medicine, University of Cambridge.

These investigators have gradually extended the scope of their studies. By 1939, when the first edition of the tables was published, they had evolved a system of analysis by which they could determine all the important organic and mineral constituents of foods with the exception of the vitamins, and had applied it to most of the foods commonly eaten in Great Britain. The method of approach had been somewhat different from that of previous workers in the same field, for the foods had been analysed not only in the raw state but also as prepared for the table. In 1946 a second edition was published which included figures for a number of foods and food materials which were characteristic of the nation's war-time and post-war diet. Since then many new foods have become available, and many of those used in war-time have disappeared from the market; and in the third edition now published more than a hundred new foods have been added to the tables, a number have been excluded, and the figures for many proprietary foods have been adjusted in accordance with changes in manufacturers' formulae.

While the revision of these tables is an essential part of the new edition, an additional feature is the inclusion of two new sets of tables giving the vitamin and amino-acid contents of foods. The authors have not themselves assayed the vitamins, since these have been the subject of intensive research by other workers. It was felt, however, that at the present time a new edition would be incomplete without the addition of tables for the vitamins. Accordingly, a comprehensive review of the literature since 1939 was undertaken, and the values published by different authors were carefully considered and compared. Those that were judged to be the most representative of British foods were used as a basis to arrive at figures which were then submitted for comment to experts in the various vitamin fields.

The study of the amino-acids in foods is comparatively new. Most of the relevant literature has been published during the last ten years, and the Council's work on this subject dates from 1955. In compiling the tables for amino-acids the authors have used values given in the literature as well as the results of their own analyses, and from these sources have been able to arrive at figures for all the main protein foods—cereals, meat, fish, eggs, and milk and its products, and for a limited number of nuts and vegetables.

There has been a steady demand for the 1st and 2nd editions of the report over the last twenty years, and it is hoped that this revised and enlarged edition will meet the widening requirements of those concerned with diet and nutrition in the prevention and treatment of disease.

MEDICAL RESEARCH COUNCIL
38 Old Queen Street
Westminster
London S.W.1*

1 June 1960

---

*Present address: 20 Park Crescent, London WIN 4AL

Acknowledgments

A. W. Haynes took an active part in the practical work involved in the preparation of the tables of Part I as they originally appeared 20 years ago; more recently, Miss Janet Adams has helped in the analyses of the foods whose composition is now appearing for the first time. We have very much enjoyed their cheerful and efficient co-operation, and we take this opportunity of thanking them for all they have done.

The late Dr. W. I. M. Holman was largely responsible for reading and abstracting the literature on the vitamins in foods. This was a great task, and his experience in the field and critical appraisal of the literature have made the tables far more valuable than they would otherwise have been.

Miss E. M. Hume, Miss M. Olliver, Dr. S. K. Kon, Dr. T. Moran, Dr. J. A. Lovern and Dr. F. Wokes have spent much time checking over the values submitted to them for the vitamins in foods. We are grateful to them all, and are the more confident of our figures because we have had the benefit of their advice.

The British Baking Industries Research Association organised the collection and preliminary drying of the loaves of bread that were analysed for the present edition, and Dr. T. Moran kindly arranged for the determinations of thiamine and nicotinic acid to be made on them.

Many other people have helped over different aspects of the study, and to each and all of them we tender our sincere thanks.

Contents

CONTENTS—*continued*

General introduction

A knowledge of the chemical composition of foods is the first essential in the dietary treatment of disease or in most quantitative studies of human nutrition. This was becoming increasingly apparent thirty years ago, and there was in consequence a demand for better and more up-to-date information about the chemistry of food. In order to provide investigators, particularly in Great Britain, with the necessary data, analytical work was carried out between 1925 and 1939, first at King's College Hospital, London, and later at the Department of Experimental Medicine, Cambridge, and the first edition of these tables represented an attempt to set out the results in a simple and practical manner. Most of the data had already been published (McCance and Shipp, 1933; Widdowson and McCance, 1935; McCance and Widdowson, 1935; McCance, Widdowson and Shackleton, 1936; Masters and McCance, 1939), but some were published for the first time.

With the advent of war some of the foods in the tables were no longer available, whereas others came on the market, and in 1946 a second edition of the tables was published, designed to include the more important war-time foods.

In the early 1950's the time seemed to have come for work to start on the preparation of a third edition. Many new proprietary foods, e.g. cereal preparations, soft drinks, and canned soups, were being extensively sold, for which no analytical figures were available, and sweets and alcoholic beverages had never been satisfactorily represented in the tables. About one hundred new foods have now been analysed for water, nitrogen, fat, carbohydrates and minerals by methods similar to those used for the earlier editions, and these are included in Part I of the present edition. All the figures for proprietary foods have been submitted to the manufacturers, and where differences of opinion have arisen the determinations have been repeated on new samples. Further, all the figures for proprietary foods published in the earlier editions have also been submitted to the firms concerned, and where the formula has been changed analyses have been made on the present-day product. The section on the chemical composition of cooked dishes has been revised and brought up-to-date.

The first and second editions of these tables contained no figures for vitamins or amino-acids. Methods for the determinations of the various vitamins and amino-acids in foods have been greatly improved since the tables were first published, and many analyses have been made in various parts of the world. This has made it possible to construct tables showing the amounts of these constituents in foodstuffs.

Part II shows the amounts of vitamin A, carotene, vitamin D, thiamine, riboflavine, nicotinic acid and ascorbic acid in 100 grams of many of the foods included in Part I, and also the amounts of pantothenic acid, vitamin B_6, biotin, folic acid, vitamin B_{12} and total tocopherols in a smaller number of foods.

1

These values are drawn almost entirely from the literature, and in all about a thousand publications have been consulted.

Part III gives figures for amino-acids in foods expressed in terms of the total nitrogen. This method of expression has been used since it simplifies and shortens the tables; for example, two sets of figures only are necessary for meat instead of the many that would have been required had the amino-acids been expressed per 100 grams of food. The values for amino-acids have been taken partly from the literature and partly from the results of original work by the author.

Details of how the figures for vitamins and amino-acids were selected are given in the introductions to Parts II and III (pp. 181, 247). For most of them a considerable number of sources from the literature were consulted. The references to both parts have been numbered, and for each part a key has been compiled which gives, by number, the references taken into consideration for each vitamin or amino-acid in every food. Copies of this key have been deposited in the library at the National Institute for Medical Research, Mill Hill, London, N.W.7, and are available on request.

Part 1
Calorific constituents, water and minerals

R. A. MCCANCE, E. M. WIDDOWSON AND D. A. T. SOUTHGATE

Introduction

The tables in this part of the report give details of the chemical composition of individual foods, both raw and cooked, and of cooked dishes made from a mixture of ingredients. The figures for individual foods were obtained by direct analysis; those for most of the cooked dishes were obtained by computation from the figures for the individual ingredients. The preparation of the cooked dishes, and the procedure followed for the computation of their composition are described on p. 7. Standard recipes were used for these dishes, and are given on pp. 8–19.

ARRANGEMENT OF THE TABLES

The tables are divided into two main sections. The first (p. 22) gives the composition of each food per 100 grams (or per 100 millilitres in the case of beverages): the second (p. 128) gives the composition per ounce. Each food is numbered and can be found under the same number in both sections and, in the case of cooked dishes, among the recipes.

Within the sections the foods have been classified into the following groups: Cereals and cereal foods; milk products and eggs; fats and oils; meat, poultry and game; fish; fruit; nuts; vegetables; sugar, preserves and sweetmeats; beverages; alcoholic beverages; condiments; cakes and pastries; puddings; meat and fish dishes; egg and cheese dishes; sauces and soups. The classification is practical rather than scientific; thus the cereal group includes starchy foods such as arrowroot, sago, tapioca, and soya products; the vegetable group includes tomatoes; and the fruit group includes rhubarb. Bovril, Oxo, Marmite, and Virol have been included in the beverage group. The majority of the cooked dishes are included in the last five groups, but there are a few in the earlier groups. Any classification must necessarily be arbitrary to some extent, and for this reason a full index is given.

Only edible material has been analysed, and the per 100 g. and per oz. composition of every item is calculated for this alone. For foods that are usually served with waste, for example fish and stone fruits, figures have also been given for the amounts of the various edible constituents that would have been obtained from 100 grams and from 1 ounce of the food as served.

In both sections of the tables the composition of each food is given in terms of protein, fat, carbohydrate, and minerals; the calorie value is also given. The tables of the first section contain additional information which is not repeated in the second section. This information includes a description of each food,

3

particulars of the method of cooking, and the nature of the edible material. For many foods particulars are given of the number of samples pooled for analysis and of their sources; for meat, fish, fruit, nuts and vegetables these details may be found in McCance and Shipp (1933), and McCance, Widdowson and Shackleton (1936). The edible matter, as eaten, is expressed as a percentage of the weight as purchased. For foods that were analysed raw and would be eaten raw the tables show the percentage of edible material in the purchased food; for foods that were analysed cooked this percentage figure allows for change of weight on cooking. The figure is usually less than 100 because for most foods there is either waste material or loss of weight on cooking. For a few cooked foods, however, for example fish fried with batter and crumbs, cooked dried pulses, and stewed fruit, the figure is greater than 100 because the added batter and crumbs, or the water taken up, outweigh the waste, if any, or the weight lost on cooking.

The tables in the first section also give figures for water; these were found by direct determination in all the analysed foods except meat and fish, where the values were obtained by difference. The available carbohydrate has been determined directly and has been differentiated into starch and sugar, the starch always being expressed as glucose. For fruits and vegetables figures for the unavailable carbohydrate are also given; these were determined as described by McCance, Widdowson, and Shackleton (1936). Figures for total nitrogen are given throughout the section, and figures for purine nitrogen are given for meat and fish.

Throughout the tables the dash (—) signifies that no estimation has been made. *Tr.* indicates that traces of the constituent in question are known to be present; an estimation may or may not have been carried out, but in any case the amount is of no quantitative dietetic significance.

NOTES ON THE DETERMINATION OF CONSTITUENTS

Protein

In the case of meat, fish, and mushrooms, Bovril, Oxo, Marmite and Nescafé protein nitrogen has been differentiated from non-protein nitrogen and the former multiplied by 6·25. In cereals the protein has been calculated by multiplying the total nitrogen by 5·7 and in milk products by 6·38. For jelly the factor 5·55 has been used, and for all other foods 6·25.

Fat

For meat and fish the figures are for true fat as determined by von Lieberman and Szekely's (1898) method. The fat in milk and milk products and in comb honey has been determined by methods similar to those recommended by the Association of Official Agricultural Chemists (1930). The fats in other foods have sometimes been determined by ether extraction in a Soxhlet apparatus, sometimes by von Lieberman's method, and often by both (see p. 5).

Available Carbohydrate

This is the sum of the starch, dextrins, and sugar, all expressed as monosaccharides. A special note has been inserted drawing attention to this fact where cane sugar and lactose are being considered.

Calculation of Calorific Values

The conversion factors used to calculate the calorific values of protein, fat, available carbohydrate (expressed as monosaccharides), and alcohol respectively were 4·1, 9·3, 3·75, and 7·0. These are the factors used in the previous edition. Since the whole question of the best factors to use is now under discussion, a brief account of the problem is given on p. 171, where the authors show why they have decided not to change the factors in this new edition.

Minerals

Some of the figures for sodium (Na), chlorine (Cl), calcium (Ca), phosphorus (P), and iron (Fe) are given in brackets. This has been done where salt or sodium bicarbonate is known to have been added in the preparation of the food, where a flour is known to have been enriched with calcium and iron, or where acid calcium phosphate has been used as a raising agent. In these instances a proportion of these particular minerals represents the work of man and not the gift of nature; the figures must be interpreted accordingly. All vegetables have been cooked in distilled water without added salt or alkali. The figures for potassium (K), and magnesium (Mg), require no comment. Copper (Cu) had not been determined in all the forms of meat and fish given in the tables. Since the nitrogen/sulphur ratio in meat and fish has been found to be very constant (Masters and McCance, 1939) the sulphur in most of these foods of animal origin has been calculated from the nitrogen found in the original mixed sample and an average nitrogen/sulphur ratio. For dietetic purposes this was deemed justifiable. For all other foods direct determinations of sulphur were made.

Acid-Base Values

The figures are expressed as milliequivalents, and have been calculated in the usual way. Sulphur and phosphorus have been taken to be divalent. No allowance has been made for the fact that certain fruits give rise to an excretion of hippuric acid (Sherman, 1937).

Phytic Acid Phosphorus

The phytic acid phosphorus in a number of foodstuffs is given on p. 170. It is expressed as a percentage of the total amount of phosphorus present. The importance of phytic acid is twofold. First, its calcium and magnesium salts are very insoluble, and if the food contains much phytic acid these insoluble salts may be precipitated in the stomach and duodenum, thus preventing the absorption and utilisation of the greater part of the calcium in the food. Secondly, the stability of phytates to intestinal disintegration prevents the phosphorus in them from being absorbed as freely as the phosphorus in other organic and inorganic compounds (McCance and Widdowson, 1935, 1942).

NOTES ON TECHNIQUE AND SOME INDIVIDUAL FINDINGS

The Soxhlet method of determining fat in malted foods gives results which are much too low, and certainly incorrect. It also gives much lower results than von Lieberman's (1898) method for many cereals. In all such instances the higher figures have been preferred. On the other hand, the Soxhlet method gives much higher results than von Lieberman's method for condiments containing volatile oils (see p. 113) Some representative figures for cereals and malted foods are given below.

Food	Fat (g/100g)		Food	Fat (g/100g)	
	By Soxhlet method	By von Lieberman's method		By Soxhlet method	By von Lieberman's method
All-Bran, Kellogg's	1·0	4·5	Grapenuts	0·4	3·0
Biscuits, digestive	13·3	20·5	Horlick's malted milk	1·2	8·6
Biscuits, rusks ..	5·0	8·4	Ryvita ..	0·5	2·1
Cornflakes, Kellogg's	0·1	0·8	Shredded Wheat	0·9	2·8
Flour, white ..	0·5	0·9	Vita-Weat ..	6·0	10·3
Flour, brown ..	0·6	2·1			

The variation in the amounts of the elements present in different foodstuffs is enormous. The lowest concentrations are often outside the range of the analytical methods. The highest are often so remarkable that it is difficult not to comment upon them. Some of the meat and vegetable extracts are very rich in sodium chloride—even up to 25 per cent. Nescafé contains more potassium than any other food analysed (5·46 per cent.). Parmesan cheese has the highest concentration of calcium (1·22 per cent.) and Marmite of phosphorus (1·89 per cent.). Carrageen moss heads the list for magnesium (0·63 per cent.) and sulphur (5·46 per cent.). Curry powder contains more than three times as much iron as any other food (75 mg. per 100g.), while liver has the highest quantity of copper (5·8 mg. per 100g.). Of all the foods analysed, low fat soya flour contains most nitrogen (7·9 per cent., corresponding to 49·6 per cent. of protein).

A few notes on individual findings given in the tables are set out below. All have been confirmed by the analysis of at least two and generally three mixed samples:

1. The sodium and chlorine in processed cheese and cheese spread are not present in the proportion usually found in cheese.

2. Fried fish tends to contain more calcium than steamed fish. This is because it is more difficult to separate the bones in the case of the fried fish, so that some small bones were almost inevitably included in the analysed (edible) material.

3. The unusually high figure for sulphur in dried apricots and dried peaches is probably to be attributed to the use of sulphur dioxide as a preservative (Leach and Winton, 1920; Monier-Williams, 1927).

4. The amount of iron in glacé cherries is much higher than would be expected from the analysis of the raw fruit. It is suggested that this is due to iron contamination during stoning.

5. Golden syrup contains 7 times as much sodium as chloride: in black treacle the ratio is reversed.

6. The amount of calcium in fruit gums (359 mg. per 100 g.) is very high; it is derived from the jelling agent, which is a calcium salt.

The chemical composition of cooked dishes containing several ingredients, and the recipes used

C.M. VERDON-ROE

REVISED BY M. W. GARDINER AND A. M. DENNY

Dietary investigations by the individual method depend upon a knowledge of the composition of cooked foods, and there has been a demand not only for the composition of individual foods but also for that of cakes, puddings, etc., made from a mixture of ingredients. For this reason a number of cooked dishes have been included in the tables. These dishes were made according to standard recipes, which are given below. As already stated, the numbering of the recipes corresponds to the numbering of the dishes in the tables.

Since pooled samples of all the ingredients used had already been analysed, to calculate an average composition for each dish the only additional information required was the loss or gain of water (and in some cases fat) occasioned by the cooking process. This was determined by weighing the mixed ingredients before they were cooked and again when they were ready for consumption. The composition of the cooked dish was then calculated from the composition of the ingredients and the change in weight on cooking. For dishes that are usually eaten hot the computations were made on the basis of their weight when hot; for cold dishes the computations were made on the basis of the weight when cold. All the foods were cooked on at least two separate occasions, and the figures are the average of the results.

Any loss in weight was assumed to be due to evaporation of water, and a gain in weight was assumed to be due to absorption of water except in cases where frying was used in the preparation of the food; in such cases it was necessary to analyse the cooked material for fat and for water before making the calculations. Computation is too inaccurate a method to apply to soups and sauces that are strained before eating, since this removes some of the solid ingredients; these dishes were therefore analysed after they had been prepared for the table. In making cakes and some other dishes it was impossible to avoid leaving some of the raw material in the mixing bowl or on the utensils. In all such cases a correction was applied to allow for the loss of material in this way.

Where flour was an ingredient, plain flour was always used, so that it was necessary to use a baking powder for cakes and for some puddings. This was a proprietary preparation consisting of sodium bicarbonate, acid calcium phosphate, acid sodium pyrophosphate, and flour; its composition is given on p. 112. One level teaspoonful of the powder was taken to weigh $3\frac{1}{2}$ grams.

Salt was added to all the savoury dishes; one level teaspoonful of salt was taken to weigh 5 grams.

All fruits were stewed in a minimum of water and without sugar. The composition of stewed fruits was calculated from the composition of the raw fruit and the ratio of cooked weight to raw weight. This ratio was found by experiment to be:—raspberries, 1·05 : 1; dried figs and prunes, 2 : 1; dried apricots and peaches, 3 : 1; and all other fruits, 1·3 : 1. The cooked weight included, of course, the weight of the added water.

RECIPES

Preserves and Sweetmeats

476. CHUTNEY, APPLE
  16 oz. cooking apples, peeled and cored   ½ teaspoon mustard
  15 oz. onions, peeled   ¼ teaspoon pepper
  3½ oz. raisins   ½ teaspoon ground ginger
  ¾ pint vinegar   2 teaspoons curry powder
  1 lb. sugar   1 teaspoon salt
  Chop the apples and onions into small pieces. Mix all the ingredients, except the sugar, and boil gently till soft. Add the sugar and boil for a further ½ hour. Pour into jars and tie down.

477. CHUTNEY, TOMATO
  2 lb. tomatoes   1 lb. sugar
  4½ oz. cooking apples, peeled and cored   ½ teaspoon mustard
  16 oz. onions, peeled   ¼ teaspoon pepper
  3½ oz. sultanas   2 teaspoons curry powder
  ¾ pint vinegar   1 teaspoon salt
Peel the tomatoes and proceed as for apple chutney.

486. LEMON CURD
  8 oz. sugar   3 eggs
  2½ oz. butter   Juice of 3 lemons (4¼ oz.)
  Place the butter, sugar and lemon juice in a double pan and stir till melted. Add the eggs one by one and cook slowly, stirring all the time until the mixture coats the back of a wooden spoon.

497. TOFFEE
  8 oz. sugar   5 oz. golden syrup
  1 oz. butter   1 tablespoon water
  1 teaspoon vinegar
  Place all the ingredients in a saucepan and heat gently till melted. Boil rapidly for 10 minutes or until a small portion, dropped into cold water, becomes brittle. Pour into buttered tins and mark into squares while still warm.

Beverages

512. LEMONADE
  Juice of one lemon (1¼ oz.)   ½ pint water
  1½ oz. sugar
  Dissolve the sugar in a little hot water. Allow to cool and add to the lemon juice and remainder of the water.

Cakes and Pastries

557. CHERRY CAKE
  8 oz. flour   3 eggs
  8 oz. margarine   6 oz. glacé cherries
  8 oz. sugar   2 level teaspoons baking powder
  Beat the butter and sugar to a cream. Beat in the egg, adding a little at a time. Sift together the flour and baking powder and fold in together with the cherries cut into pieces. Bake in a moderate oven for 1½–2 hours.

558. CHOCOLATE CAKES
  4 oz. flour   1 oz. cocoa
  3 oz. margarine   1½ level teaspoons baking
  4 oz. sugar   powder
  2 eggs   Vanilla essence
  Cream the fat and sugar and add the well beaten eggs. Sift in the flour, cocoa and baking powder. Fold in carefully. Half fill small cake tins and bake in a moderate oven for 15–20 minutes.

559. Coconut Cakes

8 oz. flour	3 oz. milk
3 oz. margarine	3 oz. desiccated coconut
3 oz. sugar	3 level teaspoons baking
1 egg	powder

Mix the flour, baking powder and sugar and rub in the fat. Add the coconut. Mix to a stiff consistency with the egg and milk. Half fill small cake tins and bake in a hot oven for 15–20 minutes.

561. Currant Cake

8 oz. flour	2 eggs
4 oz. margarine	4 oz. currants
4 oz. sugar	2 level teaspoons baking
	powder

Cream the sugar and margarine and beat in the eggs. Add the flour, baking powder and fruit. Bake in a moderate oven for 1½–2 hours.

564. Easter Biscuits

4 oz. flour	2 oz. margarine
½ level teaspoon baking powder	2 oz. sugar
pinch salt	1 oz. currants
pinch spice or cinnamon	½ egg
little grated lemon rind	

Mix the flour, baking powder, salt and spice and rub in the fat. Add the sugar, currants and lemon rind. Mix to a stiff dough with the egg, then roll out and cut into rounds. Place on a lightly greased baking sheet and bake in a moderate oven for 10–15 minutes. Dredge with sugar while still hot.

565. Eccles Cakes

8 oz. flour ⎤	2½ oz. currants
3 oz. margarine ⎬ Flaky pastry	1 oz. sugar
3 oz. lard ⎪	
3¾ oz. water ⎦	

Make the pastry, roll out, and cut into 3-inch squares. Place some currants in the middle of each square and sprinkle with half a teaspoonful of sugar. Fold in the edges, turn over and roll out. Bake in a hot oven for about 20 minutes.

566. Ginger Biscuits

8 oz. flour	3½ oz. golden syrup
3 oz. margarine	¼ oz. ground ginger
3 oz. sugar	1 level teaspoon sodium
1 egg	bicarbonate

Mix the dry ingredients. Add the previously melted fat and syrup and finally the beaten egg. Form into small balls. Bake in a moderate oven for 15–30 minutes.

567. Gingerbread

6 oz. flour	1 egg
2 oz. margarine	1¾ oz. milk
2 oz. sugar	¼ oz. ground ginger
4 oz. golden syrup	½ level teaspoon sodium
	bicarbonate

Put the butter, sugar and syrup into a saucepan and heat gently till melted. Beat the egg well. Mix all the ingredients together and bake in a moderate oven for about 1½ hours.

568. Imperial Biscuits

2 oz. margarine	4 oz. flour
2 oz. castor sugar	¼ teaspoon cinnamon
pinch of salt	(optional)
¼ egg	¼ level teaspoon baking
	powder
	2 oz. jam

Cream the margarine, sugar and salt together and beat in the egg. Sift together the flour, cinnamon and baking powder and work into the creamed mixture. Roll out, cut into rounds, removing a small round from the centre of half the rounds. Bake in a moderate oven for 20 minutes. When cold, dust the holed rounds with icing sugar and sandwich them to the complete rounds with jam.

B

569. JAM TARTS

      6 oz. raw pastry (short)   6 oz. jam

Make the pastry in the usual way, roll out and cut into rounds to fit the tart tins. Fill each tart with jam and bake in a hot oven for about 15 minutes.

570. LEMON CURD TARTS

      7 oz. raw short pastry   4½ oz. lemon curd

                                                      (Recipe No. 486)

Make the tarts in the same way as the jam tarts.

571. MINCE PIES

      10 oz. raw short pastry   5 oz. mincemeat

Roll out the pastry and cut into rounds. Place half the rounds in tart tins. Fill up with mincemeat and cover with the remaining rounds. Bake in a moderate oven for about 20 minutes.

572 and 573. ORANGE CAKE (ICED OR PLAIN)

5 oz. flour	4 oz. icing sugar	⎫ Icing
4 oz. margarine	¾ oz. orange juice	⎭
4 oz. sugar Cake	1½ oz. butter	⎫
2 eggs	1½ oz. icing sugar	⎬ Filling
1¼ level teaspoons baking powder	Orange essence	⎭
Grated rind of an orange		

Cake: Cream the fat and sugar, add the eggs slowly, beating well. Sift in the flour and baking powder and add the grated rind. Bake in a moderate oven for 1–1¼ hours. *Filling:* Sieve the icing sugar into a bowl, add the butter, and cream well, adding essence to flavour. Split the cake and spread on the filling. *Icing:* Mix the sugar for icing with juice, and ice top of cake.

574 and 575. PASTRY, FLAKY

      8 oz. flour   3 oz. lard

      3 oz. margarine   3¾ oz. water

                                             ½ level teaspoon salt

Make the pastry according to the standard method described in all cookery books.

576 and 577. PASTRY, SHORT

      8 oz. flour   2 oz. lard

      2 oz. margarine   1¼ oz. water

                                             ½ level teaspoon salt

Make the pastry according to the standard method described in all cookery books.

578. PLAIN FRUIT CAKE

6 oz. flour	3 oz. margarine
Pinch salt	3 oz. sugar
3 level teaspoons baking powder	1 oz. each of currants,
¼ level teaspoons each of	sultanas and seedless raisins
cinnamon, ginger and nutmeg	½ oz. chopped peel
1½ eggs	Grated rind of ¼ lemon
Milk (2–3 tablespoonfuls)	

Sift together the flour, salt, baking powder and spices, and rub in the fat. Add the fruit, peel and grated lemon rind. Mix with the egg and milk to a dropping consistency and bake in a moderate oven for about 1 hour.

579. QUEEN CAKES

6 oz. flour	2 oz. currants
4 oz. margarine	1½ level teaspoons baking
4 oz. sugar	powder
	2 eggs

Cream the butter and sugar. Add the beaten egg a little at a time and beat well. Fold in the sifted flour and baking powder and the fruit. Half fill small cake tins and bake in a moderate oven for about 20 minutes.

580. ROCK CAKES

8 oz. flour	4 oz. currants
3 oz. margarine	1¼ oz. milk
3 oz. sugar	3 level teaspoons baking
1 egg	powder

Rub the fat, flour, baking powder and sugar well together. Add the currants. Mix in the beaten egg and milk. Drop the mixture in small portions on to a baking sheet. Bake in a hot oven for about 15 minutes.

581. SCONES

8 oz. flour	5 oz. milk
1½ oz. margarine	4 level teaspoons baking
¼ oz. sugar	powder

Rub the fat into the flour, baking powder and sugar. Mix in the milk. Roll out and cut into rounds. Bake in a hot oven for about 10 minutes.

582. SHORTBREAD

8 oz. flour	2 oz. castor sugar
4 oz. butter	

Beat the butter and sugar to a cream. Mix in the flour and knead till smooth. Press into a flat tin to about ½ inch in thickness. Bake in a moderate oven for 45–60 minutes.

583. SPONGE CAKE

2 oz. flour	2 eggs
2 oz. sugar	

Whisk the sugar and eggs together, in a basin over hot water till stiff. Fold in the flour. Bake in a moderate oven for 20–30 minutes.

584. VICTORIA SANDWICH

4 oz. butter or margarine	4 oz. flour
4 oz. castor sugar	1 level teaspoon baking powder
2 eggs	Pinch salt
	2 oz. raspberry jam

Cream together the fat and sugar and beat in the egg. Sift together the flour, baking powder and salt, and fold lightly into the creamed mixture. Divide the mixture between two prepared 7-inch sandwich tins and bake in a moderate oven for about 20 minutes. When cold, sandwich together with jam and dredge the top with either icing or castor sugar.

585. WELSH CHEESE CAKES

6 oz. flour	⎫	2 oz. margarine	
1½ oz. margarine	⎬ Short pastry	2 oz. sugar	
1½ oz. lard	⎪	1 egg	
1 oz. water	⎭	1 level teaspoon baking powder	
2½ oz. jam			
3 oz. flour			

Make the pastry in the usual way. Line some tins with pastry and put a little jam in the bottom of each. Cream the butter and sugar, and add the egg, beating well. Sift the flour and baking powder together and fold in lightly. Spread the mixture on top of the jam. Bake in a moderate oven for about half an hour.

Puddings

586. APPLE DUMPLING

6 oz. flour	⎫	3 apples (18½ oz. peeled and	
1½ oz. margarine	⎬ Short pastry	cored)	
1½ oz. lard	⎪	1½ oz. sugar	
1 oz. water	⎭		

Make the pastry. Divide into three and roll out. Peel and core the apples. Place one on each piece of pastry. Fill the centre of the apple with sugar. Work the pastry round the apple until it is well covered. Bake for 30–40 minutes in a moderate oven.

587. Apple Pudding

6 oz. flour	⎫		10 oz. apples, peeled and cored
3 oz. suet	⎪		3 oz. sugar
3½ oz. water	⎬ Suet crust		1 oz. water
1½ level teaspoons	⎪		
baking powder	⎭		

Make the suet crust. Roll out and line a basin. Trim off the uneven edges. Fill with peeled apples and a little water and sugar. Roll out the trimmings to cover the basin. Steam for 2 hours.

588. Apple Pie

| 7 oz. raw short pastry | 3 oz. sugar |
| 1 lb. apples, peeled and cored | 1 oz. water |

Place the prepared apples, sugar and water in a pie dish. Roll out the pastry and place over the dish. Bake in a moderate oven for 30–40 minutes.

589. Banana Custard

1 pint milk	⎫		
1 oz. custard powder	⎬ Custard		6 bananas (9½ oz. peeled)
1½ oz. sugar	⎭		

Make the custard (Recipe No. 597) and slice the bananas into it. Serve when cold.

590. Blancmange

| 1 pint milk | 1½ oz. sugar |
| 1½ oz. cornflour | Vanilla essence |

Mix the cornflour to a smooth paste with a little of the milk. Heat the remainder of the milk and sugar together. When hot stir into the paste and then transfer the whole to the saucepan. Cook gently with stirring for about 5 minutes. Stir in 2 or 3 drops of vanilla essence. Turn into a mould and allow to set.

591. Bread and Butter Pudding

1 pint milk	1 oz. currants
1 oz. sugar	2½ oz. bread
2 eggs	¾ oz. butter

Cut the bread very thinly and spread with butter. Beat the eggs with the sugar and add the milk. Place the bread and the currants in a pie dish in alternate layers. Pour the egg and the milk over the bread and bake in a moderate oven for about 30 minutes.

592. Canary Pudding

6 oz. flour	2 eggs
4 oz. margarine	½ oz. milk
4 oz. sugar	2 level teaspoons baking powder

Cream the butter and sugar together and beat in the eggs. Sift together the flour and baking powder, and fold in together with the milk. Bake in a moderate oven for about 45 minutes.

593. Castle Pudding (Steamed)

3 oz. flour	2 oz. sugar
2 oz. margarine	½ level teaspoon baking powder
1 egg	⅔ oz. milk

Cream the butter and sugar together and beat in the egg. Fold in the sieved flour and baking powder and add the milk. Put in greased dariole tins, cover with greased greaseproof paper, and steam for 40 minutes.

594. Chocolate Mould

1 pint milk	1½ oz. cornflour
2 oz. sugar	¼ oz. cocoa
	Vanilla essence

Mix the cornflour and cocoa to a smooth paste with a little of the milk. Heat the rest of the milk and the sugar. Pour the hot liquid on to the paste. Return to the pan and boil for 5 minutes, stirring all the time. Stir in the essence. Pour into a mould and allow to set.

595. CUSTARD, EGG (BAKED)
    1 pint milk   1 oz. sugar
    2 eggs

Beat the eggs and sugar together. Add the milk and strain into a greased pie dish. Stand in a pan of water and bake in a moderate oven until set. (About 40 minutes).

596. CUSTARD SAUCE (EGG)
    1 pint milk   2 oz. sugar
    2 eggs   Vanilla essence

Beat the eggs and sugar together. Warm the milk and pour over the mixture, stirring all the time. Strain into the pan, and add vanilla essence. Stir for a few minutes until the mixture thickens and coats the back of a spoon. Remove from the heat immediately. Allow to cool.

597. CUSTARD, POWDER
    1 pint milk   1½ oz. sugar
    1 oz. custard powder

Blend the custard powder with a little of the milk. Add the sugar to the remainder of the milk, bring to the boil and pour immediately over the paste, stirring all the time. Return to the pan, bring to boiling point, stirring, then serve.

598. CUSTARD TART
    6 oz. flour   ⎫   ½ pint milk
    1½ oz. margarine   ⎬ Short pastry   1 egg
    1½ oz. lard   ⎪   1 oz. sugar
    1 oz. water   ⎭

Make the pastry and line a shallow tin. Make the custard (Recipe No. 595) and use as filling. Bake in a moderate oven till set.

599. DUMPLING
    4 oz. flour   2½ oz. water
    1½ oz. suet   1 level teaspoon baking powder
                                                   ½ teaspoon salt

Mix all the ingredients together with cold water to form a soft dough. Divide into twelve balls. Flour each one and place in boiling water. Boil for half an hour.

600. GOOSEBERRY PIE
    7 oz. raw short pastry   3 oz. sugar
    1 lb. gooseberries   1 oz. water

Place the prepared gooseberries, sugar and water in a pie dish. Roll out the pastry and place over the dish. Bake in a hot oven until the pastry has set, then lower the heat and cook until fruit is tender (30–40 minutes in all).

601. JAM OMELETTE
    2 eggs   1 oz. jam
    ¼ oz. butter   ½ oz. sugar

Beat the yolks and sugar together. Whisk the whites stiffly and fold into the yolks. Pour the mixture into an omelette pan, previously heated with the butter, and cook very slowly until well risen. Brown slightly under the grill. Turn out on to paper. Spread with jam and fold into two.

602. JAM ROLL, BAKED
    8 oz. flour   ⎫   6 oz. jam
    2 oz. lard   ⎬ Short pastry
    2 oz. margarine   ⎪
    1¼ oz. water   ⎭

Make the pastry. Roll out and spread with jam. Damp the edges and roll up. Bake in a moderate oven for 40–50 minutes.

603. JELLY
    6½ oz. jelly cubes   Water

Dissolve the jelly cubes in hot water. Make up to a pint with water. Pour into a mould and allow to set.

604. JELLY (MILK)

6½ oz. jelly cubes   ¼ pint water
½ pint milk

Dissolve the jelly cubes in ¼ pint hot water. Allow to cool. Add the milk slowly, stirring all the time, making up to a pint of mixture. Leave to set in a mould.

605. LEICESTER PUDDING

2½ oz. margarine   4 oz. flour
2½ oz. castor sugar   1 level teaspoon baking powder
1 egg   1 tablespoonful jam
Pinch of salt   A little milk

Put the jam into the bottom of a greased basin. Cream together the fat and sugar, beat in the egg a little at a time and fold in the sifted flour, salt and baking powder, adding milk to give a soft dropping consistency. Turn into the basin and steam for 1½ to 2 hours.

606. MIXED FRUIT PUDDING

4 oz. flour   1 oz. sultanas
Pinch of salt   ½ oz. chopped mixed peel
2 level teaspoons baking powder   A little grated lemon rind
2 oz. margarine   ½ egg
1½ oz. sugar   About 3 teaspoonfuls milk
1 oz. currants

Sift together the flour, salt and baking powder and rub in the fat. Add the sugar, fruit, chopped peel and grated lemon rind. Mix with the egg and milk to give a medium dropping consistency. Steam for 2 to 2½ hours.

607. PANCAKES

4 oz. flour   2 oz. sugar
½ pint milk   1½ oz. lard
1 egg

Break the egg into the flour, add a little milk and stir till smooth. Add the rest of the milk by degrees, beating all the time. Heat a little lard in a frying pan. Pour into the pan enough batter just to cover the bottom thinly. Cook both sides and then turn on to sugared paper. Repeat till all the batter is used up. (Sufficient for about 12 small pancakes).

608. PLUM PIE

7 oz. raw short pastry   3 oz. sugar
1 lb. plums (weighed with stones)   1 oz. water

Place the plums, sugar and water in a pie dish. Roll out the pastry and cover the dish. Bake in a moderate oven for about 30–40 minutes.

609. QUEEN OF PUDDINGS

½ pint milk   3 oz. sugar
2 oz. breadcrumbs   2 oz. jam
2 eggs   Rind and juice of half a lemon
1 oz. butter

Pour the heated milk and butter over the breadcrumbs and 1 oz. of the sugar. Allow to stand for a few minutes. Add the beaten yolks, grated lemon rind and juice and pour into a greased pie dish. Bake in a moderate oven till set (20 minutes). Remove from the oven and spread with jam. Whisk the whites stiffly, then whisk in 2 oz. sugar one teaspoonful at a time, and pile on top. Return to a slow oven and bake till golden brown.

610. RHUBARB PIE

7 oz. raw short pastry   4 oz. sugar
1 lb. rhubarb (weighed after preparing)

Place the prepared rhubarb and sugar in a pie dish. Roll out the pastry and cover the dish. Bake in a moderate oven for about 30–40 minutes.

611. RICE PUDDING

1 pint milk   1 oz. sugar
1½ oz. rice   1 oz. butter

Place the rice, milk, butter and sugar in a pie dish. Bake in a slow oven for about 3 hours, stirring 2 or 3 times during the first hour, and then leaving undisturbed.

612. SAGO PUDDING
      1 pint milk   1½ oz. sugar
      2 oz. sago

Soak the sago in the milk for 20 minutes. Add the sugar and bake in a slow oven for about 1 hour, stirring well after the first 15 minutes, and then leaving undisturbed.

613. SEMOLINA PUDDING
      1 pint milk   1½ oz. sugar
      2 oz. semolina

Heat the milk and sprinkle in the semolina, Bring slowly to the boil and simmer till the grain is soft. Add the sugar and pour into a pie dish. Bake in a moderate oven for about 20 minutes.

614. SUET PUDDING, PLAIN
      2 oz. flour   1½ oz. sugar
      2 oz. breadcrumbs   3 oz. milk
      2 oz. suet   1 level teaspoon baking
                                             powder

Place all the dry ingredients together in a basin. Mix to a soft paste with the milk. Pour into a greased basin. Steam for 2½ hours.

615. SUET PUDDING WITH RAISINS
      2 oz. flour   1½ oz. sugar
      2 oz. breadcrumbs   3½ oz. milk
      2 oz. suet   1 level teaspoon baking
      2 oz. raisins   powder

Place the flour, breadcrumbs, suet, sugar, raisins and baking powder in a basin and mix to a soft paste with the milk. Pour into a greased basin. Steam for 2½ hours.

616. SWISS APPLE PUDDING
     14 oz. apples, peeled and cored   4 oz. sugar
      3 oz. fresh breadcrumbs
      1½ oz. suet

Grease a pie dish and line with breadcrumbs. Fill the dish with alternate layers of apple, suet, sugar and breadcrumbs. Cover the top with crumbs and bake in a moderate oven till golden brown.

617. SYRUP SPONGE PUDDING

Recipe and method as for LEICESTER PUDDING, substituting 2 tablespoonfuls of syrup for 1 tablespoonful jam.

618. TAPIOCA PUDDING
      1 pint milk   1½ oz. sugar
      2 oz. tapioca (pearl)

Soak the tapioca in the milk for 20 minutes. Add the sugar and bake in a slow oven for about 1 hour, stirring well after the first 15 minutes and then leaving undisturbed.

619. TREACLE TART
     12 oz. raw short pastry   1¾ oz. fresh breadcrumbs
     10 oz. golden syrup

Line shallow tins with pastry. Pour in the golden syrup. Sprinkle with breadcrumbs. Bake in a hot oven for 20–30 minutes.

620. TRIFLE
     3 oz. sponge cake   1 oz. whipped cream ⎫
     1 oz. jam   ¼ oz. nuts   ⎬ **For**
     2 oz. fruit juice   ¼ oz. cherries   ⎰ decoration
     3 oz. tinned fruit   Angelica   ⎭
     1 oz. sherry
     ½ pint custard powder custard

Slice the sponge cake, spread with jam, sandwich together and cut into 1½ inch cubes. Soak in the fruit juice and sherry. Mix with the fruit, cover with the cold custard and decorate with piped cream, nuts, cherries and angelica.

621. YORKSHIRE PUDDING
     ½ pint milk   ¾ oz. dripping
     4 oz. flour   1 level teaspoon salt
     1 egg

   Salt the flour and break the egg into it. Beat till smooth, gradually adding about half the milk. Add the remainder of the milk. Pour into a tin containing very hot dripping. Bake in a hot oven for 30–45 minutes.

Meat and Fish Dishes

622. BEEF STEAK PUDDING
     6 oz. flour   ⎫   12 oz. raw steak
     3 oz. suet   ⎪   ⅛ oz. flour
     3½ oz. water   ⎬ Suet crust   1 oz. water
     1¼ level teaspoons   ⎪   1 level teaspoon salt
        baking powder   ⎪
     ¼ teaspoon salt   ⎭

   Make the suet crust pastry and line a pudding basin, leaving sufficient for a lid. Cut the meat into slices and roll in the salted flour. Put into the basin. Add a little water and cover with the remainder of the pastry. Steam for about 3 hours.

623. BEEF STEW
     8 oz. stewing steak (raw)   10 oz. water
     2 oz. carrot   ½ oz. flour
     2 oz. onion   1 level teaspoon salt
     ½ oz. dripping   Pepper

   Melt the dripping in a casserole and fry the meat, cut in large pieces, until brown. Remove the meat from the fat and add the sliced onion. Fry the onion till brown, then add the flour and cook the roux. Gradually blend in the water, add the meat, carrots and seasoning, bring to the boil and finish cooking in a moderate oven for 2–2½ hours, or simmer gently in a saucepan.

624. CURRIED MEAT
     9½ oz. cooked meat   ½ oz. desiccated coconut
     2½ oz. dripping   1 oz. flour
     3 onions, peeled (12¾ oz.)   1 oz. curry powder
     1 apple, peeled and cored (2½ oz.)   1 pint water
     2 oz. sultanas   2 level teaspoons salt

   Chop the onions and fry in the dripping. Add the chopped apple, sultanas and coconut, then the flour and curry powder, and fry for a minute or two. Add the water and bring to the boil. Simmer for 5 minutes. Add the cooked meat, which has been cut into pieces, and reheat.

625. FISH CAKES
     8 oz. steamed cod   ½ oz. margarine
     4 oz. mashed potato   1 oz. dried breadcrumbs
     1 egg   1 level teaspoon salt
     ¼ oz. flour   Pepper

   Heat the fat in a pan and add the coarsely chopped fish, potato and half the beaten egg. Mix well and allow to cool. Shape into six flat round cakes. Coat with flour, then with the other half of the egg and finally with breadcrumbs. Fry in very hot deep fat for 2 minutes.

626. HOT POT
     8 oz. raw steak   8 oz. raw potato, peeled
     2 onions, peeled (5 oz.)   4 oz. water
     2 carrots, scraped (3 oz.)   2 level teaspoons salt
                                                   Pepper

   Cut the steak into small pieces and arrange in layers with slices of carrot and onion. Add water and seasoning. Slice the potatoes and place on top. Cover and bake in a slow oven for about 2½ hours, removing lid for last ½ hour to brown potatoes.

627. IRISH STEW
     8 oz. neck of mutton (weighed with bone)   12 oz. water
     8 oz. potato, peeled   ½ oz. pearl barley
     4 oz. onion, peeled   ¼ teaspoon salt
                                                   Pepper

   Cut up the meat, potato and onion and put into a saucepan. Add the water and barley and bring to the boil. Skim well and allow to simmer slowly for 1¼ hours.

628. KEDGEREE

8 oz. smoked fillet, steamed	2 eggs (one hard boiled)
2 oz. rice	½ teaspoon salt
1 oz. margarine	Pepper

Boil the rice. Melt the margarine and add the boiled rice, flaked fish, beaten egg and seasoning. Mix well and stir in the chopped hard boiled egg. Put in a pie dish and cook in a moderate oven for 20 minutes.

629 and 630. SAUSAGE ROLL

5½ oz. raw flaky pastry ⎫ or ⎰ 7½ oz. raw short pastry
2 oz. raw sausage meat ⎭ ⎱ 3½ oz. raw sausage meat

Make the pastry, roll out and cut into squares of 4 inches. Place some sausage in the middle of each. Fold over, and bake in a hot oven for 20–30 minutes.

631. SHEPHERD'S PIE

12 oz. beef, cooked	¾ oz. margarine
3½ oz. onion, boiled	6 oz. water
18½ oz. potato, boiled	2 level teaspoons salt
2 oz. milk	Pepper

Mince the meat and chop up the onion. Moisten with water and add the seasoning. Mash the potatoes with the milk and margarine. Place the mince and onion in a pie dish. Pile the potato on top. Bake in a hot oven till brown.

632. STEAK AND KIDNEY PIE

14 oz. raw flaky pastry	4 oz. water
15 oz. raw beef steak	2 level teaspoons salt
7 oz. raw kidney	½ oz. flour

Make the pastry. Cut the steak and kidney into pieces and roll in flour. Place with water and seasoning in the pie dish. Cover with pastry. Bake in a hot oven for 20 minutes, then reduce the heat and cover with greaseproof paper. Continue cooking slowly for 2–2½ hours.

633. TOAD-IN-THE-HOLE

½ pint milk ⎫
4 oz. flour ⎬ Batter
2 eggs ⎭

8 oz. raw sausage
2 oz. dripping
2 level teaspoons salt

Make the batter, add the salt, and pour into a small tin containing hot dripping. Skin the sausages and place them in the batter. Bake in a hot oven for about 40 minutes.

Egg and Cheese Dishes

634. BUCK RAREBIT

1½ or 2 slices toast, buttered (1¼ oz.)	Pepper, cayenne
1½ oz. grated cheese	1 egg
1 level teaspoonful cornflour	¼ level teaspoon dry mustard
About 1 tablespoonful milk	¼ level teaspoon salt

Mix the cheese, cornflour and seasoning to a stiff paste with the milk. Spread on buttered toast and brown under the grill. Poach the egg and place on top of the toasted cheese.

635. CHEESE OMELETTE

2 eggs	¼ oz. butter
1¼ oz. cheese	1 level teaspoon salt

Beat the eggs with the seasoning. Heat the butter in an omelette pan, pour in the mixture and stir till it begins to thicken evenly. While still creamy, sprinkle with the grated cheese, fold the omelette and turn on to a hot dish.

636. CHEESE STRAWS

2 oz. flour	½ an egg yolk
2 oz. butter	¼ oz. water
3 oz. cheese	¼ teaspoon salt
	Pepper, cayenne

Rub the butter into the flour. Add the grated cheese and seasoning. Bind to a stiff paste with the yolk and water. Roll out thinly and cut into narrow strips. Bake in a moderate oven for about 10 minutes.

637. CHEESE PUDDING

2 oz. breadcrumbs	Mustard and cayenne pepper
½ pint milk	3 oz. grated cheese
½ level teaspoon salt	2 eggs

Heat the milk, pour over the breadcrumbs and leave to stand for about 15 minutes. Add the grated cheese, seasonings and egg yolks. Fold in the stiffly whipped egg whites and bake in a moderately hot oven until well risen and golden brown.

638. MACARONI CHEESE

½ pint milk	2 oz. macaroni
1 oz. margarine	3 oz. cheese
1 oz. flour	½ level teaspoon salt

Break the macaroni into small pieces and boil; drain well. Make a sauce of the milk, flour and margarine. Stir in the salt and three-quarters of the grated cheese. Add the boiled macaroni. Put the mixture in a pie dish and sprinkle the remainder of the cheese on top. Brown under the grill.

639. OMELETTE

2 eggs	½ oz. water
¼ oz. butter	½ level teaspoon salt

Beat the eggs with the salt and add the water. Heat the butter in an omelette pan, pour in the mixture and stir till it begins to thicken evenly. While still creamy, fold the omelette and serve.

640. SCOTCH EGG

3 eggs	½ oz. flour
8 oz. raw sausage	⅜ oz. beaten egg
⅝ oz. breadcrumbs	

Hard boil the eggs, cool and remove shells. Skin the sausages and flatten each on a floured board. Dip each egg in flour and cover with sausage meat. Brush with beaten egg and coat with crumbs. Fry in very hot deep fat for about 3 minutes.

641. SCRAMBLED EGGS

2 eggs	½ oz. milk
¾ oz. butter	½ level teaspoon salt

Beat the eggs with the seasoning and add the milk. Heat the butter in a pan and add the beaten eggs and milk. Stir over a gentle heat until the mixture thickens.

642. WELSH RAREBIT

1½ or 2 slices toast, buttered (1½ oz.)	About 1 tablespoonful milk
1½ oz. grated cheese	¼ level teaspoon dry mustard
1 level teaspoonful cornflour	¼ level teaspoon salt
Pepper, cayenne	

Mix the cheese, cornflour and seasoning to a stiff paste with the milk. Spread on buttered toast and brown under the grill.

Sauces and Soups

645. BREAD SAUCE

½ pint milk	1 small onion stuck with 2
2 oz. fresh breadcrumbs	cloves
¼ oz. butter	½ teaspoon salt

Put the milk and onion in a saucepan and bring to the boil. Add the breadcrumbs, and simmer gently for about 20 minutes, using a double pan. Remove the onion and add the seasoning, stir in the butter and serve.

647. BROWN SAUCE

¾ oz. dripping	¾ pint brown stock
1½ oz. onion	Salt and pepper to taste
1½ oz. turnip	Small bouquet garni (bayleaf,
1 oz. carrot	mixed herbs, mace, pepper-
½ oz. bacon rinds	corns, parsley)
1 oz. flour	

Fry the pieces of vegetable and the bacon rinds in the dripping to a good brown colour. Add the flour and continue to fry very gently, stirring well, until the flour assumes a light brown colour. Add the stock, seasoning and bouquet garni, bring to the boil and allow to simmer gently for 40 minutes. Adjust the consistency and colour with gravy browning if necessary, and strain.

648. CHEESE SAUCE

½ pint milk ⎫
¾ oz. flour ⎬ White sauce
¾ oz. margarine ⎭

1½ oz. cheese
½ level teaspoon salt
Pepper, cayenne

Melt the fat in a pan. Add the flour, and cook gently for a few minutes, stirring all the time. Add the milk, and cook until the mixture thickens, stirring continually. Add the grated cheese and seasoning. Reheat to soften the cheese and serve immediately.

650. EGG SAUCE

½ pint milk ⎫
¾ oz. flour ⎬ White sauce
¾ oz. margarine ⎭

1 hard-boiled egg
1 level teaspoon salt
Pepper

Make the sauce and add the chopped egg and seasoning.

651. LENTIL SOUP

4 oz. lentils
1 small carrot (1 oz.)
½ turnip (1½ oz.)
1 small onion (1½ oz.)
1 ham bone
Bouquet garni (bayleaf, mixed herbs, mace, peppercorns, parsley)

1 oz. margarine
1 oz. flour
1 quart brown stock
1 gill milk
Salt and pepper to taste

Melt the dripping and toss the lentils and sliced vegetables in it over a gentle heat. Add the stock, seasoning, bouquet garni and ham bone and bring to the boil. Simmer for 2 to 2½ hours, stirring at intervals. Sieve and return to the pan with the flour blended to a smooth cream with the milk. Cook for about 5 minutes. Adjust seasoning.

652. ONION SAUCE

½ pint milk ⎫
¾ oz. flour ⎬ White sauce
¾ oz. margarine ⎭

8 oz. onion, boiled
1 level teaspoon salt
Pepper

Make the sauce and add the chopped onion and seasoning.

653. POTATO SOUP

13¼ oz. potatoes, peeled
1 onion, peeled (4¾ oz.)
1 oz. dripping

½ pint milk
½ pint water
2 level teaspoons salt
Pepper

Melt the fat in a pan. Slice the vegetables and fry in the fat. Add the water and seasoning. Bring to the boil, cover and simmer for an hour. Rub through a sieve, add the milk and reheat.

659. TOMATO SAUCE

1 lb tomatoes
1 oz. carrots
1½ oz. onion
½ oz. bacon

½ oz. margarine
½ pint stock
¾ oz. flour
Bouquet garni

Cut the tomato, carrot and onion into small pieces and fry gently with the margarine and bacon. Stir in the flour, blended with some of the stock, then the rest of the stock and the bouquet garni. Bring to the boil, stirring, and allow to simmer for 40 minutes. Rub through a hair sieve. Reheat, adjust seasoning and serve.

662. WHITE SAUCE, SAVOURY

½ pint milk
¾ oz. flour

¾oz. margarine
1 level teaspoon salt
Pepper

Melt the fat in a pan. Add the flour, and cook for a few minutes, stirring all the time. Add the milk and seasoning, and cook gently until the mixture thickens, stirring continually.

663. WHITE SAUCE, SWEET

½ pint milk
¾ oz. flour

¾ oz. margarine
1 oz. sugar

Make the sauce in the same way as the savoury sauce, adding the sugar instead of salt.

Tables to Part 1

COMPOSITION PER 100 GRAMS

Cereals and Cereal Foods

No.	Food	Description and number of samples	Water	g. per 100 g.		
				Sugar (as invert sugar)	Starch and dextrins (as glucose)	Total nitrogen
1	All-Bran, Kellogg's	2 packets from different shops	8·0*	18·2	39·8	2·20
2	Arrowroot	2 samples from different shops	12·2	Tr.	94·0	0·07
3	Barley, pearl, raw	2 samples from different shops	10·6	Tr.	83·6	1·35
4	Barley, pearl, boiled	2 samples from different shops (boiled in water)	69·6	Tr.	27·6	0·46
5	Bemax	6 packets from different shops	6·8	16·0	28·7	4·88
6	Biscuits, cream crackers	6 varieties	4·3	Tr.	68·3	1·66
7	Biscuits, digestive	3 varieties	4·5	16·4	49·6	1·68
8	Biscuits, plain mixed	Marie (3 varieties), Osborne (3 varieties)	5·2	15·8	59·5	1·29
9	Biscuits, rusks	2 varieties	6·4	11·8	69·8	1·06
10	Biscuits, sweet mixed	3 varieties	0·7	25·0	41·5	0·97
11	Biscuits, water	3 varieties	4·5	2·3	73·5	1·89
12	Bread, Allinson's	Mean of 2 pooled samples†	40·1	2·1	45·0	1·44
13	Bread, brown	Mean of 2 pooled samples†	37·7	1·8	48·1	1·52
14	Bread, currant	4 samples from different shops	37·7	13·0	38·8	1·12
15	Bread, Hovis	Mean of 2 pooled samples†	39·7	2·5	45·1	1·58
16	Bread, malt	3 varieties	39·0	18·6	30·8	1·46
17	Bread, Procea	6 samples from different shops	34·5	1·4	48·9	1·87
18	Bread, white, large loaves	Mean of 3 pooled samples†	38·3	1·7	51·0	1·37
19	Bread, white, small loaves	Mean of 3 pooled samples†	35·6	1·8	52·6	1·45
20	Bread, white, batch loaves	Mean of 3 pooled samples†	38·4	2·0	49·7	1·40

* When freshly packed the moisture content may be between 2 and 3 per cent.

† The samples of bread analysed were those described by Coppock, Knight, and Vaughan (1958). Twenty-five loaves from different parts of England, Scotland and Wales were air-dried and allotted into three samples representing large, small and batch loaves, and were then analysed. This was done on three occasions, so that in all nine samples were analysed. The samples were prepared at the British Baking Industries Research Station, Chorley Wood, and analysed by the authors. Sampling of brown, Hovis and Allinson's wholemeal bread was carried out in the same way on two occasions.

Cereals and Cereal Foods—continued

No.	Food	Protein (N × 5.7)	Fat	Available carbohydrate (as monosaccharides)	Calories per 100 g.	Na	K	Ca	Mg	Fe	Cu	P	S	Cl	Acid	Base
		g. per 100 g.				mg. per 100 g.									Acid-base balance, m-equiv. per 100 g.	
1	All-Bran, Kellogg's	12·6	4·5	58·0	311	(1210)	955	82·1	420	10·80	0·46	815	182	(2020)	4·3	—
2	Arrowroot	0·4	0·1	94·0	355	4·8	18	7·0	7·8	1·95	0·22	27	2	7·1	0·4	
3	Barley, pearl, raw	7·7	1·7	83·6	360	2·6	123	9·7	20·2	0·67	0·12	206	107	105·0	17·5	
4	Barley, pearl, boiled	2·6	0·6	27·6	120	0·8	40	3·4	6·8	0·23	0·04	70	36	35·5	6·0	
5	Bemax	27·8	9·3	44·7	368	7·9	1150	54·2	289	7·68	1·07	1100	—	80·2	—	
6	Biscuits, cream crackers	9·6	16·3	68·3	447	(611)	123	(106)	24·6	(1·65)	—	110	87	(83)		1·7
7	Biscuits, digestive	9·6	20·5	66·0	481	(435)	156	(111)	32·0	(2·01)	0·23	134	72	(43)		5·7
8	Biscuits, plain mixed	7·4	13·2	75·3	435	(244)	170	(126)	14·3	(1·78)	0·08	41	83	(26)		7·3
9	Biscuits, rusks	6·0	8·4	81·6	409	(206)	140	(181)	27·3	(3·29)	0·21	81	107	(174)		7·1
10	Biscuits, sweet mixed	5·5	30·7	66·5	556	(216)	136	(83)	14·0	(1·20)	0·12	66	32	(37)		1·5
11	Biscuits, water	10·7	12·5	75·8	444	(472)	142	(121)	18·9	(1·60)	0·08	87	100	(673)		1·0
12	Bread, Allinson's*	8·2	2·0	47·1	228	(466)	261	26·0	89·3	2·88	0·46	240	81	(773)	7·2	
13	Bread, brown*	8·7	2·1	49·9	242	(549)	230	(95)	60·4	2·44	0·35	178	85	(911)	3·1	
14	Bread, currant	6·4	3·4	51·8	252	(164)	250	(90)	24·7	(2·70)	0·09	121	59	(284)		0·6
15	Bread, Hovis*	9·0	2·3	47·6	237	(529)	236	(107)	60·5	2·68	0·35	204	89	(813)	1·9	
16	Bread, malt	8·3	3·3	49·4	250	(275)	381	(94)	77·8	(3·59)	0·06	253	114	(526)	5·3	
17	Bread, Procea	10·7	2·4	50·3	255	(487)	140	(140)	26·8	1·77	0·17	109	105	(807)	2·2	
18	Bread, white, large loaves*	7·8	1·4	52·7	243	(515)	106	(92)	22·6	(1·80)	0·13	81	77	(844)	2·2	
19	Bread, white, small loaves*	8·3	1·8	54·4	255	(520)	117	(90)	23·7	(1·90)	0·18	89	81	(842)	3·1	
20	Bread, white, batch loaves*	8·0	1·4	51·7	240	(614)	110	(91)	24·2	(1·82)	0·17	81	78	(996)	1·3	

* See note (†) p. 22.

Cereals and Cereal Foods – *continued*

No.	Food	Description and number of samples	g. per 100 g.			
			Water	Sugar (as invert sugar)	Starch and dextrins (as glucose)	Total nitrogen
21	Bread, white, dried crumbs*	Mean of several samples ..	9·7	2·6	74·9	2·03
22	Bread, white, fried*	Mean of 3 pooled samples	4·0	1·7	49·6	1·33
23	Bread, white, toasted*	Mean of 3 pooled samples	24·0	2·1	62·8	1·69
24	Cornflakes, Kellogg's	2 packets from different shops	8·0†	10·4	77·8	1·16
25	Cornflour	3 samples from different shops	12·5	Tr.	92·0	0·09
26	Custard powder	Take as cornflour				
27	Energen Rolls	5 samples from different shops	8·5	1·6	44·1	7·72
28	Farex	6 samples from different shops	9·7	4·0	69·0	2·26
29	Figgerrolls	4 samples from different shops	7·1	2·4	42·6	7·70
30	Flour, English (100% whole wheat)	Composite sample of 19 varieties, weighted for popularity. (See *Biochem, J.*, 1945. **39**, 213.)	15·0	Tr.	73·4	1·56
31	Flour, English (85%)		15·0	Tr.	79·1	1·50
32	Flour, English (80%)		15·0	Tr.	80·8	1·44
33	Flour, English (75%)		15·0	Tr.	81·5	1·40
34	Flour, English (70%)		15·0	Tr.	81·9	1·39
35	Flour, English (Patent)		15·0	Tr.	83·2	1·34
36	Flour, Manitoba (100% whole wheat)	Composite sample from 24 shiploads (12 No. 1 Manitoba and 12 No. 2 Manitoba). (See *Biochem. J.*, 1945. **39**, 213.)	15·0	Tr.	69·1	2·39
37	Flour, Manitoba (85%)		15·0	Tr.	75·0	2·38
38	Flour, Manitoba (80%)		15·0	Tr.	75·5	2·32
39	Flour, Manitoba (75%)		15·0	Tr.	76·3	2·29
40	Flour, Manitoba (70%)		15·0	Tr.	76·9	2·24
41	Flour, Manitoba (Patent)		15·0	Tr.	78·2	2·07

* *See note (†) p. 22.*
† When freshly packed the moisture content may be between 2 and 3 per cent.

Cereals and Cereal Foods – continued

No.	Food	g. per 100 g.			Calories per 100 g.	mg. per 100 g.									Acid-base balance, m-equiv. per 100 g.	
		Protein (N × 5.7)	Fat	Available carbohydrate (as monosaccharides)		Na	K	Ca	Mg	Fe	Cu	P	S	Cl	Acid	Base
21	Bread, white, dried crumbs*	11·6	1·9	77·5	355	(755)	151	(132)	33·9	(2·79)	0·20	121	105	(113·0)	3·1	
22	Bread, white, fried*	7·6	37·2	51·3	569	(502)	103	(90)	22·0	(1·75)	0·13	79	75	(82·2)	2·3	
23	Bread, white, toasted*	9·6	1·7	64·9	299	(635)	131	(113)	27·8	(2·22)	0·16	100	95	(104·0)	2·6	
24	Cornflakes, Kellogg's	6·6	0·8	88·2	367	(1050)	114	7·4	16·5	2·80	0·09	58	93	(152·0)	2·0	
25	Cornflour	0·5	0·7	92·0	354	51·6	61	15·3	7·2	1·43	0·13	39	1·1	71·0		0·6
26	Custard powder							Take as Cornflour								
27	Energen Rolls	44·0	4·1	45·7	390	22·4	134	46·6	62·6	3·96	0·52	186	—	85·1	—	
28	Farex	12·9	2·3	73·0	348	(276)	296	885	84·0	(24·1)	0·34	589	—	(44)	—	
29	Figgerrolls	43·9	4·1	45·0	387	(601)	157	52·8	72·3	3·91	0·48	205	—	(99)	—	
30	Flour, English (100%)	8·9	2·2	73·4	333	3·4	361	35·5	106·0	3·05	0·65	340	—	35·5	—	
31	Flour, English (85%)	8·6	1·5	79·1	346	2·9	179	24·5	35·0	2·22	0·36	153	—	42·2	—	
32	Flour, English (80%)	8·2	1·3	80·8	348	2·1	151	21·5	24·0	1·65	0·27	118	—	44·4	—	
33	Flour, English (75%)	8·0	1·1	81·5	349	2·2	118	19·2	16·8	1·35	0·22	93	—	44·9	—	
34	Flour, English (70%)	7·9	1·0	81·9	349	2·1	111	18·9	13·9	1·40	0·22	84	—	45·0	—	
35	Flour, English (Patent)	7·6	0·8	83·2	352	—	99	15·2	8·7	0·95	0·20	68	—	41·5	—	
36	Flour, Manitoba (100%)	13·6	2·5	69·1	339	3·2	312	27·6	141·0	3·81	0·60	350	—	38·5	—	
37	Flour, Manitoba (85%)	13·6	1·7	74·0	350	4·1	146	18·5	61·8	2·70	0·34	188	—	44·5	—	
38	Flour, Manitoba (80%)	13·2	1·4	75·5	350	2·9	112	15·4	44·6	2·47	0·27	139	—	48·5	—	
39	Flour, Manitoba (75%)	13·1	1·3	76·3	353	—	87	13·1	30·4	2·27	0·22	109	—	48·0	—	
40	Flour, Manitoba (70%)	12·8	1·2	76·9	352	2·2	82	12·8	26·9	2·23	0·18	97	—	47·8	—	
41	Flour, Manitoba (Patent)	11·8	0·9	78·2	351	1·8	71	11·1	21·5	2·08	0·15	82	—	45·0	—	

* See note (†) p. 22.

C

Cereals and Cereal Foods – *continued*

| No. | Food | Description and number of samples | Water | g. per 100 g. | | Total nitrogen |
				Sugar (as invert sugar)	Starch and dextrins (as glucose)	
42	Flour, mixed grist, basic grade .. :	Mixed samples supplied by British Baking Industries Research Association	13·9	1·6	75·9	1·96
43	Flour, mixed grist, Patent .. :		14·1	1·4	76·6	1·89
44	Grapenuts .. : :	2 packets from different shops .. :	4·8	11·9	63·3	2·05
45	Macaroni, raw .. : :	2 samples from different shops .. :	12·4	Tr.	79·2	1·87
46	Macaroni, boiled .. :	2 samples from different shops (boiled in water)	72·2	Tr.	25·2	0·58
47	Oatmeal, raw .. :	Coarse, medium and fine. Two samples of each from different shops.	8·9	Tr.	72·8	2·12
48	Oatmeal porridge .. :	2½ oz. mixed sample and 2 level teaspoons salt per pint of water.	89·1	Tr.	8·2	0·24
49	Puffed Wheat .. :	4 packets from different shops .. :	7·8*	2·2	73·1	2·44
50	Rice Krispies .. :	4 packets from different shops .. :	7·2*	7·8	77·3	1·00
51	Rice, polished, raw .. :	5 samples from different shops .. :	11·7	Tr.	86·8	1·09
52	Rice, polished, boiled .. :	5 samples from different shops (boiled in water)	69·9	Tr.	29·6	0·37
53	Rye (100%) .. :		15·0	Tr.	75·9	1·40
54	Rye (85%) .. :	Commercial grist of all-English rye.	15·0	Tr.	80·2	1·28
55	Rye (75%) .. :		15·0	Tr.	82·5	1·17
56	Rye (60%) .. :		15·0	Tr.	85·8	0·99
57	Ryvita .. :	12 packets from different shops .. :	7·5	6·4	70·4	1·60
58	Sago .. :	2 samples from different shops .. :	12·6	Tr.	94·0	0·04
59	Semolina .. :	2 samples from different shops (coarse and fine)	14·0	Tr.	77·5	1·87
60	Shredded Wheat .. :	2 packets from different shops .. :	8·0*	Tr.	79·0	1·69
61	Soya. Full fat flour .. :	Mixed sample, supplied by the Cereals Research Station.	7·0	Tr.	13·3	6·45
62	Soya. Low fat flour or grits .. :		7·0	Tr.	17·2	7·94

* When freshly packed the moisture content may be between 2 and 3 per cent.

Cereals and Cereal Foods – continued

No.	Food	g. per 100 g.			Calories per 100 g.	mg. per 100 g.									Acid-base balance, m-equiv. per 100 g.	
		Protein (N × 5.7)	Fat	Available carbohydrate (as monosaccharides)		Na	K	Ca	Mg	Fe	Cu	P	S	Cl	Acid	Base
42	Flour, mixed, grist, basic grade	11.2	1.5	77.5	350	2.7	132	(118)	34.1	(1.93)	0.17	111	110	62.0	3.1	
43	Flour, mixed grist, Patent	10.8	1.3	78.0	349	2.7	102	(110)	18.5	(1.66)	0.11	89	109	53.7	4.5	
44	Grapenuts	11.7	3.0	75.2	358	(658)	423	47.8	153.0	5.64	0.19	333	144	(905)	1.4	
45	Macaroni, raw ..	10.7	2.0	79.2	360	25.6	217	26.3	57.3	1.43	0.07	152	95	31.4	3.8	
46	Macaroni, boiled ..	3.4	0.6	25.2	114	7.9	67	8.1	17.6	0.45	0.02	47	29	9.7	1.2	
47	Oatmeal, raw ..	12.1	8.7	72.8	404	33.4	368	55.3	113.0	4.12	0.23	380	155	73.0	13.2	
48	Oatmeal porridge ..	1.4	0.9	8.2	45	(578)	42	6.3	12.7	0.47	0.03	43	18	(890)	1.5	
49	Puffed Wheat ..	13.9	2.0	75.3	358	5.8	431	35.3	129.0	3.29	0.58	331	—	65.0	—	
50	Rice Krispies ..	5.7	1.1	85.1	351	(799)	144	6.1	36.2	0.72	0.16	128	—	(1280)	—	
51	Rice, polished, raw	6.2	1.0	86.8	361	6.3	113	3.7	13.1	0.45	0.06	99	78	27.0	7.6	
52	Rice, polished, boiled	2.1	0.3	29.6	122	2.2	38	1.3	4.4	0.16	0.02	34	27	9.2	2.6	
53	Rye (100%) ..	8.0	2.0	75.9	335	—	412	31.5	92.0	2.70	—	359	—	—	—	—
54	Rye (85%)	7.3	1.6	80.2	347	—	203	26.1	45.0	1.97	—	193	—	—	—	—
55	Rye (75%)	6.7	1.3	82.5	350	—	172	19.5	26.0	1.72	—	129	—	—	—	—
56	Rye (60%)	5.6	1.0	85.8	354	—	140	15.3	16.0	1.32	—	78	—	—	—	—
57	Ryvita	9.1	2.1	76.8	345	(615)	469	40.5	90.7	3.73	0.15	295	87	(935)	2.5	
58	Sago	0.2	0.2	94.0	355	3.4	5	9.8	2.5	1.18	0.03	29	0.5	12.3	1.3	
59	Semolina	10.7	1.8	77.5	352	11.8	166	18.2	32.0	1.04	0.15	114	92	71.0	6.7	
60	Shredded Wheat ..	9.7	2.8	79.0	362	16.5	303	34.8	120.0	4.48	0.45	287	86	71.0	5.7	
61	Soya. Full fat flour ..	40.3*	23.5	13.3†	433	—	1660	208	235	6.93	—	597	—	—	—	—
62	Soya. Low fat flour or grits	49.6*	7.2	17.2†	335	—	2025	241	286	9.14	—	643	—	—	—	—

* Total N × 6.25.   † 75 per cent. total carbohydrate taken to be available.

C2

Cereals and Cereal Foods – continued

No.	Food	Description and number of samples	g. per 100 g.			
			Water	Sugar (as invert sugar)	Starch and dextrins (as glucose)	Total nitrogen
63	Spaghetti	6 samples from different shops	12·4	2·7	81·3	1·74
64	Tapioca	4 varieties (medium pearl, seed pearl, coarse and flake)	12·2	Tr.	95·0	0·07
65	Vita-Weat	12 packets from different shops	4·9	Tr.	77·8	1·50
66	Weetabix	5 packets from different shops	8·2*	5·9	71·0	1·92

* When freshly packed the moisture content may be between 2 and 3 per cent.

Milk Products and Eggs

No.	Food	Description and number of samples	g. per 100 g.	
			Water	Total nitrogen
	Milk and milk products			
67	Butter, slightly salted ..	6 samples from different shops (Foreign, Australian and N.Z. and English) ..	13·9	0·07
68	Cheese, Camembert ..	3 samples from different shops	47·5	3·58
69	Cheese, Cheddar	6 samples from different shops	37·0	3·98
70	Cheese, Cheshire	4 samples from different shops	36·4	4·05
71	Cheese, cream (home-made) ..	1 sample only	10·0	0·51

Cereals and Cereal Foods – continued

No.	Food	g. per 100 g.			Calories per 100 g.	mg. per 100 g.									Acid base-balance, m-equiv. per 100 g.	
		Protein (N×5·7)	Fat	Available carbohydrate (as monosaccharides)		Na	K	Ca	Mg	Fe	Cu	P	S	Cl	Acid	Base
63	Spaghetti	9·9	1·0	84·0	365	4·8	161	22·6	34·9	1·21	0·27	124	97	63·0	7·5	—
64	Tapioca	0·4	0·1	95·0	359	4·2	20	8·2	2·0	0·32	0·07	30	3·5	13·1	1·2	
65	Vita-Weat	8·6	10·3	77·8	423	(605)	430	44·0	118·0	3·40	0·19	372	93	(845)	4·3	
66	Weetabix	10·9	1·9	77·0	351	(316)	340	35·5	119·0	4·11	0·48	288	—	(500)	—	

Milk Products and Eggs – continued

No.	Food	g. per 100 g.			Calories per 100 g.	mg. per 100 g.									Acid-base balance, m-equiv. per 100 g.	
		Protein (N×6·38)	Fat	Available carbohydrate (as monosaccharides)		Na	K	Ca	Mg	Fe	Cu	P	S	Cl	Acid	Base
	Milk and milk products															
67	Butter, slightly salted	0·4	85·1	Tr.	793	(223)*	15	15	2·4	0·16	0·03	24	9	(332)=	0·4	—
68	Cheese, Camembert	22·8	23·2	Tr.	309	(1403)	111	152	17·4	0·76	0·08	285	—	(2323)	—	—
69	Cheese, Cheddar	25·4	34·5	Tr.	425	(612)	116	810	46·9	0·57	0·03	545	230	(1060)	5·4	
70	Cheese, Cheshire	25·8	30·6	Tr.	389	(700)	95	619	20·9	0·21	0·04	459	—	(1178)	—	
71	Cheese, cream	3·3	86·0	Tr.	813	(110)	47	30	5·2	0·14	0·04	44	64	(15)	3·4	

* Salt-free butter contains approximately 7 mg. Na and 10 mg. Cl per 100 grams. Salted butters contain up to 900 mg. Na and 1400 mg. Cl per 100 grams.

Milk Products and Eggs – *continued*

No.	Food	Description and number of samples	g. per 100 g.	
			Water	Total nitrogen
72	Cheese, Danish Blue	4 samples from different shops	40·5	3·61
73	Cheese, Edam	4 samples from different shops	43·7	3·82
74	Cheese, Gorgonzola	4 samples from different shops	41·0	3·97
75	Cheese, Gouda	4 samples from different shops	42·4	3·54
76	Cheese, Gouda, matured	2 samples from different shops	34·9	4·16
77	Cheese, Gruyère	4 samples from different shops	21·9	5·90
78	Cheese, Norwegian Mysost	1 sample only	12·4	1·70
79	Cheese, Parmesan	3 samples from different shops	28·0	5·50
80	Cheese, processed	6 varieties	43·0	3·60
81	Cheese Spread	6 varieties	51·0	2·87
82	Cheese, St. Ivel	8 samples from different shops	45·7	3·70
83	Cheese, Stilton	3 samples from different shops	28·2	4·02
84	Cheese, Wensleydale	4 samples from different shops	38·0	4·59
85	Cream, double	3 samples from different shops	48·6	0·24
86	Cream, single	3 samples from different shops	71·9	0·38
87	Milk, fresh, whole	8 samples from different dairies	87·0	0·53
88	Milk, fresh, skimmed	Calculated on the assumption that skimmed milk contains 0·2 per cent .of fat	90·2	0·55
89	Milk, condensed, whole, sweetened	3 varieties	20·3	1·28
90	Milk, condensed, whole, unsweetened	3 varieties	67·9	1·22

Milk Products and Eggs – continued

No.	Food	g. per 100 g. Protein (N× 6·38)	g. per 100 g. Fat	g. per 100 g. Available carbohydrate (as monosaccharides)	Calories per 100 g.	mg. per 100 g. Na	K	Ca	Mg	Fe	Cu	P	S	Cl	Acid base-balance, m-equiv. per 100 g. Acid	Base
72	Cheese, Danish Blue	23·0	29·2	Tr.	366	(1417)	186	578	20·4	0·17	0·09	425	—	(2393)	—	—
73	Cheese, Edam	24·4	22·9	Tr.	313	(983)	159	739	27·7	0·21	0·03	523	—	(1640)	—	—
74	Cheese, Gorgonzola	25·4	31·1	Tr.	393	(1220)	172	540	37·8	0·50	0·15	375	177	(1800)	0·3	—
75	Cheese, Gouda	22·6	26·6	Tr.	340	(1054)	124	622	24·5	0·34	0·06	469	—	(1711)	—	—
76	Cheese, Gouda, matured	26·5	30·4	Tr.	390	(1202)	141	719	28·0	0·46	0·07	535	206	(1951)	—	—
77	Cheese, Gruyère	37·6	33·4	T.	465	(542)	128	1080	45·0	0·26	0·27	698	206	(825)	—	3·6
78	Cheese, Norwegian Mysost	10·8	28·7	42·0†	468	(301)	1477	319	62·8	0·43	0·03	412	—	(838)	—	—
79	Cheese, Parmesan	35·1	29·7	Tr.	420	(755)	153	1220	49·6	0·37	0·36	772	251	(1110)	—	5·1
80	Cheese, processed	23·0	30·1	Tr.	374	(918)	86	724	47·6	0·57	0·03	480	321	(1080)	—	0·5
81	Cheese Spread	17·9	22·9	0·9†	290	(1166)	150	509	24·6	0·69	0·09	436	—	(760)	—	—
82	Cheese, St. Ivel	23·6	30·5	Tr.	380	(567)	68	483	23·2	0·72	0·02	375	186	(910)	8·9	—
83	Cheese, Stilton	25·6	40·0	Tr.	477	(1150)	161	362	27·2	0·46	0·03	304	228	(1720)	7·8	—
84	Cheese, Wensleydale	29·3	30·7	Tr.	406	(364)	214	691	26·5	0·30	0·03	529	—	(55)	—	—
85	Cream, double	1·5	48·2	2·0†	462	26·8	79	50	3·8	0·20	0·13	21	—	46	—	—
86	Cream, single	2·4	21·2	3·2†	219	42·2	124	79	6·0	0·31	0·20	44	—	72	—	—
87	Milk, fresh, whole	3·4	3·7	4·8†	66	50·0	160	120	14·0	0·08	0·02	95	29	98	—	2·7
88	Milk, fresh, skimmed	3·5	0·2	5·1†	35	52·0	166	124	14·5	0·08	0·02	98	30	102	—	2·9
89	Milk, condensed, whole, sweetened	8·2	12·0	56·0	354	143	408	344	36·0	0·17	0·08	238	83	284	—	8·4
90	Milk, condensed, whole, unsweetened	7·8	8·8	†12·3	159	161	502	290	34·8	0·18	0·11	254	75	277		8·4

† See p. 4.

Milk Products and Eggs – *continued*

No.	Food	Description and number of samples	g. per 100 g.	
			Water	Total nitrogen
91	Milk, condensed, skimmed, sweetened ..	2 varieties	27·0	1·55
92	Milk, dried, skimmed	5 tins from different shops	5·0	5·46
93	Milk, dried, whole.. ..	Calculated on the assumption that dried milk is 8 times as concentrated as fresh milk. The figures for iron and copper may vary with the method of manufacture.	1·3	4·24
94	Human milk, transitional	Mixed sample from 15 mothers on tenth day *post partum*	90·2	0·31
94a	Human milk, mature	Mixed sample from 9 mothers 5—16 weeks *post partum* ..	87·1	0·19
95	Milk substitute, low Na " Edosol "	Supplied by local hospital	2·7	4·75
96	Milk substitute, low Ca " Locasol "	Supplied by local hospital	2·6	3·57
97	Ostermilk, No. 1 ..	6 tins from different shops	2·6	2·91
97a	Yoghurt, low fat ..	6 cartons from different shops	87·7	0·74
98	Eggs, fresh, whole ..	34 eggs, English and Danish, from different shops	73·4	1·90
99	Egg white ..	34 eggs, English and Danish, from different shops	88·3	1·44
100	Egg yolk ..	34 eggs, English and Danish, from different shops	51·0	2·58
101	Eggs, dried ..	6 packets from different shops	7·0	6·97
102	Eggs, fried ..	6 eggs from different shops	63·3	2·26
103	Eggs, poached ..	6 eggs from different shops	74·7	1·99

Milk Products and Eggs — continued

No.	Food	Protein (N× 6·38)*	Fat	Available carbohydrate (as monosaccharides)	Calories per 100 g.	Na	K	Ca	Mg	Fe	Cu	P	S	Cl	Acid	Base
		g. per 100 g.				mg. per 100 g.									Acid-base balance, m-equiv. per 100 g.	
91	Milk, condensed, skimmed, sweetened	9·9	0·3	60·0	267	180	498	384	37·7	0·29	0·03	270	94	310		10·9
92	Milk, dried, skimmed ..	34·5	0·3	†49·1	326	600	1335	1265	111·0	0·52	1·39‡	1050	300	1130		14·5
93	Milk, dried, whole ..	27·0	29·7	†38·8	530	400	1280	960	112·0	0·64	0·16	760	234	784		21·6
94	Human milk, transitional	2·0	3·7	†6·9	68	48	68	25	2·3	0·07	0·04	16	—	85	—	—
94a	Human milk, mature ..	1·2	5·1	†6·7	78	15	52	29	3·0	0·05	—	14	—	64	—	—
95	Milk substitute, low Na "Edosol"	30·3	26·4	37·9	510	43	739	846	17·1	0·58	0·10	604	—	(207)	—	—
96	Milk substitute, low Ca "Locasol"	22·8	19·9	51·9	474	218	604	46	57·2	1·50	0·09	343	—	240	—	—
97	Ostermilk No. 1 ::	18·6	17·5	†57·7	453	285	895	672	57·5	(4·04)	0·08	502	—	554	—	—
97a	Yoghurt, low fat ::	4·7	1·8	†4·9	54	62	177	163	15·2	0·05	—	118	—	119		
98	Eggs, fresh, whole ::	11·9	12·3	Tr.	163	135	138	56	12·3	2·53	0·03	218	173	159	16·2	
99	Egg white ::	9·0	Tr.	Tr.	37	192	148	5	10·7	0·10	0·03	33	183	170	5·0	
100	Egg yolk ::	16·2	30·5	Tr.	350	50	123	131	14·9	6·13	0·02	495	165	142	33·2	
101	Eggs, dried ::	43·4	43·3	Tr.	580	519	483	190	41·4	7·85	0·18	799	630	592	59·8	
102	Eggs, fried ::	14·1	19·5	Tr.	239	220	176	64	13·9	2·53	0·05	256	206	199	16·5	
103	Eggs, poached ::	12·4	11·7	Tr.	160	111	118	52	11·2	2·30	0·03	239	181	155	19·7	

* Eggs N× 6·25.   † See p. 4.   ‡ Most of this copper was probably derived from the manufacturing machinery.

Fats and Oils

No.	Food							Description and number of samples									g. per 100 g.	
																	Water	Total nitrogen
104	Cod liver oil	..	..	..	..	..	..	3 samples from different shops	..	..	..	..	..	..	..	..	Tr.	Tr.
105	Compound cooking fat	..	..	..	..	..	..	7 samples from different shops	..	..	..	..	..	..	..	..	Tr.	Tr.
106	Dripping, beef	..	..	..	..	..	..	Analysed as purchased	..	..	..	..	..	..	..	..	1·0	Tr.
107	Lard	..	..	..	..	..	..	Analysed as purchased	..	..	..	..	..	..	..	..	1·0	Tr.
108	Margarine	..	..	..	..	..	..	4 samples from different shops	..	..	..	..	..	..	..	..	13·7	0·03
109	Olive oil	..	..	..	..	..	..	One sample only	..	..	..	..	..	..	..	..	Tr.	Tr.
110	Suet..	..	..	..	..	..	..	Analysed as purchased	..	..	..	..	..	..	..	..	Tr.	0·15

Fats and Oils – *continued*

No.	Food	g. per 100 g.			Calories per 100 g.	mg. per 100 g.									Acid-base balance, m-equiv. per 100 g.	
		Protein (N × 6·25)	Fat	Carbohydrate		Na	K	Ca	Mg	Fe	Cu	P	S	Cl	Acid	Base
104	Cod liver oil	—	99·9	0·0	930	Tr.	Tr.	Tr.	Tr.	Tr.	Tr.	Tr.	Tr.	Tr.	—	—
105	Compound cooking fat	—	99·3	0·0	925	Tr.	Tr.	Tr.	Tr.	Tr.	Tr.	Tr.	Tr.	Tr.	—	—
106	Dripping, beef	Tr.	99·0	0·0	920	5	4	0·8	Tr.	0·2	—	13	9	2	1·1	
107	Lard	Tr.	99·0	0·0	920	2	1	0·8	1·3	0·1	0·02	3	25	4	1·6	
108	Margarine	0·2	85·3	0·0	795	(318)	5	4·1	0·9	0·3	0·04	12	12	(495)	1·3	
109	Olive oil	Tr.	99·9	0·0	930	0·1	Tr.	0·5	0·4	0·1	0·07	Tr.	Tr.	Tr.		⟨0·1
110	Suet	0·9	99·0	0·0	925	21	13	6·0	1·1	0·4	0·04	7	20	18	0·6	

Meat, Poultry and Game

No.	Food	Method of cooking	Nature of edible (analysed) material	Edible matter, as eaten, expressed as a percentage of the weight as purchased	g. per 100 g. Water	g. per 100 g. Total nitrogen	g. per 100 g. Purine nitrogen
111	*Bacon, Danish Wilts, tank cured	Raw	Average of 6 medium lean sides (rind and bone excluded)	—	46·9	2·23	0·037
112	*Bacon, Danish Wilts, tank cured	Raw	Fore ends of above sides (26·6 per cent. of total) (rind and bone excluded)	—	51·2	2·35	0·039
113	*Bacon, Danish Wilts., tank cured	Raw	Middle of above sides (50·6 per cent. of total) (rind and bone excluded)	—	40·9	2·07	0·035
114	*Bacon, Danish Wilts,. tank cured	Raw	Gammon of above sides (22·8 per cent. of total) rind and bone excluded)	—	55·4	2·45	0·041
115	*Bacon, English Wilts,. dry cured	Raw	Average of 3 sides (rind and bone excluded)	—	36·3	2·00	0·034
116	*Bacon, English Midland, dry cured	Raw	Average of 3 sides (rind and bone excluded)	—	25·3	1·67	0·028
117	Bacon, back	Rashers fried	Fat and lean	48	12·7	4·12	0·069
118	Bacon, collar	Rashers fried	Fat and lean	50	27·3	4·58	0·080
119	Bacon, gammon	Rashers fried	Fat and lean	58	24·9	5·28	0·086
120	Bacon, streaky	Rashers fried	Fat and lean	41	20·0	3·99	0·066
121	Beef, corned	Canned	All	100	58·5	3·60	0·036
122	Beef, frozen (Argentine, N.Z., Australia, S. Africa)	Raw	All	—	70·3	3·40	0·050
123	Beef, silverside	Boiled	All	74	46·2	4·62	0·055
124	Beef, sirloin	Roast (underdone in centre)	Lean only	44	58·4	4·47	0·060
125	Beef, sirloin	Roast (underdone in centre)	All except bone	60	45·2	3·54	0·046
126	Beef, steak	Raw	Lean only	—	68·3	3·19	0·058
127	Beef, steak	Fried (lightly cooked)	Lean with some fat	81	56·9	3·42	0·061

*These bacons were green, i.e., unsmoked. About 5 per cent. of the total weight is lost on smoking.

Meat, Poultry and Game – continued

No.	Food	Protein	Fat	Carbohydrate (as glucose)	Calories per 100 g.	Na	K	Ca	Mg	Fe	Cu	P	S	Cl	Acid	Base
		g. per 100 g.				*mg. per 100 g.*									*Acid-base balance, m-equiv. per 100 g.*	
	Bacon, raw															
111	Danish Wilts, average	14·0	37·4	0·0	405	(1220)	250	13·5	14·5	1·3	0·19	122	162	(1870)	7·5	
112	Danish Wilts, fore end	14·7	31·7	0·0	355	(1350)	265	14·4	15·5	1·1	0·20	138	170	(2070)	10·7	
113	Danish Wilts, middle ..	13·0	44·6	0·0	468	(1160)	227	13·5	13·8	1·3	0·19	119	150	(1760)	4·8	
114	Danish Wilts, gammon	15·3	28·2	0·0	325	(1200)	285	12·6	14·8	1·7	0·17	111	178	(1880)	9·8	
115	English Wilts.	12·5	49·3	0·0	509	(975)	268	13·5	12·3	0·9	0·27	94	145	(1510)	6·7	
116	English Midland	10·4	61·1	0·0	612	(830)	281	7·2	10·4	1·0	0·26	92	121	(1300)	5·8	
117	Bacon, back, fried	24·6	53·4	0·0	597	(2790)	517	11·5	25·7	2·8	—	229	298	(4150)	12·9	
118	Bacon, collar, fried	27·4	35·0	0·0	438	(3050)	492	23·2	25·8	3·9	—	236	332	(4790)	22·6	
119	Bacon, gammon, fried	31·3	33·9	0·0	444	(2330)	638	24·9	32·7	2·8	—	303	383	(4210)	40·8	
120	Bacon, streaky, fried	24·0	46·0	0·0	526	(3090)	462	52·3	25·1	3·2	0·16	238	299	(4750)	17·0	
121	Beef, corned ..	22·3	15·0	0·0	231	(1380)	117	12·8	29·0	9·8	0·19	119	212	(2080)	13·7	
122	Beef, frozen, raw	20·3	7·3	0·0	151	74	350	8·0	25·0	3·7	0·19	200	215	74	13·7	
123	Beef, silverside, boiled ..	28·0	20·0	0·0	301	(1470)	288	23·3	20·0	3·7	0·19	243	292	(2320)	25·2	
124	Beef, sirloin, roast, lean only	26·8	12·3	0·0	224	70	357	6·5	25·0	5·3		284	283	74	23·5	
125	Beef, sirloin, roast, lean and fat	21·3	32·1	0·0	385	62	290	5·8	19·9	4·6	0·17	237	224	64	19·0	
126	Beef steak, raw ..	19·3	10·5	0·0	177	69	334	5·4	24·5	4·3	—	276	202	70	18·5	
127	Beef steak, fried	20·4	20·4	0·0	273	80	371	5·2	24·8	6·0	—	257	216	90	17·3	

Meat, Poultry and Game – continued

No.	Food	Method of cooking	Nature of edible (analysed) material	Edible matter, as eaten, expressed as a percentage of the weight as purchased	g. per 100 g. Water	Total nitrogen	Purine nitrogen
128	Beef, steak	Grilled	All	73	50·5	4·24	0·085
129	Beef, steak	Stewed 4 hours	Lean only	57	58·1	5·19	0·061
130	Beef, topside	Boiled	Lean only	59	56·6	5·44	0·072
131	Beef, topside	Roast	Lean only	79	56·2	4·40	0·073
132	Beef, topside	Roast	All	89	50·0	3·99	0·066
133	Brain, calf	Boiled 10–15 min.	All	90	80·2	1·96	0·040
134	Brain, sheep	Boiled	All	95	79·7	1·92	0·031
135	Chicken	Raw	Pectoral muscle only	—	73·7	3·71	—
136	Chicken	Boiled	Flesh only	48	61·0	4·37	0·061
136a	Chicken (weighed with bone)	Boiled	Flesh only	48	39·6	2·85	0·040
137	Chicken	Roast (with basting)	Flesh only	40	61·1	4·84	0·072
137a	Chicken (weighed with bone)	Roast (with basting)	Flesh only	40	33·0	2·61	0·039
138	Duck	Roast (with basting)	Flesh only	42	52·0	3·67	0·064
138a	Duck (weighed with bone)	Roast (with basting)	Flesh only	42	28·1	1·98	0·035
139	Goose	Roast (with basting)	Flesh only	39	46·7	4·69	0·100
139a	Goose (weighed with bone)	Roast (with basting)	Flesh only	39	27·1	2·72	0·058
140	Grouse	Roast (with basting)	Flesh only	51	61·6	5·00	0·098
140a	Grouse (weighed with bone)	Roast (with basting)	Flesh only	51	40·6	3·30	0·065
141	Guinea-fowl	Roast (with basting)	Flesh only	41	56·9	5·32	0·142
141a	Guinea-fowl (weighed with bone)	Roast (with basting)	Flesh only	41	30·1	2·83	0·075
142	Ham, York	Raw	Average of 3 hams (all except bone)	—	31·0	2·40	—

Meat, Poultry and Game – continued

No.	Food	g. per 100 g.			Calories per 100 g.	mg. per 100 g.									Acid-base balance, m-equiv. per 100 g.	
		Protein	Fat	Carbohydrate (as glucose)		Na	K	Ca	Mg	Fe	Cu	P	S	Cl	Acid	Base
128	Beef steak, grilled	25·2	21·6	0·0	304	67	368	9·2	25·2	5·2	—	303	268	64	23·2	
129	Beef steak, stewed	30·8	8·6	0·0	206	38	153	3·0	21·1	5·1	—	229	328	35	28·9	
130	Beef, topside, boiled	33·3	8·2	0·0	213	46	220	3·6	25·9	8·3	—	247	345	49	28·9	
131	Beef, topside, roast, lean only	26·7	15·0	0·0	249	76	370	6·2	28·1	4·7	0·25	286	279	62	22·2	
132	Beef, topside, roast, lean and fat	24·2	23·8	0·0	321	72	337	5·9	25·4	4·4	0·23	264	252	59	20·4	
133	Brain, calf, boiled	12·0	5·8	0·0	103	147	270	16·0	13·3	2·0	—	355	132	167	20·7	
134	Brain, sheep, boiled	11·7	6·7	0·0	110	170	268	10·8	17·8	2·2	—	339	129	144	17·7	
135	Chicken, muscle, raw	23·2	2·1	0·0	115	46	407	5·8	29·0	0·7	—	248	268	61	19·5	
136	Chicken, boiled	26·2	10·3	0·0	203	98	381	10·7	26·4	2·1	—	270	293	62	20·7	
136a	Chicken, boiled (weighed with bone)	17·0	6·7	0·0	132	64	248	7·0	17·2	1·4	—	175	190	40	13·5	
137	Chicken, roast	29·6	7·3	0·0	189	80	355	14·5	23·0	2·6	—	271	324	100	25·4	
137a	Chicken, roast (weighed with bone)	16·0	3·9	0·0	102	43	192	7·8	12·4	1·4	—	146	175	54	13·7	
138	Duck, roast	22·8	23·6	0·0	313	195	319	19·0	23·9	5·8	—	231	395	158	24·4	
138a	Duck, roast (weighed with bone)	12·3	12·8	0·0	169	105	172	10·2	12·9	3·1	—	125	213	85	13·2	
139	Goose, roast	28·0	22·4	0·0	323	145	406	10·4	30·8	4·6	—	267	319	159	21·8	
139a	Goose, roast (weighed with bone)	16·2	13·0	0·0	187	84	236	6·0	17·8	2·7	—	155	185	92	12·7	
140	Grouse, roast	30·1	5·3	0·0	173	96	466	29·8	40·6	7·6	—	338	340	34	25·8	
140a	Grouse, roast (weighed with bone)	20·0	3·5	0·0	114	63	308	19·6	26·8	5·0	—	223	224	88	17·0	
141	Guinea-fowl, roast	32·5	8·2	0·0	210	136	430	19·2	28·7	9·3	—	292	363	179	26·3	
141a	Guinea-fowl, roast (weighed with bone)	17·2	4·3	0·0	112	72	228	10·2	15·2	4·9	—	155	192	95	13·9	
142	Ham, York, raw	15·0	49·0	0·0	517	(1120)	345	14·2	15·6	1·2	—	104	174	(1170)	7·6	

Meat, Poultry and Game – continued

No.	Food	Method of cooking	Nature of edible (analysed) material	Edible matter, as eaten, expressed as a percentage of the weight as purchased	Water	g. per 100 g.	
						Total nitrogen	Purine nitrogen
143	Ham	Boiled (purchased cooked and sliced)	Lean only	67	55·8	3·86	0·064
144	Ham	Boiled (purchased cooked and sliced)	As purchased, lean and fat	100	48·6	2·72	0·045
145	Ham or Pork, chopped	Canned, as purchased	Six varieties	100	53·6	2·43	—
146	Hare	Roast (with basting)	Flesh only	38	59·0	5·18	0·099
146a	Hare (weighed with bone)	Roast (with basting)	Flesh only	38	40·1	3·52	0·067
147	Hare	Stewed	Flesh only	44	60·7	4·78	0·060
147a	Hare (weighed with bone)	Stewed	Flesh only	44	44·3	3·48	0·044
148	Heart, pig	Raw	All	—	79·2	2·74	—
149	Heart, sheep	Roast	Ventricles only	53	57·3	4·18	0·174
150	Kidney, ox	Raw	All	—	75·5	2·82	0·094
151	Kidney, ox	Stewed	All	54	66·0	4·24	0·147
152	Kidney, sheep	Raw	Pelvis and capsule removed	—	77·4	2·86	0·103
153	Kidney, sheep	Fried	Pelvis and capsule removed	53	59·3	4·71	0·137
154	Liver, mixed sample	Raw	All	—	73·3	2·73	0·081
155	Liver, pig	Raw	All	—	71·6	3·17	—
156	Liver, calf	Sliced and fried after rolling in flour	All	64	50·8	4·78	0·143
157	Liver, ox	Sliced and fried after rolling in flour	All	67	47·7	4·84	0·143
158	Luncheon meat, canned	Raw	6 samples from different shops	100	52·4	1·82	—
159	Meat paste	Analysed as purchased	Chicken and ham, 3 varieties; ham and tongue, 2 varieties	100	60·5	3·15	—
160	Mutton chop	Raw	Lean only	37	67·1	3·18	0·081
160a	Mutton chop (weighed with fat and bone)	Raw	Lean only	37	24·9	1·18	0·030
161	Mutton chop	Raw	Lean and fat	77	32·3	2·28	0·049

Meat, Poultry and Game – continued

No.	Food	g. per 100 g.			Calories per 100 g.	mg. per 100 g.									Acid-base balance m-equiv. per 100 g.	
		Protein	Fat	Carbo-hydrate (as glucose)		Na	K	Ca	Mg	Fe	Cu	P	S	Cl	Acid	Base
143	Ham, boiled, lean only..	23·1	13·4	0·0	219	(2100)	454	17·0	23·5	2·6	—	244	280	(3350)	22·3	|
144	Ham, boiled, lean and fat	16·3	39·6	0·0	435	(1490)	322	12·7	17·4	2·5	—	192	198	(2350)	16·2	
145	Ham or Pork, chopped	15·2	29·9	Tr.	340	(1540)	223	11·8	16·6	1·5	0·09	136	—	(2120)		
146	Hare, roast	31·2	7·0	0·0	193	53	403	28·2	30·0	9·8	0·24	337	347	108	30·0	
146a	Hare, roast (weighed with bone)	21·3	4·8	0·0	131	36	274	19·2	20·4	6·7	0·16	229	236	74	20·4	
147	Hare, stewed ..	29·2	8·0	0·0	194	40	211	20·7	22·2	10·8	—	248	320	74	28·1	
147a	Hare, stewed (weighed with bone)	21·3	5·8	0·0	142	29	154	15·1	16·2	7·9	—	181	234	54	20·5	
148	Heart, pig, raw ..	17·1	2·7	0·0	95	80	300	5·7	19·7	4·8	—	76	198	113	11·3	
149	Heart, sheep, roast	25·0	14·7	0·0	239	153	370	9·5	34·9	8·1	—	389	296	125	27·6	
150	Kidney, ox, raw..	17·0	5·3	0·0	119	245	231	14·2	18·3	15·0	—	262	161	256	15·3	
151	Kidney, ox, stewed	25·7	5·8	0·0	159	164	164	20·8	22·4	7·1	0·31	392	242	144	30·3	
152	Kidney, sheep, raw	16·8	3·1	0·0	98	250	254	13·3	15·8	11·7	0·30	254	166	255	15·7	
153	Kidney, sheep, fried	28·0	9·1	0·0	199	261	304	16·6	26·7	14·5	5·80	433	274	288	31·0	
154	Liver, raw ..	16·5	8·1	0·0	143	86	325	8·4	20·8	13·9	—	313	239	100	23·6	
155	Liver, pig, raw ..	19·8	7·6	0·0	152	85	319	5·1	23·3	13·0	—	372	228	102	24·8	
156	Liver, calf, fried..	29·0	14·5	2·4	262	122	407	8·8	23·8	21·7	—	576	431	120	49·5	
157	Liver, ox, fried ..	29·5	15·9	4·0	284	92	386	8·6	26·5	20·7	—	550	410	82	46·9	|
158	Luncheon meat, canned	11·4	29·0	5·0	335	(873)	207	17·5	9·4	1·1	0·07	166	—	(1200)	—	
159	Meat paste ..	19·7	12·7	4·2	215	(940)	206	26·5	21·7	3·7	0·09	132	131	(1500)	9·6	
160	Mutton chop, raw, lean only	18·8	11·8	0·0	187	91	350	12·6	27·2	1·7	0·16	195	208	34	12·1	
160a	Mutton chop, raw, lean only (weighed with fat and bone)	7·0	4·4	0·0	69	34	130	4·7	10·1	0·6	0·06	72	77	31	4·5	
161	Mutton chop, raw, lean and fat	13·7	52·5	0·0	544	75	246	12·6	18·7	1·0	0·16	173	149	70	10·7	

Meat, Poultry and Game – *continued*

No.	Food	Method of cooking	Nature of edible (analysed) material	Edible matter, as eaten, expressed as a percentage of the weight as purchased	g. per 100 g.		
					Water	Total nitrogen	Purine nitrogen
161a	Mutton chop (weighed with bone)	Raw	Lean and fat	77	24·8	1·76	0·038
162	Mutton chop	Grilled	Lean only	34	53·7	4·38	0·061
162a	Mutton chop (weighed with fat and bone)	Grilled	Lean only	34	25·2	2·06	0·029
163	Mutton chop	Grilled	Lean and fat	55	33·6	3·26	0·046
163a	Mutton chop (weighed with bone)	Grilled	Lean and fat	55	25·4	2·46	0·035
164	Mutton chop	Covered with egg and breadcrumbs and fried	Lean only	36	44·2	3·82	0·063
164a	Mutton chop (weighed with fat and bone)	Covered with egg and breadcrumbs and fried	Lean only	36	16·6	1·43	0·024
165	Mutton chop	Covered with egg and breadcrumbs and fried	Lean and fat	78	20·6	2·54	0·040
165a	Mutton chop (weighed with bone)	Covered with egg and breadcrumbs and fried	Lean and fat	78	16·8	2·07	0·033
166	Mutton, leg	Boiled	All except bone	63	45·5	4·29	0·091
167	Mutton, leg	Roast	All except bone	48	52·4	4·15	0·077
168	Mutton, scrag and neck	Stewed	All except bone	46	49·7	3·96	0·056

Meat, Poultry and Game – *continued*

No.	Food	g. per 100 g.			Calories per 100 g.	mg. per 100 g.									Acid-base balance, m-equiv. per 100 g.	
		Protein	Fat	Carbohydrate (as glucose)		Na	K	Ca	Mg	Fe	Cu	P	S	Cl	Acid	Base
161a	Mutton chop, raw, lean and fat (weighed with bone)	10·6	40·5	0·0	419	58	190	9·7	14·4	0·8	0·12	133	115	54	8·3	
162	Mutton chop, grilled, lean only	26·5	17·5	0·0	271	127	400	20·9	30·0	2·5	0·18	239	286	110	17·0	
162a	Mutton chop, grilled, lean only (weighed with fat and bone)	12·4	8·2	0·0	127	60	188	9·8	14·1	1·2	0·09	112	134	52	8·0	
163	Mutton chop, grilled, lean and fat	19·9	45·0	0·0	500	102	305	17·8	22·8	2·4	0·18	206	213	90	14·1	
163a	Mutton chop, grilled, lean and fat (weighed with bone)	15·0	34·0	0·0	378	77	230	13·5	17·3	1·8	0·14	156	161	68	10·7	
164	Mutton chop, fried, lean only	22·8	25·2	5·7	341	116	349	15·4	26·1	3·1	0·13	222	250	134	16·6	
164a	Mutton chop, fried, lean only (weighed with fat and bone)	8·6	9·4	2·1	127	44	131	5·8	9·8	1·2	0·05	83	94	50	6·2	
165	Mutton chop, fried, lean and fat	15·4	60·1	2·6	629	86	241	14·0	17·9	2·6	0·12	184	166	92	12·6	
165a	Mutton chop, fried, lean and fat (weighed with bone)	12·6	49·0	2·1	512	70	196	11·4	14·6	2·1	0·10	150	135	75	10·3	
166	Mutton, leg, boiled	25·8	16·6	0·0	260	64	273	3·6	27·3	5·1	0·24	238	280	67	22·5	
167	Mutton, leg, roast	25·0	20·4	0·0	292	71	346	4·3	26·4	4·3	—	242	271	62	19·9	
168	Mutton, scrag and neck, stewed	24·2	24·4	0·0	326	66	186	50·0	26·6	6·8	—	220	259	82	20·3	

D2

Meat, Poultry and Game – *continued*

No.	Food	Method of cooking	Nature of edible (analysed) material	Edible matter, as eaten, expressed as a percentage of the weight as purchased	Water	g. per 100 g. Total nitrogen	g. per 100 g. Purine nitrogen
168a	Mutton, scrag and neck (weighed with bone)	Stewed..	All except bone	46	37·3	2·97	0·042
169	Partridge (weighed with bone)	Roast (with basting)	Flesh only	39	54·5	5·87	0·145
169a	Partridge (weighed with bone)	Roast (with basting)	Flesh only	39	32·7	3·52	0·087
170	Pemmican (Bovril)	—	6 cans supplied by makers	100	3·3	7·21	—
171	Pheasant	Roast (with basting)	Flesh only	45	56·9	5·15	0·095
171a	Pheasant (weighed with bone)	Roast (with basting)	Flesh only	45	35·8	3·24	0·060
172	Pigeon	Boiled..	Flesh only	36	62·1	3·57	0·083
172a	Pigeon (weighed with bone)	Boiled..	Flesh only	36	27·4	1·57	0·036
173	Pigeon	Roast (with basting)	Flesh only	28	57·2	4·44	0·096
173a	Pigeon (weighed with bone)	Roast (with basting)	Flesh only	28	25·2	1·95	0·043
174	Pork	Raw	Lean only	—	74·9	3·58	—
175	Pork, leg	Roast	All except bone	42	49·7	4·07	0·066
176	Pork, loin	Roast	Lean only	39	54·2	3·92	0·064
177	Pork, loin	Roast	Lean and fat	62	38·6	3·21	0·051
178	Pork, loin	Salt smoked (purchased cooked)	Lean only	100	54·0	3·90	0·050
179	Pork, loin chops	Grilled..	Lean only	31	48·9	4·20	0·068
179a	Pork, loin chops (weighed with bone)	Grilled..	Lean only	31	20·0	1·72	0·028

Meat, Poultry and Game – continued

No.	Food	g. per 100 g.			Calories per 100 g.	mg. per 100 g.									Acid-base balance, m-equiv. per 100 g.	
		Protein	Fat	Carbohydrate (as glucose)		Na	K	Ca	Mg	Fe	Cu	P	S	Cl	Acid	Base
168a	Mutton, scrag and neck, stewed (weighed with bone)	18·2	18·3	0·0	245	50	140	37·5	20·0	5·1	—	165	194	61	15·2	—
169	Partridge, roast	35·2	7·2	0·0	211	100	407	45·8	36·0	7·7	—	313	399	99	27·9	
169a	Partridge, roast (weighed with bone)	21·1	4·3	0·0	127	60	244	27·5	21·6	4·6	—	188	239	59	16·7	
170	Pemmican (Bovril)	45·1	43·5	0·0	590	(1630)	1020	28·9	67·3	11·8	0·29	521	—	(2430)	—	—
171	Pheasant, roast	30·8	9·3	0·0	213	104	411	49·3	35·0	8·4	—	308	306	108	21·6	
171a	Pheasant, roast (weighed with bone)	19·4	5·9	0·0	134	66	259	31·0	22·1	5·3	—	194	193	68	13·6	
172	Pigeon, boiled	21·7	13·9	0·0	218	74	299	17·6	31·2	9·8	—	352	243	75	25·7	
172a	Pigeon, boiled (weighed with bone)	9·6	6·1	0·0	96	33	131	7·8	13·7	4·3	—	155	107	33	11·3	
173	Pigeon, roast	26·8	13·2	0·0	233	105	410	16·3	33·8	19·4	—	404	302	99	29·1	
173a	Pigeon, roast (weighed with bone)	11·8	5·8	0·0	102	46	180	7·2	14·9	8·5	—	178	133	44	12·8	
174	Pork, raw	22·4	2·6	0·0	116	45	400	4·3	26·1	1·4	—	223	258	49	17·2	
175	Pork, leg, roast	24·6	23·2	0·0	317	66	308	5·2	22·6	1·7	—	363	253	83	28·6	
176	Pork, loin, roast, lean only	23·6	20·1	0·0	284	69	353	7·4	23·6	2·6	0·09	206	243	101	17·0	
177	Pork, loin, roast, lean and fat	19·5	40·4	0·0	455	60	287	7·5	18·0	2·3	0·09	185	199	77	14·6	
178	Pork, loin, salt, smoked, lean only	23·7	15·7	0·0	243	(1800)	300	27·3	24·1	2·3	—	219	242	(3100)	27·4	
179	Pork chops, grilled, lean only	25·3	23·7	0·0	325	76	347	9·2	20·7	2·9	0·09	211	261	113	18·7	
179a	Pork chops, grilled, lean only (weighed with bone)	10·4	9·7	0·0	133	31	142	3·8	8·5	1·2	0·04	86	107	46	7·7	

Meat, Poultry and Game – continued

No.	Food	Method of cooking	Nature of edible (analysed) material	Edible matter, as eaten, expressed as a percentage of the weight as purchased	g. per 100 g.		
					Water	Total nitrogen	Purine nitrogen
180	Pork, loin chops	Grilled	Lean and fat	60	29·6	3·06	0·049
180a	Pork, loin chops (weighed with bone)	Grilled	Lean and fat	60	24·6	2·54	0·041
181	Rabbit	Stewed	Flesh only	35	63·9	4·37	0·061
181a	Rabbit (weighed with bone)	Stewed	Flesh only	35	32·5	2·23	0·031
182	Sausage, beef	Fried	All	82	49·2	2·20	—
183	Sausage, pork	Raw	All	—	50·7	1·41	—
184	Sausage, pork	Fried	All	88	48·5	1·83	—
185	Sausage, black	Analysed as purchased	All except skin	—	55·8	0·85	0·002
186	Sausage, breakfast	Analysed as purchased	All	100	52·2	1·40	—
187	Sweetbreads	Stewed	All	59	65·6	3·70	0·426
188	Tongue, ox	Pickled in NaCl and sugar and boiled	Muscular portion only, fat at base of tongue and skin discarded	38	48·6	3·12	0·048
189	Tongue, sheep's	Stewed	Muscular portion only, fat at base of tongue and skin discarded	33	56·9	2·91	0·052
190	Tripe, dressed	Stewed (treated with lime before purchase)	All	54	77·6	3·00	0·022
191	Turkey	Roast (with basting)	Flesh only	46	59·0	5·07	0·079
191a	Turkey (weighed with bone)	Roast (with basting)	Flesh only	46	35·4	3·04	0·049
192	Veal, fillet	Raw	All	—	74·9	3·37	0·080
193	Veal, frozen (Uruguay and N.Z.)	Raw	All	—	75·2	3·19	0·050
194	Veal cutlet	Covered with egg and breadcrumbs and fried	All	74	54·6	5·02	0·106
195	Veal, fillet	Roast	All	75	55·1	5·06	0·089
196	Venison, haunch	Roast	Flesh only	58	56·8	5·60	0·097

Meat, Poultry and Game — continued

No.	Food	g. per 100 g.			Calories per 100 g.	mg. per 100 g.									Acid-base balance, m-equiv. per 100 g.	
		Protein	Fat	Carbohydrate (as glucose)		Na	K	Ca	Mg	Fe	Cu	P	S	Cl	Acid	Base
180	Pork chops, grilled, lean and fat	18·6	50·3	0·0	544	59	258	8·3	14·9	2·4	0·09	178	190	72	14·2	
180a	Pork chops, grilled, lean and fat (weighed with bone)	15·4	41·9	0·0	451	49	214	6·9	12·4	2·0	0·07	148	158	50	11·8	
181	Rabbit, stewed	26·6	7·7	0·0	180	32	210	11·3	21·6	1·9	0·20	199	245	43	20·1	
181a	Rabbit, stewed (weighed with bone)	13·6	3·9	0·0	92	16	107	5·8	11·0	1·0	0·10	102	125	22	10·2	
182	Sausage, beef, fried	13·8	18·4	15·7	287	(1130)	255	21·2	16·6	4·1	0·17	168	163	(170)	12·9	
183	Sausage, pork, raw	8·8	28·8	9·8	341	(770)	158	15·1	11·5	2·5	0·12	108	73	(100)	2·5	
184	Sausage, pork, fried	11·5	24·8	12·7	326	(999)	205	19·7	14·9	3·3	0·15	141	95	(100)	3·6	
185	Sausage, black	5·3	22·5	14·7	286	(900)	130	31·2	15·0	19·5	0·26	27	173	(120)	4·4	
186	Sausage, breakfast	8·7	20·4	16·8	288	(880)	170	21·9	16·4	1·9	0·08	86	79	(100)	2·0	
187	Sweetbreads, stewed	22·7	9·1	0·0	178	69	231	14·3	15·4	1·6	—	596	185	74	11·7	
188	Tongue, ox, pickled	19·1	23·9	2·3	309	(1870)	152	30·9	16·2	3·0	—	229	200	(300)	23·6	
189	Tongue, sheep's, stewed	18·0	24·0	0·0	297	79	109	11·1	13·2	3·4	—	196	187	80	18·7	
190	Tripe, stewed	18·0	3·0	0·0	102	72	9	(127)	7·9	1·6	—	132	145	30	8·1	
191	Turkey, roast	30·2	7·7	0·0	196	130	367	38·3	28·2	3·8	—	320	234	23	19·5	
191a	Turkey, roast (weighed with bone)	18·1	4·6	0·0	118	78	220	23·0	16·9	2·3	—	192	140	74	11·7	
192	Veal, fillet, raw	20·1	2·7	0·0	108	107	357	7·6	25·0	2·3	—	258	220	68	16·1	
193	Veal, frozen, raw	18·7	3·6	0·0	110	95	370	10·2	25·0	1·8	0·15	200	208	98	12·4	
194	Veal, cutlet, fried	30·4	8·1	4·4	216	106	422	10·0	32·7	2·6	—	283	329	115	23·5	
195	Veal, fillet, roast	30·5	11·5	0·0	232	97	427	14·3	27·6	2·5	—	355	330	113	28·5	
196	Venison, roast	33·5	6·4	0·0	197	86	364	29·0	33·4	7·8	—	286	321	89	23·8	

Fish

No.	Food	Nature of raw material	Method of cooking	Nature of edible (analysed) material	Edible matter, as eaten, expressed as a percentage of the weight as purchased	g. per 100 g.		
						Water	Total nitrogen	Purine nitrogen
197	Bass	Whole fish, excluding guts	Steamed	Flesh and skin ..	47	73·3	3·26	0·073
197a	Bass (weighed with bones)	Whole fish, excluding guts	Steamed	Flesh and skin ..	47	38·9	1·73	0·039
198	Bloaters	Body of fish without heads, roes or guts	Grilled	Flesh only ..	65	55·6	3·76	0·133
198a	Bloaters (weighed with bones and skin)	Body of fish without heads, roes or guts	Grilled	Flesh only ..	65	41·1	2·78	0·098
199	Bream, Red	Whole fish, excluding guts	Steamed	Flesh and skin ..	47	73·5	3·39	0·069
199a	Bream, Red (weighed with bones)	Whole fish, excluding guts	Steamed	Flesh and skin ..	47	38·2	1·76	0·036
200	Bream, Sea	Whole fish, excluding guts	Steamed	Flesh and skin ..	58	76·5	3·07	0·072
200a	Bream, Sea (weighed with bones)	Whole fish, excluding guts	Steamed	Flesh and skin ..	58	49·7	2·00	0·047
201	Brill	Pieces from tail end	Steamed	Flesh only ..	63	74·2	3·39	0·061
201a	Brill (weighed with bones and skin)	Pieces from tail end	Steamed	Flesh only ..	63	50·5	2·30	0·042
202	Catfish	Middle cuts, skinned	Steamed	All except bones ..	64	73·6	3·43	0·060
202a	Catfish (weighed with bones)	Middle cuts, skinned	Steamed	All except bones ..	64	62·5	2·92	0·051
203	Catfish	Middle cuts, skinned	Covered with batter and crumbs and fried	All except bones ..	90	61·9	3·17	0·065
203a	Catfish (weighed with bones)	Middle cuts, skinned	Covered with batter and crumbs and fried	All except bones ..	90	58·0	2·98	0·061

Fish – continued

No.	Food	g. per 100 g.			Calories per 100 g.	mg. per 100 g.									Acid-base balance, m-equiv. per 100 g.	
		Protein	Fat	Carbohydrate (as glucose)		Na	K	Ca	Mg	Fe	Cu	P	S	Cl	Acid	Base
197	Bass, steamed	19·5	5·1	0·0	127	75	326	46·9	26·9	0·7	—	220	233	35	15·0	
197a	Bass, steamed (weighed with bones)	10·4	2·7	0·0	67	40	173	24·9	14·2	0·4	—	117	124	45	7·9	
198	Bloaters, grilled	22·6	17·4	0·0	255	(703)	446	123·0	44·7	2·2	—	355	308	(1110)	74·1	
198a	Bloaters, grilled (weighed with bones and skin)	16·7	12·9	0·0	189	(520)	330	91·0	33·1	1·6	—	263	228	(818)	55·0	
199	Bream, Red, steamed	19·7	4·0	0·0	118	119	345	27·9	29·9	0·4	—	213	242	138	14·8	
199a	Bream, Red, steamed (weighed with bones)	10·2	2·1	0·0	61	62	179	14·5	15·6	0·2	—	111	126	72	7·7	
200	Bream, Sea, steamed	17·8	3·0	0·0	101	113	281	35·0	26·7	0·6	—	238	219	122	16·4	
200a	Bream, Sea, steamed (weighed with bones)	11·6	2·0	0·0	66	73	182	22·7	17·4	0·4	—	155	142	79	10·6	
201	Brill, steamed	20·4	3·4	0·0	115	94	264	15·3	31·0	0·7	0·13	230	214	125	17·5	
201a	Brill, steamed (weighed with bones and skin)	13·9	2·3	0·0	78	64	180	10·4	21·1	0·5	0·09	157	146	85	11·9	
202	Catfish, steamed	20·4	3·7	0·0	118	108	317	13·9	26·6	0·6	—	212	215	108	14·5	
202a	Catfish, steamed (weighed with bones)	17·4	3·2	0·0	100	92	269	11·8	22·6	0·5	—	180	183	92	12·3	
203	Catfish, fried	18·8	10·5	6·5	200	120	323	19·1	25·7	2·3	—	228	199	50	14·8	
203a	Catfish, fried (weighed with bones)	17·7	9·9	6·1	188	113	304	18·0	24·2	2·2	—	215	187	41	13·9	

Fish – *continued*

No.	Food	Nature of raw material	Method of cooking	Nature of edible (analysed) material	Edible matter, as eaten, expressed as a percentage of the weight as purchased	g. per 100 g.		
						Water	Total nitrogen	Purine nitrogen
204	Cockles	Purchased cooked without shells	.. .. ..	All	100	78·9	1·80	0·051
205	Cod	Middle cuts ..	Steamed	Flesh only ..	66	79·2	2·98	0·062
205a	Cod (weighed with bones and skin)	Middle cuts ..	Steamed	Flesh only ..	66	64·1	2·42	0·050
206	Cod, fried	Purchased cooked..	Fried in batter	Analysed as purchased	100	60·9	3·14	—
207	Cod	Steaks	Covered with batter and crumbs and fried	All except bones ..	114	69·4	3·44	0·063
207a	Cod (weighed with bones) ..	Steaks	Covered with batter and crumbs and fried	All except bones ..	114	63·1	3·13	0·057
208	Cod	Steaks	Grilled with added butter	Flesh only ..	54	64·6	4·56	0·082
208a	Cod (weighed with bones and skin)	Steaks	Grilled with added butter	Flesh only ..	54	54·9	3·87	0·070
209	Cod roe	Half a roe ..	Parboiled, sliced and fried in crumbs	All	93	62·0	3·35,	0·112
210	Cod roe	Half a roe	Baked in vinegar ..	All	98	71·1	3·85	0·130
211	Conger	Cut from behind head	Steamed	Flesh only ..	60	73·3	3·77	0·063
211a	Conger (weighed with bones and skin)	Cut from behind head	Steamed	Flesh only ..	60	55·0	2·83	0·047
212	Conger	Steaks from behind head	Covered with batter and crumbs and fried	All except bones ..	91	52·7	3·10	0·070

Fish – continued

No.	Food	g. per 100 g.			Calories per 100 g.	mg. per 100 g.									Acid-base balance, m-equiv. per 100 g.	
		Protein	Fat	Carbohydrate (as glucose)		Na	K	Ca	Mg	Fe	Cu	P	S	Cl	Acid	Base
204	Cockles	11·0	0·3	Tr.	48	(3520)	43	127·0	51·0	26·0	—	204	322	(≤220)	15·6	—
205	Cod, steamed	18·0	0·9	0·0	82	100	360	14·6	20·6	0·5	0·10	242	212	120	16·2	
205a	Cod, steamed (weighed with bones and skin) ..	14·6	0·7	0·0	66	81	292	11·8	16·7	0·4	0·08	196	172	97	13·1	
206	Cod, fried (purchased cooked)	19·6	10·3	7·5	204	102	365	80·0	24·2	0·5	0·07	202	—	252	—	
207	Cod, fried	20·7	4·7	2·9	140	161	342	49·6	26·8	1·0	0·10	261	243	145	15·6	
207a	Cod, fried (weighed with bones)	18·8	4·3	2·6	127	146	311	45·2	24·4	0·9	0·09	238	221	132	14·2	
208	Cod, grilled	27·0	5·3	0·0	160	110	407	31·0	36·0	1·0	—	274	323	130	21·8	
208a	Cod, grilled (weighed with bones and skin) ..	22·9	4·5	0·0	136	94	346	26·4	30·6	0·9	—	233	274	111	18·5	
209	Cod roe, fried	20·6	11·9	3·0	206	127	258	16·8	10·5	1·6	—	504	238	138	38·8	
210	Cod roe, baked in vinegar	24·0	3·2	0·0	128	73	132	13·0	8·0	2·3	—	402	272	173	40·0	
211	Conger, steamed ..	22·8	1·8	0·0	110	99	347	29·8	28·4	0·5	—	220	269	82	16·3	
211a	Conger, steamed (weighed with bones and skin)	17·1	1·4	0·0	83	74	260	22·4	21·3	0·4	—	165	202	62	12·2	
212	Conger, fried	18·7	20·0	6·5	287	108	353	24·2	29·4	1·0	—	247	222	156	16·8	

Fish – continued

No.	Food	Nature of raw material	Method of cooking	Nature of edible (analysed) material	Edible matter, as eaten, expressed as a percentage of the weight as purchased	g. per 100 g.		
						Water	Total nitrogen	Purine nitrogen
212a	Conger (weighed with bones)	Steaks from behind head	Covered with batter and crumbs and fried	All except bones	91	46·3	2·73	0·062
213	Crab	Alive	Boiled in fresh water	Flesh only	16	72·5	3·21	0·061
213a	Crab (weighed with shell)	Alive	Boiled in fresh water	Flesh only	16	14·5	0·64	0·012
214	Dabs	Whole fish, excluding guts	Covered with batter and crumbs and fried	All except bones	91	19·9	3·19	0·065
214a	Dabs (weighed with bones)	Whole fish, excluding guts	Covered with batter and crumbs and fried	All except bones	91	15·9	2·55	0·052
215	Dogfish	Tail ends, skinned	Covered with batter and crumbs and fried	All except bones	90	44·4	3·66	0·050
215a	Dogfish (weighed with bone)	Tail ends, skinned	Covered with batter and crumbs and fried	All except bones	90	40·3	3·33	0·045
216	Eels, elvers	Whole fish	Raw	All	100	81·8	2·02	—
217	Eels, silver	Live eels	Raw	Flesh only	66	57·1	2·31	—
217a	Eels, silver (weighed with bones and skin)	Live eels	Raw	Flesh only	66	37·8	1·52	—
218	Eels, silver	Live eels	Stewed in half their weight of water	Flesh only	50	49·2	2·84	—
219	Eels, yellow	Live eels	Raw	Flesh only	67	71·3	2·66	—
219a	Eels, yellow (weighed with bones and skin)	Live eels	Raw	Flesh only	67	47·8	1·78	—

Fish – *continued*

No.	Food	g. per 100 g.			Calories per 100 g.	mg. per 100 g.									Acid-base balance, m-equiv. per 100 g.	
		Protein	Fat	Carbohydrate (as glucose)		Na	K	Ca	Mg	Fe	Cu	P	S	Cl	Acid	Base
212a	Conger, fried (weighed with bones)	16·4	17·6	5·7	252	95	310	21·3	25·8	0·9	—	217	195	137	14·8	
213	Crab, boiled	19·2	5·2	0·0	127	366	271	29·4	47·9	1·3	—	350	465	570	39·5	
213a	Crab, boiled (weighed with shell)	3·8	1·0	0·0	25	73	54	5·9	9·6	0·3	—	70	93	114	7·9	
214	Dabs, fried	19·2	14·3	9·8	249	127	284	130·0	29·1	1·0	0·07	250	259	245	17·5	
214a	Dabs, fried (weighed with bones)	15·4	11·4	7·8	199	102	227	104·0	23·3	0·8	0·06	200	207	196	14·0	
215	Dogfish, fried	17·9	25·2	6·0	330	163	245	12·5	20·0	1·3	—	269	210	203	20·5	
215a	Dogfish, fried (weighed with bone)	16·3	22·9	5·5	300	148	223	11·4	18·2	1·2	—	244	191	134	18·6	
216	Eels, elvers, raw	12·6	2·2	0·0	72	67	230	515·0	31·0	4·0	Tr.	440	141	55	1·6	
217	Eels, silver, raw	14·4	27·8	0·0	318	77	215	12·6	14·3	0·8	0·03	192	162	69	13·8	
217a	Eels, silver, raw (weighed with bones and skin)	9·5	18·4	0·0	211	51	142	8·3	9·4	0·5	0·02	127	107	46	9·1	
218	Eels, silver, stewed	17·7	32·4	0·0	374	73	200	14·4	14·8	1·0	—	200	199	64	16·8	
219	Eels, yellow, raw	16·6	11·3	0·0	173	89	267	18·5	19·0	0·7	0·05	223	187	57	14·5	
219a	Eels, yellow, raw (weighed with bones and skin)	11·1	7·4	0·0	115	60	179	12·4	12·7	0·5	0·03	150	125	33	9·6	

Fish – *continued*

No.	Food	Nature of raw material	Method of cooking	Nature of edible (analysed) material	Edible matter, as eaten, expressed as a percentage of the weight as purchased	g. per 100 g.		
						Water	Total nitrogen	Purine nitrogen
220	Fillet, smoked	Fillet as purchased	Steamed	All	67	75·2	3·25	0·048
221	Fish paste	Analysed as purchased		Salmon and shrimp 3 varieties; salmon and anchovy, 2 varieties; bloater, 3 varieties	100	64·5	2·38	—
222	Flounder	Body of fish without head or guts	Steamed	Flesh only	45	76·6	3·24	0·086
222a	Flounder (weighed with bones and skin)	Body of fish without head or guts	Steamed	Flesh only	45	42·8	1·81	0·048
223	Flounder	Body of fish without head or guts	Covered with batter and crumbs and fried	Flesh and skin	74	61·5	2·84	0·061
223a	Flounder (weighed with bones)	Body of fish without head or guts	Covered with batter and crumbs and fried	Flesh and skin	74	42·4	1·96	0·042
224	Gurnet, grey	Body of fish without head or guts	Steamed	Flesh only	61	72·0	3·46	0·085
224a	Gurnet, grey (weighed with bones and skin)	Body of fish without head or guts	Steamed	Flesh only	61	58·2	2·80	0·069
225	Gurnet, red	Body of fish without head or guts	Steamed	Flesh only	57	71·6	3·54	0·079
225a	Gurnet, red (weighed with bones and skin)	Body of fish without head or guts	Steamed	Flesh only	57	50·9	2·51	0·056
226	Haddock, fresh	Fillets	Raw	Flesh only	—	81·3	2·68	0·067
227	Haddock, fresh	Middle cut	Steamed	Flesh only	59	75·1	3·65	0·072

Fish – *continued*

No.	Food	g. per 100 g.			Calories per 100 g.	mg. per 100 g.									Acid-base balance, m-equiv. per 100 g.	
		Protein	Fat	Carbohydrate (as glucose)		Na	K	Ca	Mg	Fe	Cu	P	S	Cl	Acid	Base
220	Fillet, smoked, steamed	19·4	0·9	0·0	88	(1080)	268	19·6	43·9	1·0	—	222	248	(1550)	14·9	
221	Fish paste	14·9	9·5	6·5	174	(1480)	307	146·0	30·1	6·0	0·06	210	185	(2380)	10·3	
222	Flounder, steamed ..	19·4	1·7	0·0	95	115	318	55·1	25·0	1·3	—	296	231	148	19·7	
222a	Flounder, steamed (weighed with bones and skin)	10·9	1·0	0·0	53	64	178	30·9	14·0	0·7	—	166	129	83	11·0	
223	Flounder, fried	17·0	12·9	6·5	214	130	282	74·5	22·6	1·1	—	218	203	200	13·9	
223a	Flounder, fried (weighed with bones)	11·7	8·9	4·5	147	90	194	51·3	15·6	0·8	—	150	140	138	9·6	
224	Gurnet, grey, steamed ..	21·0	5·2	0·0	134	117	305	13·1	23·9	0·8	—	196	247	117	15·8	
224a	Gurnet, grey, steamed (weighed with bones and skin)	17·0	4·2	0·0	108	95	247	10·6	19·4	0·6	—	158	200	95	12·8	
225	Gurnet, red, steamed ..	21·3	4·7	0·0	131	186	350	20·9	30·9	0·7	—	241	253	141	14·6	
225a	Gurnet, red, steamed (weighed with bones and skin)	15·1	3·3	0·0	93	132	248	14·8	21·9	0·5	—	171	180	100	10·4	
226	Haddock, fillets, raw ..	15·9	0·6	0·0	71	125	302	31·7	22·5	1·0	—	216	223	155	15·6	
227	Haddock, fresh, steamed	22·0	0·8	0·0	97	121	323	54·6	27·8	0·7	0·13	234	304	78	17·7	

Fish – *continued*

No.	Food	Nature of raw material	Method of cooking	Nature of edible (analysed) material	Edible matter, as eaten, expressed as a percentage of the weight as purchased	g. per 100 g. Water	g. per 100 g. Total nitrogen	g. per 100 g. Purine nitrogen
227a	Haddock, fresh (weighed with bones and skin)	Middle cut ..	Steamed ..	Flesh only ..	59	57·1	2·77	0·055
228	Haddock, fresh ..	Body of fish without head or guts	Covered with batter and crumbs and fried	All except bones ..	115	65·1	3·42	0·083
228a	Haddock, fresh (weighed with bones)	Body of fish without head or guts	Covered with batter and crumbs and fried	All except bones ..	115	60·0	3·15	0·076
229	Haddock, smoked ..	As purchased ..	Steamed ..	Flesh only ..	55	71·6	3·73	0·065
229a	Haddock, smoked (weighed with bones and skin)	As purchased ..	Steamed ..	Flesh only ..	55	46·5	2·42	0·042
230	Hake ..	Middle cut ..	Steamed ..	Flesh only ..	63	76·1	3·11	0·061
230a	Hake (weighed with bones and skin)	Middle cut ..	Steamed ..	Flesh only ..	63	61·0	2·49	0·049
231	Hake ..	Steaks ..	Covered with batter and crumbs and fried	All except bones ..	106	62·0	3·18	0·052
231a	Hake (weighed with bones)	Steaks ..	Covered with batter and crumbs and fried	All except bones ..	106	58·3	2·99	0·049
232	Halibut ..	Middle cut ..	Steamed ..	Flesh only ..	66	70·9	3·80	0·068
232a	Halibut (weighed with bones and skin)	Middle cut ..	Steamed ..	Flesh only ..	66	53·8	2·88	0·052
233	Herring ..	Fillets ..	Raw ..	All except bones ..	—	63·5	2·70	0·119
234	Herring ..	Body of fish without head or guts	Covered with oatmeal and fried	Flesh, skin and roes	77	58·7	3·69	0·172

Fish – *continued*

No.	Food	g. per 100 g.			Calories per 100 g.	mg. per 100 g.									Acid-base balance, m-equiv. per 100 g.	
		Protein	Fat	Carbohydrate (as glucose)		Na	K	Ca	Mg	Fe	Cu	P	S	Cl	Acid	Base
227a	Haddock, fresh, steamed (weighed with bones and skin)	16·7	0·6	0·0	74	92	245	41·4	21·2	0·5	0·10	178	231	59	13·4	
228	Haddock, fresh, fried	20·4	8·3	3·6	175	177	348	114·0	30·6	1·2	—	247	285	181	14·0	
228a	Haddock, fresh, fried (weighed with bones)	18·8	7·6	3·3	161	163	320	105·0	28·2	1·1	—	227	262	166	12·9	
229	Haddock, smoked, steamed	22·3	0·9	0·0	100	(1220)	293	57·5	25·4	1·0	—	248	253	(1900)	19·7	
229a	Haddock, smoked, steamed (weighed with bones and skin)	14·5	0·6	0·0	65	(793)	190	37·4	16·5	0·7	—	162	164	(1230)	12·8	
230	Hake, steamed	18·5	3·3	0·0	107	118	310	15·9	26·7	0·6	0·12	218	193	95	12·7	
230a	Hake, steamed (weighed with bones and skin)	14·8	2·6	0·0	86	95	248	12·7	21·4	0·5	0·10	175	154	76	10·2	
231	Hake, fried	19·3	11·4	5·3	205	153	297	25·8	29·0	0·9	0·17	259	197	134	14·8	
231a	Hake, fried (weighed with bones)	18·2	10·7	5·0	193	144	279	24·3	27·3	0·8	0·16	244	185	125	13·9	
232	Halibut, steamed	22·7	4·0	0·0	130	111	340	13·0	23·2	0·6	0·07	255	255	80	18·6	
232a	Halibut, steamed (weighed with bones and skin)	17·3	3·0	0·0	99	84	258	9·9	17·6	0·5	0·05	194	194	61	14·1	
233	Herring, raw	16·7	18·1	0·0	273	130	317	101·0	31·7	1·5	—	272	191	122	11·5	
234	Herring, fried	21·8	15·1	1·5	235	101	415	38·6	34·7	1·9	—	339	261	125	21·9	

E

Fish – *continued*

No.	Food	Nature of raw material	Method of cooking	Nature of edible (analysed) material	Edible matter, as eaten, expressed as a percentage of the weight as purchased	g. per 100 g.		
						Water	Total nitrogen	Purine nitrogen
234a	Herring (weighed with bones)	Body of fish without head or guts	Covered with oatmeal and fried	Flesh, skin and roes	77	51·6	3·24	0·151
235	Herring	Body of fish without head or guts	Baked in vinegar ..	Flesh, skin and roes	78	67·5	2·89	0·160
235a	Herring (weighed with bones)	Body of fish without head or guts	Baked in vinegar ..	Flesh, skin and roes	78	62·0	2·65	0·147
236	Herring roe (soft) ..	Whole roes	Rolled in flour and fried	All	80	52·3	3·85	0·484
237	John Dory	Whole fish without head, guts or fins	Steamed	Flesh only	50	76·7	3·28	0·057
237a	John Dory (weighed with bones and skin)	Whole fish without head, guts or fins	Steamed	Flesh only	50	47·5	2·04	0·035
238	Kippers	As purchased ..	Baked	Flesh only	45	58·7	4·08	0·091
238a	Kippers (weighed with bones and skin)	As purchased ..	Baked	Flesh only	45	31·6	2·20	0·049
239	Lemon sole	Whole fish without head, guts or fins	Steamed	Flesh only	62	77·2	3·29	0·054
239a	Lemon sole (weighed with bones and skin)	Whole fish without head, guts or fins	Steamed	Flesh only ..	62	54·9	2·34	0·038
240	Lemon sole	Whole fish without head, guts or fins	Covered with batter and crumbs and fried	All except bones ..	91	60·4	2·57	0·044
240a	Lemon sole (weighed with bones)	Whole fish without head, guts or fins	Covered with batter and crumbs and fried	All except bones ..	91	47·7	2·03	0·035

Fish – *continued*

No.	Food	g. per 100 g.			Calories per 100 g.	mg. per 100 g.									Acid-base balance, m-equiv. per 100 g.	
		Protein	Fat	Carbo-hydrate (as glucose)		Na	K	Ca	Mg	Fe	Cu	P	S	Cl	Acid	Base
234a	Herring, fried (weighed with bones) ..	19·2	13·3	1·3	208	89	365	34·0	30·5	1·7	—	298	230	110	19·3	
235	Herring, baked in vinegar ..	16·9	12·9	0·0	189	62	233	58·2	21·8	1·6	—	326	205	119	23·8	
235a	Herring, baked in vinegar (weighed with bones)	15·5	11·8	0·0	174	57	214	53·5.	20·1	1·5	—	300	188	109	21·9	
236	Herring roe, fried ..	23·4	15·8	4·7	260	87	239	15·7	8·1	1·5	—	915	242	123	66·2	
237	John Dory, steamed ..	19·9	1·4	0·0	95	139	287	23·0	29·0	0·6	—	251	234	143	17·9	
237a	John Dory, steamed (weighed with bones and skin)	12·3	0·9	0·0	59	86	178	14·3	18·0	0·4	—	156	145	89	11·1	
238	Kippers, baked	23·2	11·4	0·0	201	(990)	520	64·8	47·5	1·4	—	426	280	(1520)	24·5	
238a	Kippers, baked (weighed with bones and skin)	12·5	6·2	0·0	108	(535)	281	35·0	25·7	0·8	—	230	151	(824)	13·2	
239	Lemon sole, steamed ..	19·9	0·9	0·0	90	115	279	20·6	20·0	0·6	0·12	247	241	117	19·4	
239a	Lemon sole steamed (weighed with bones and skin)	14·1	0·6	0·0	64	82	198	14·6	14·2	0·4	0·09	175	171	83	13·8	
240	Lemon sole, fried ..	15·4	13·0	9·3	219	136	250	95·0	22·3	1·1	0·16	241	189	124	11·9	
240a	Lemon sole, fried (weighed with bones)	12·2	10·3	7·4	173	108	198	75·0	15·8	0·9	0·13	190	149	58	8·4	

E2

Fish – *continued*

No.	Food	Nature of raw material	Method of cooking	Nature of edible (analysed) material	Edible matter, as eaten, expressed as a percentage of the weight as purchased	g. per 100 g.		
						Water	Total nitrogen	Purine nitrogen
241	Ling	Sections from body	Steamed	Flesh only	60	74·6	3·73	0·060
241a	Ling (weighed with bones and skin)	Sections from body	Steamed	Flesh only	60	55·9	2·79	0·045
242	Ling	Steaks	Covered with batter and crumbs and fried	All except bones	100	62·1	2·85	0·056
242a	Ling (weighed with bones)	Steaks	Covered with batter and crumbs and fried	All except bones	100	55·2	2·54	0·050
243	Lobster	Alive	Boiled in fresh water	Flesh only	29	72·4	3·54	0·073
243a	Lobster (weighed with shell)	Alive	Boiled in fresh water	Flesh only	29	26·1	1·27	0·026
244	Mackerel	Body of fish without head or guts	Fried	Flesh only	61	65·6	3·44	0·100
244a	Mackerel (weighed with bones and skin)	Body of fish without head or guts	Fried	Flesh only	61	47·8	2·51	0·073
245	Megrim	Fillets	Raw	All except bones	—	80·0	2·85	0·046
246	Megrim	Whole fish without guts	Steamed	Flesh only	54	75·9	3·45	0·057
246a	Megrim (weighed with bones)	Whole fish without guts	Steamed	Flesh only	54	50·8	2·32	0·038
247	Megrim	Whole fish without head, fins or guts	Covered with batter and crumbs and fried	All except bones	92	57·0	3·29	0·065
247a	Megrim (weighed with bones)	Whole fish without head, fins or guts	Covered with batter and crumbs and fried	All except bones	92	48·5	2·80	0·055

Fish – continued

| No. | Food | g. per 100 g. | | | Calories per 100 g. | mg. per 100 g. | | | | | | | | | Acid-base balance, m-equiv. per 100 g. | |
		Protein	Fat	Carbohydrate (as glucose)		Na	K	Ca	Mg	Fe	Cu	P	S	Cl	Acid	Base
241	Ling, steamed	22·4	0·8	0·0	99	120	370	17·6	36·9	0·5	—	221	266	99	14·9	
241a	Ling, steamed (weighed with bones and skin)	16·8	0·6	0·0	74	90	278	13·2	27·7	0·4	—	166	199	74	11·2	
242	Ling, fried	16·8	12·4	6·3	208	145	312	39·8	32·0	0·8	—	228	203	157	12·8	
242a	Ling, fried (weighed with bones)	15·0	11·0	5·6	185	129	278	35·4	28·5	0·7	—	203	181	140	11·4	
243	Lobster, boiled	21·2	3·4	0·0	119	325	258	61·9	34·3	0·8	—	283	514	525	38·4	
243a	Lobster, boiled (weighed with shell)	7·6	1·2	0·0	43	117	93	22·2	12·3	0·3	—	102	185	189	13·8	
244	Mackerel, fried	20·0	11·3	0·0	187	153	418	28·4	34·8	1·2	0·20	280	210	114	12·7	
244a	Mackerel, fried (weighed with bones and skin)	14·6	8·3	0·0	136	112	305	20·7	25·4	0·9	0·15	204	153	83	9·3	
245	Megrim, raw	17·1	1·0	0·0	79	121	269	61·8	29·4	1·2	—	187	204	122	10·5	
246	Megrim, steamed	20·7	1·3	0·0	97	96	214	76·0	27·7	0·9	—	218	246	119	17·1	
246a	Megrim, steamed (weighed with bones and skin)	13·9	0·9	0·0	65	64	144	50·9	18·6	0·6	—	146	165	80	11·5	
247	Megrim, fried	19·5	11·6	9·5	224	177	251	62·8	31·0	0·6	—	219	235	183	14·1	
247a	Megrim, fried (weighed with bones)	16·6	9·9	8·1	190	150	214	53·4	26·4	0·5	—	186	200	156	12·0	

Fish – *continued*

No.	Food	Nature of raw material	Method of cooking	Nature of edible (analysed) material	Edible matter, as eaten, expressed as a percentage of the weight as purchased	Water	Total nitrogen	Purine nitrogen
							g. per 100 g.	
248	Monkfish	Tail ends skinned ..	Steamed	All except bones ..	53	75·4	3·58	0·053
248a	Monkfish (weighed with bones)	Tail ends skinned ..	Steamed	All except bones ..	53	61·1	2·90	0·043
249	Monkfish	Tail ends skinned ..	Covered with batter and crumbs and fried	All except bones ..	78	66·3	2·88	0·066
249a	Monkfish (weighed with bones)	Tail ends skinned ..	Covered with batter and crumbs and fried	All except bones ..	78	57·0	2·48	0·057
250	Mullet, grey	Whole fish without guts	Steamed	Flesh only	55	72·7	3·52	0·073
250a	Mullet, grey (weighed with bones and skin)	Whole fish without guts	Steamed	Flesh only	55	46·5	2·25	0·047
251	Mullet, red	Whole fish without guts	Steamed	Flesh and skin ..	53	71·6	3·62	0·081
251a	Mullet, red (weighed with bones)	Whole fish without guts	Steamed	Flesh and skin ..	53	47·3	2·38	0·054
252	Mussels	Alive in shells ..	Raw..	Flesh only	32	84·1	1·93	0·199
253	Mussels	Alive in shells ..	Boiled in fresh water	Flesh only	20	79·0	2·75	0·154
253a	Mussels (weighed with shells)	Alive in shells ..	Boiled in fresh water	Flesh only	20	23·7	0·83	0·046
254	Oysters	Alive in shells ..	Raw..	Flesh only	12	85·7	1·72	0·044
254a	Oysters (weighed with shells)	Alive in shells ..	Raw..	Flesh only	12	10·3	0·21	0·005
255	Pilchards	Canned, with added water and salt	.. ..	Fish, except backbone	79	65·5	3·50	—
256	Pilchards	Canned, with added water and salt	.. ..	Everything in can except backbone	97	64·0	3·02	—

Fish – *continued*

No.	Food	g. per 100 g.			Calories per 100 g.	mg. per 100 g.									Acid-base balance, m-equiv. per 100 g.	
		Protein	Fat	Carbohydrate (as glucose)		Na	K	Ca	Mg	Fe	Cu	P	S	Cl	Acid	Base
248	Monkfish, steamed	21·8	0·9	0·0	98	135	356	10·4	29·6	0·5	—	215	256	136	15·7	
248a	Monkfish, steamed (weighed with bones)	17·7	0·7	0·0	79	109	288	8·4	24·0	0·4	—	174	207	110	12·7	
249	Monkfish, fried	17·0	8·2	6·1	169	164	400	11·3	31·7	1·2	—	206	206	197	11·1	
249a	Monkfish, fried (weighed with bones)	14·6	7·1	5·2	145	141	344	9·7	27·2	1·0	—	177	177	169	9·6	
250	Mullet, grey, steamed	21·6	4·0	0·0	126	94	275	14·2	30·0	2·0	—	256	252	77	20·1	
250a	Mullet, grey, steamed (weighed with bones and skin)	13·8	2·6	0·0	81	60	176	9·1	19·2	1·3	—	164	161	49	12·8	
251	Mullet, red, steamed	21·4	4·3	0·0	128	118	364	29·2	32·8	0·9	—	282	258	101	18·5	
251a	Mullet, red, steamed (weighed with bones)	14·1	2·8	0·0	85	78	240	19·3	21·7	0·6	—	186	171	67	12·2	
252	Mussels, raw	11·7	1·9	Tr.	66	289	315	88·0	22·7	5·8	—	236	367	163	24·4	
253	Mussels, boiled	16·8	2·0	Tr.	87	210	92	197·0	25·0	13·5	—	331	348	315	28·7	
253a	Mussels, boiled (weighed with shells)	5·0	0·6	Tr.	26	63	28	59·0	7·5	4·1	—	99	104	95	8·6	
254	Oysters, raw	10·2	0·9	Tr.	50	505	258	186·0	41·8	6·0	—	267	249	815	14·4	
254a	Oysters, raw (weighed with shells)	1·2	0·1	Tr.	6	61	31	22·3	5·0	0·7	—	32	30	98	1·7	
255	Pilchards, canned (fish only)	21·9	10·8	0·0	191	(595)	305	231·0	41·6	3·1	0·21	296	245	(905)	12·4	
256	Pilchards, canned (whole contents of can)	18·9	15·4	0·0	221	(573)	290	190·0	38·0	2·6	0·19	269	212	(856)	9·9	

Fish – *continued*

No.	Food	Nature of raw material	Method of cooking	Nature of edible (analysed) material	Edible matter, as eaten, expressed as a percentage of the weight as purchased	g. per 100 g.		
						Water	Total nitrogen	Purine nitrogen
257	Plaice	Fillets	Raw	All except bones	—	80·8	2·59	0·065
258	Plaice	Body of fish without head, fins or guts	Steamed	Flesh only	49	78·0	3·02	0·053
258a	Plaice (weighed with bones)	Body of fish without head, fins or guts	Steamed	Flesh only	49	42·1	1·63	0·029
259	Plaice	Body of fish without head, fins or guts	Covered with batter and crumbs and fried	All except bones	61	58·5	3·02	0·047
259a	Plaice (weighed with bones)	Body of fish without head, fins or guts	Covered with batter and crumbs and fried	All except bones	61	35·6	1·84	0·029
260	Pollack	Middle cut	Steamed	Flesh only	68	20·7	3·33	0·071
260a	Pollack (weighed with bones and skin)	Middle cut	Steamed	Flesh only	68	17·8	2·86	0·061
261	Pollack	Steaks	Covered with batter and crumbs and fried	All except bones	100	67·5	2·77	0·075
261a	Pollack (weighed with bones)	Steaks	Covered with batter and crumbs and fried	All except bones	100	62·0	2·55	0·069
262	Pollan	Whole fish without guts	Steamed	Flesh only	59	77·1	3·09	0·082
262a	Pollan (weighed with bones and skin)	Whole fish without guts	Steamed	Flesh only	59	47·0	1·88	0·050
263	Pollan	Whole fish without guts	Covered with oat-meal and fried	Flesh and skin	65	64·3	3·19	0·096

Fish – continued

No.	Food	Protein (g. per 100 g.)	Fat (g. per 100 g.)	Carbohydrate (as glucose) (g. per 100 g.)	Calories per 100 g.	Na (mg. per 100 g.)	K	Ca	Mg	Fe	Cu	P	S	Cl	Acid (m-equiv. per 100 g.)	Base
257	Plaice, raw	15·3	1·8	0·0	79	96	353	16·6	22·0	0·8	—	218	214	83	14·0	
258	Plaice, steamed	18·1	1·9	0·0	92	120	278	37·7	23·9	0·6	—	246	249	112	18·4	
258a	Plaice, steamed (weighed with bones and skin)	9·8	1·0	0·0	50	65	150	20·4	12·9	0·3	—	133	134	61	9·9	
259	Plaice, fried	18·0	14·4	7·0	234	124	219	44·9	24·4	0·8	0·15	251	249	174	21·4	
259a	Plaice, fried (weighed with bones)	11·0	8·8	4·3	142	76	134	27·4	14·9	0·5	0·09	153	152	105	13·1	
260	Pollack, steamed	19·5	0·8	0·0	87	95	438	12·8	32·7	0·5	—	202	238	114	12·4	
260a	Pollack, steamed (weighed with bones and skin)	16·8	0·7	0·0	75	82	376	11·0	28·1	0·4	—	174	205	98	10·7	
261	Pollack, fried	16·5	6·9	6·6	157	162	333	128·0	45·4	2·8	—	241	198	225	9·9	
261a	Pollack, fried (weighed with bones)	15·2	6·4	6·1	145	149	306	118·0	41·7	2·6	—	222	182	253	9·1	
262	Pollan, steamed	18·1	2·1	0·0	95	69	373	82·0	23·0	0·9	—	287	220	71	15·7	
262a	Pollan, steamed (weighed with bones and skin)	11·0	1·3	0·0	58	42	227	50·0	14·0	0·5	—	175	134	43	9·6	
263	Pollan, fried	18·7	12·2	1·7	196	64	390	200·0	25·9	1·2	—	367	228	54	14·8	

Fish – *continued*

No.	Food	Nature of raw material	Method of cooking	Nature of edible (analysed) material	Edible matter, as eaten, expressed as a percentage of the weight as purchased	g. per 100 g.		
						Water	Total nitrogen	Purine nitrogen
263a	Pollan (weighed with bones)	Whole fish without guts	Covered with oatmeal and fried	Flesh and skin ..	65	46·4	2·29	0·069
264	Prawns	Purchased cooked	..	Flesh only ..	38	70·0	3·62	0·070
264a	Prawns (weighed with shells)	Purchased cooked	..	Flesh only ..	38	26·6	1·38	0·027
265	Saithe ..	Pieces from tail end	Steamed	Flesh only ..	65	74·8	3·73	0·078
265a	Saithe (weighed with bones and skin)	Pieces from tail end	Steamed	Flesh only ..	65	63·5	3·17	0·066
266	Salmon, fresh..	Shoulder cut ..	Steamed	Flesh only ..	73	65·4	3·21	0·078
266a	Salmon, fresh (weighed with bones and skin)	Shoulder cut ..	Steamed	Flesh only ..	73	53·0	2·60	0·063
267	Salmon ..	Canned, as purchased	..	All except backbone	98	69·9	3·43	0·101
268	Sardines ..	Canned, as purchased	..	All, after draining off oil	100	50·7	3·49	0·234
269	Scallops ..	Flesh only. No shells	Steamed	All ..	56	73·1	3·71	0·117
270	Shrimps ..	Purchased cooked..	..	Flesh only ..	33	62·5	3·80	0·072
270a	Shrimps (weighed with shells)	Purchased cooked..	..	Flesh only	33	20·6	1·26	0·024
271	Skate ..	"Wings" skinned..	Covered with batter and crumbs and fried	All except bones ..	95	55·4	3·09	0·041
271a	Skate (weighed with bones)	"Wings" skinned..	Covered with batter and crumbs and fried	All except bones ..	95	46·0	2·56	0·034
272	Smelts ..	Whole fish without guts	Rolled in flour and fried	All except heads ..	48	34·3	4·29	0·168

Fish – *continued*

No.	Food	g. per 100 g.			Calories per 100 g.	mg. per 100 g.									Acid-base balance, m-equiv. per 100 g.	
		Protein	Fat	Carbohydrate (as glucose)		Na	K	Ca	Mg	Fe	Cu	P	S	Cl	Acid	Base
263a	Pollan, fried (weighed with bones)	13·5	8·8	1·2	142	46	281	144·0	18·5	0·9	—	264	164	46	10·6	
264	Prawns	21·2	1·8	0·0	104	(1590)	260	145·0	42·0	1·1	—	349	366	(2550)	30·7	
264a	Prawns (weighed with shells)	8·1	0·7	0·0	40	(605)	99	55·0	16·0	0·4	—	132	139	(970)	11·7	
265	Saithe, steamed	22·6	0·6	0·0	98	97	348	18·6	30·8	0·6	—	250	266	35	18·4	
265a	Saithe, steamed (weighed with bones and skin)	19·2	0·5	0·0	83	83	296	15·8	26·2	0·5	—	213	226	71	15·6	
266	Salmon, fresh, steamed	19·1	13·0	0·0	199	107	333	28·9	28·7	0·8	—	302	190	64	16·2	
266a	Salmon, fresh, steamed (weighed with bones and skin)	15·5	10·5	0·0	161	87	269	23·4	23·2	0·6	—	245	154	52	13·1	
267	Salmon, canned	19·7	6·0	0·0	137	(538)	320	66·4	29·8	1·3	0·05	285	235	(855)	20·1	
268	Sardines, canned	20·4	22·6	0·0	294	(785)	433	409·0	41·3	4·0	0·04	683	283	(1200)	26·5	
269	Scallops, steamed	22·4	1·4	Tr.	105	265	476	115·0	38·3	3·0	—	338	570	410	36·2	
270	Shrimps	22·3	2·4	0·0	114	(3840)	404	320·0	105·0	1·8	0·80	270	340	(5850)	1·6	
270a	Shrimps (weighed with shells)	7·4	0·8	0·0	38	(1260)	133	105·5	34·6	0·6	0·26	89	112	(1930)	0·5	
271	Skate, fried	15·0	16·4	7·5	242	182	236	19·4	23·2	1·2	—	238	213	265	19·3	
271a	Skate, fried (weighed with bones)	12·4	13·6	6·2	201	151	196	16·1	19·2	1·0	—	198	177	221	16·0	
272	Smelts, fried	25·0	30·8	5·0	408	148	517	686·0	58·8	3·3	—	535	302	38		3·9

Fish – continued

No.	Food	Nature of raw material	Method of cooking	Nature of edible (analysed) material	Edible matter, as eaten, expressed as a percentage of the weight as purchased	g. per 100 g.		
						Water	Total nitrogen	Purine nitrogen
272a	Smelts (weighed with heads)	Whole fish without guts	Rolled in flour and fried	All except heads	48	29·2	3·64	0·143
273	Sole	Body of fish without head or guts	Steamed	Flesh only	57	78·9	2·94	0·053
273a	Sole (weighed with bones and skin)	Body of fish without head or guts	Steamed	Flesh only	57	47·3	1·76	0·032
274	Sole	Body of fish without head or guts	Covered with batter and crumbs and fried	All except bones	110	53·8	3·32	0·052
274a	Sole (weighed with bones)	Body of fish without head or guts	Covered with batter and crumbs and fried	All except bones	110	47·3	2·92	0·046
275	Sprats, fresh	Whole fish	Fried in deep fat	All except heads	59	33·7	3·98	0·125
275a	Sprats, fresh (weighed with heads)	Whole fish	Fried in deep fat	All except heads	59	29·6	3·50	0·110
276	Sprats, smoked	Whole fish	Grilled	Flesh and skin	89	45·8	4·18	0·250
276a	Sprats, smoked (weighed with heads)	Whole fish	Grilled	Flesh and skin	89	40·7	3·72	0·223
277	Stockfish (dried salt cod)	As purchased	Soaked in water 24 hours, then boiled	Flesh only	99	64·9	5·20	0·113
277a	Stockfish (weighed with bones and skin)	As purchased	Soaked in water 24 hours, then boiled	Flesh only	99	53·8	4·32	0·094
278	Sturgeon	Sections from middle of fish, skinned	Steamed	All except bone	43	67·5	4·07	0·050
278a	Sturgeon (weighed with bones)	Sections from middle of fish, skinned	Steamed	All except bone	43	45·8	2·77	0·034

Fish – *continued*

No.	Food	g. per 100 g.			Calories per 100 g.	mg. per 100 g.									Acid-base balance, m-equiv. per 100 g.	
		Protein	Fat	Carbohydrate (as glucose)		Na	K	Ca	Mg	Fe	Cu	P	S	Cl	Acid	Base
272a	Smelts, fried (weighed with heads)	21·3	26·2	4·3	346	126	438	582·0	50·0	2·8	—	455	257	1·8		3·3
273	Sole, steamed	17·6	1·3	0·0	84	110	240	113·0	28·2	0·7	—	270	235	132	16·9	
273a	Sole, steamed (weighed with bones and skin)	10·6	0·8	0·0	50	66	144	68·0	16·9	0·4	—	162	141	79	10·2	
274	Sole, fried	20·1	18·4	5·4	274	192	236	131·3	27·9	1·4	—	260	265	193	15·5	
274a	Sole, fried (weighed with bones)	17·7	16·2	4·8	241	169	208	115·5	24·5	1·2	—	228	233	170	13·6	
275	Sprats, fresh, fried ..	22·3	37·9	0·0	444	132	409	707·0	45·8	4·5	—	635	284	132	8·5	
275a	Sprats, fresh, fried (weighed with heads)	19·6	33·4	0·0	390	116	360	620·0	40·3	4·0	—	559	250	150	7·5	
276	Sprats, smoked, grilled..	25·1	23·2	0·0	319	(845)	483	436·0	40·0	5·7	—	565	275	(1330)	16·9	
276a	Sprats, smoked, grilled (weighed with heads)	22·3	20·6	0·0	284	(751)	430	388·0	35·6	5·1	—	502	245	(1180)	15·0	
277	Stockfish, boiled ..	32·0	0·9	0·0	140	(396)	31	22·4	35·0	1·8	—	163	372	(670)	30·7	
277a	Stockfish, boiled (weighed with bones and skin)	26·6	0·8	0·0	116	(329)	26	18·6	29·0	1·5	—	135	309	(556)	25·5	
278	Sturgeon, steamed ..	24·7	5·7	0·0	154	108	235	15·2	18·5	2·0	—	263	291	138	26·1	
278a	Sturgeon, steamed (weighed with bones)	16·8	3·9	0·0	105	74	160	10·4	12·6	1·4	—	179	198	94	17·8	

Fish – *continued*

No.	Food	Nature of raw material	Method of cooking	Nature of edible (analysed) material	Edible matter, as eaten, expressed as a percentage of the weight as purchased	g. per 100 g.		
						Water	Total nitrogen	Purine nitrogen
279	Torsk	Middle cut	Steamed	Flesh only	48	74·3	3·75	0·065
279a	Torsk (weighed with bones and skin)	Middle cut	Steamed	Flesh only	48	43·9	2·21	0·038
280	Torsk	Slices from middle of fish	Covered with batter and crumbs and fried	Flesh only	70	65·8	3·27	0·064
280a	Torsk (weighed with bones and skin)	Slices from middle of fish	Covered with batter and crumbs and fried	Flesh only	70	46·6	2·32	0·045
281	Trout	Whole fish, without guts	Steamed	Flesh only	54	70·6	3·76	0·092
281a	Trout (weighed with bones and skin)	Whole fish, without guts	Steamed	Flesh only	54	46·5	2·48	0·061
282	Trout, Sea	Middle cut	Steamed	Flesh only	68	70·9	3·62	0·095
282a	Trout, Sea (weighed with bones and skin)	Middle cut	Steamed	Flesh only	68	55·9	2·86	0·075
283	Turbot	Sections from middle of fish	Steamed	Flesh only	56	75·6	3·48	0·064
283a	Turbot (weighed with bones and skin)	Section from middle of fish	Steamed	Flesh only	56	49·8	2·30	0·042
284	Whelks	Purchased cooked		All except shells	15	77·5	2·96	0·065
284a	Whelks (weighed with shells)	Purchased cooked		All except shells	15	11·6	0·44	0·010
285	Whitebait	Whole fish	Rolled in flour and fried	All	77	23·5	3·12	0·335
286	Whiting	Body of fish without head or guts	Steamed	Flesh only	57	76·9	3·35	0·090

Fish – continued

No.	Food	g. per 100 g.			Calories per 100 g.	mg. per 100 g.									Acid-base balance, m-equiv. per 100 g.	
		Protein	Fat	Carbohydrate (as glucose)		Na	K	Ca	Mg	Fe	Cu	P	S	Cl	Acid	Base
279	Torsk, steamed	22·4	0·7	0·0	99	74	386	27·0	26·4	1·0	—	283	278	101	21·8	
279a	Torsk, steamed (weighed with bones and skin)	13·2	0·4	0·0	58	44	228	15·9	15·6	0·6	—	167	164	60	12·9	
280	Torsk, fried	19·3	4·3	7·8	148	93	372	64·8	24·9	0·6	—	298	234	153	19·3	
280a	Torsk, fried (weighed with bones and skin)	13·7	3·1	5·5	105	66	264	45·9	17·7	0·4	—	212	166	109	13·7	
281	Trout, steamed	22·3	4·5	0·0	133	88	374	35·8	30·9	1·0	—	270	218	70	15·2	
281a	Trout, steamed (weighed with bones and skin)	14·7	3·0	0·0	88	58	246	23·6	20·4	0·7	—	178	144	46	10·0	
282	Trout, Sea, steamed ..	21·1	4·8	0·0	131	207	314	12·4	30·1	1·0	—	290	259	261	22·1	
282a	Trout, Sea, steamed (weighed with bones and skin)	16·6	3·8	0·0	104	153	248	9·8	23·8	0·8	—	229	204	206	17·4	
283	Turbot, steamed ..	20·7	1·6	0·0	100	90	255	13·5	23·9	0·5	—	188	247	142	18·4	
283a	Turbot, steamed (weighed with bones and skin)	13·6	1·1	0·0	66	59	168	8·9	15·8	0·3	—	124	163	94	12·1	
284	Whelks	17·8	1·9	Tr.	91	(265)	316	54·0	160·0	6·2	—	227	448	(185)	23·5	
284a	Whelks (weighed with shells)	2·7	0·3	Tr.	14	(40)	47	8·1	24·0	0·9	—	34	67	(85)	3·5	
285	Whitebait, fried ..	18·3	47·5	5·3	537	225	112	859·0	50·3	5·1	—	856	269	325	21·4	
286	Whiting, steamed ..	19·9	0·9	0·0	90	127	299	42·0	28·3	1·0	—	189	307	93	16·4	

Fish – *continued*

No.	Food	Nature of raw material	Method of cooking	Nature of edible (analysed) material	Edible matter, as eaten, expressed as a percentage of the weight as purchased	g. per 100 g.		
						Water	Total nitrogen	Purine nitrogen
286a	Whiting (weighed with bones and skin)	Body of fish without head or guts	Steamed ..	Flesh only ..	57	52·2	2·28	0·061
287	Whiting	Body of fish without head or guts	Covered with batter and crumbs and fried	All except bones ..	102	63·0	2·90	0·094
287a	Whiting (weighed with bones)	Body of fish without head or guts	Covered with batter and crumbs and fried	All except bones ..	102	56·8	2·61	0·085
288	Winkles, edible portion ..	Purchased cooked..	Probably boiled in salt water	All except shells ..	19	79·1	2·45	0·066
288a	Winkles (weighed with shells)	Purchased cooked	Probably boiled in salt water	All except shells ..	19	15·1	0·47	0·013
289	Winkles	In shells as purchased	Boiled in fresh water	All except shells ..	15	76·8	2·90	0·070
289a	Winkles (weighed with shells)	In shells as purchased	Boiled in fresh water	All except shells ..	15	11·5	0·44	0·011
290	Witch	Body of fish without head, fins or guts	Steamed ..	Flesh only ..	48	77·7	3·18	0·053
290a	Witch (weighed with bones and skin)	Body of fish without head, fins or guts	Steamed ..	Flesh only ..	48	46·5	1·91	0·032
291	Witch	Body of fish without head, fins or guts	Covered with batter and crumbs and fried	All except bones ..	113	58·1	2·96	0·055
291a	Witch (weighed with bones)	Body of fish without head, fins or guts	Covered with batter and crumbs and fried	All except bones ..	113	48·9	2·49	0·046

Fish – *continued*

No.	Food	g. per 100 g.			Calories per 100 g.	mg. per 100 g.									Acid-base balance, m-equiv. per 100 g.	
		Protein	Fat	Carbohydrate (as glucose)		Na	K	Ca	Mg	Fe	Cu	P	S	Cl	Acid	Base
286a	Whiting, steamed (weighed with bones and skin)	13·5	0·6	0·0	61	86	203	28·6	19·2	0·7	—	128	208	63	11·2	
287	Whiting, fried	17·3	10·3	7·0	193	199	317	47·7	32·5	0·7	—	258	267	194	16·9	
287a	Whiting, fried (weighed with bones and skin)	15·6	9·3	6·3	174	179	285	42·9	29·3	0·6	—	233	240	175	15·2	
288	Winkles, boiled in salt water	15·2	1·4	Tr.	75	(1140)	154	136·0	358·0	15·0	—	219	377	(1800)		2·0
288a	Winkles, boiled in salt water (weighed with shells)	2·9	0·3	Tr.	14	(218)	29	25·8	68·0	2·9	—	42	72	(342)		0·4
289	Winkles, boiled in fresh water	17·6	2·6	Tr.	96	266	211	165·0	414·0	17·1	—	277	446	500	0·1	
289a	Winkles, boiled in fresh water (weighed with shells)	2·6	0·4	Tr.	14	40	32	24·8	62·0	2·6	—	42	67	75	0·1	
290	Witch, steamed	19·0	1·1	0·0	88	136	304	30·1	24·1	0·9	—	233	252	123	17·0	
290a	Witch, steamed (weighed with bones and skin)	11·4	0·7	0·0	53	82	182	18·1	14·4	0·5	—	140	151	74	10·2	
291	Witch, fried	17·6	14·1	7·9	233	176	300	52·2	24·4	0·8	—	187	235	187	12·1	
291a	Witch, fried (weighed with bones and skin)	14·8	11·8	6·6	196	148	252	43·8	20·5	0·7	—	157	197	157	10·2	

F

Fruit

No.	Food	Description	Nature of edible (analysed) material	Edible matter, as eaten, expressed as a percentage of the weight as purchased	g. per 100 g.				
					Water	Unavailable carbohydrate	Sugar (as monosaccharides)	Starch (as glucose)	Total nitrogen
292	Apples, imported eating	Raw..	Flesh only, no skin or core	75	84·1	1·7	12·2	Tr.	0·04
292a	Apples, imported eating (weighed with skin and core)	Raw..	Flesh only, no skin or core	75	63·1	1·3	9·2	Tr.	0·03
293	Apples, English eating	Raw..	Flesh only, no skin or core	79	84·5	2·2	11·4	0·3	0·04
293a	Apples, English eating (weighed with skin and core)	Raw..	Flesh only, no skin or core	79	66·8	1·7	9·0	0·2	0·03
294	Apples, English cooking	Raw..	Flesh only, no skin or core	81	85·6	2·4	9·2	0·4	0·05
295	Apples, English cooking	Baked without sugar	Flesh only, no skin (cored before cooking)	70	85·0	2·5	9·6	0·4	0·05
295a	Apples, English cooking (weighed with skin)	Baked without sugar	Flesh only, no skin (cored before cooking)	70	68·0	2·0	7·7	0·3	0·04
296	Apples, English cooking	Stewed without sugar	Flesh and juice (peeled and cored before cooking)	177	88·9	1·8	7·1	0·3	0·04
297	Apricots, fresh	Raw..	Flesh and skin, no stones	92	86·6	2·1	6·7	0·0	0·09
297a	Apricots, fresh (weighed with stones)	Raw..	Flesh and skin, no stones	92	79·6	1·9	6·2	0·0	0·08
298	Apricots, fresh	Stewed without sugar	Flesh and skin, no stones	116	89·7	1·6	5·2	0·0	0·07
299	Apricots, dried	Raw..	All	100	14·7	24·0	43·4	0·0	0·76
300	Apricots, dried	Stewed without sugar	Fruit and juice	300	71·6	8·0	14·4	0·0	0·25
301	Apricots	Canned in syrup	Fruit and syrup as purchased	100	67·8	1·3	27·7	0·0	0·08
302	Avocado pears	Raw..	Flesh only, no skin or stone	62	81·3	2·0	2·5	0·0	0·17

Fruit – *continued*

No.	Food	g. per 100 g.			Calories per 100 g.	mg. per 100 g.									Acid base-balance, m-equiv. per 100 g.	
		Protein (N×6·25)	Fat	Available carbohydrate (as monosaccharides)		Na	K	Ca	Mg	Fe	Cu	P	S	Cl	Acid	Base
292	Apples, imported eating	0·3	Tr.	12·2	47	2·7	116	3·6	5·0	0·29	0·14	6·8	3·7	<1·0		3·0
292a	Apples, imported eating (weighed with skin and core)	0·2	Tr.	9·2	35	2·0	87	2·7	3·8	0·22	0·11	5·1	2·8	<1·0		2·3
293	Apples, English eating	0·3	Tr.	11·7	45	2·0	120	3·5	4·3	0·29	0·07	8·5	7·6	2·0		2·6
293a	Apples, English eating (weighed with skin and core)	0·2	Tr.	9·2	36	1·6	95	2·8	3·4	0·23	0·06	6·7	6·0	1·5		2·1
294	Apples, cooking, raw	0·3	Tr.	9·6	37	2·1	123	3·6	2·9	0·29	0·09	16·2	2·9	4·5		2·3
295	Apples, cooking, baked	0·3	Tr.	10·0	39	2·2	128	3·7	3·0	0·30	0·09	16·8	3·0	4·8		2·4
295a	Apples, cooking, baked (weighed with skin)	0·2	Tr.	8·0	31	1·8	102	3·0	2·4	0·24	0·07	13·4	2·4	3·8		1·9
296	Apples, cooking, stewed without sugar	0·2	Tr.	7·4	28	0·2	95	2·8	2·2	0·22	0·07	12·5	2·2	3·5		1·7
297	Apricots, fresh ..	0·6	Tr.	6·7	28	<1·0	320	17·2	12·3	0·37	0·12	21·3	6·1	<1·0		8·4
297a	Apricots, fresh (weighed with stones)	0·6	Tr.	6·2	26	<1·0	294	15·8	11·3	0·34	0·11	19·6	5·6	<1·0		7·7
298	Apricots, fresh, stewed without sugar	0·5	Tr.	5·2	22	<1·0	246	13·2	9·5	0·28	0·09	16·4	4·7	<1·0		6·4
299	Apricots, dried, raw ..	4·8	Tr.	43·4	183	56·4	1880	92·4	65·2	4·09	0·27	118·0	164·0	54·5		41·9
300	Apricots, dried, stewed without sugar	1·6	Tr.	14·4	61	18·8	627	30·8	21·7	1·36	0·09	37·0	54·7	11·5		13·9
301	Apricots, canned in syrup	0·5	Tr.	27·7	106	0·9	256	12·0	7·2	0·70	0·05	13·0	1·0	1·5		6·9
302	Avocado pears	1·1	8·0	2·5	88	16·0	396	15·3	29·4	0·53	0·21	30·8	19·4	5·9		10·7

F2

Fruit – *continued*

No.	Food	Description	Nature of edible (analysed) material	Edible matter, as eaten, expressed as a percentage of the weight as purchased	g. per 100 g.				
					Water	Unavailable carbohydrate	Sugar (as monosaccharides)	Starch (as glucose)	Total nitrogen
303	Bananas	Raw	Flesh only, no skin	59	70·7	3·4	16·2	3·0	0·18
303a	Bananas (weighed with skin)	Raw	Flesh only, no skin	59	41·6	2·0	9·6	1·8	0·11
304	Blackberries	Raw	Whole fruit	100	82·0	7·3	6·4	0·0	0·20
305	Blackberries	Stewed without sugar	Fruit and juice	130	86·2	5·6	4·9	0·0	0·15
306	Cherries, eating	Raw	Flesh and skin, no stalks or stones	87	81·5	1·7	11·9	0·0	0·09
306a	Cherries, eating (weighed with stones)	Raw	Flesh and skin, no stalks or stones	87	71·0	1·5	10·4	0·0	0·08
307	Cherries, cooking	Raw	Flesh and skin, no stalks or stones	84	79·8	1·7	11·6	0·0	0·09
307a	Cherries, cooking (weighed with stones)	Raw	Flesh and skin, no stalks or stones	84	67·0	1·4	9·8	0·0	0·08
308	Cherries, cooking (weighed with stones)	Stewed without sugar	Fruit and juice, no stones	114	84·6	1·3	8·9	0·0	0·07
309	Cranberries	Raw	Whole fruit	100	87·0	4·2	3·5	0·0	0·06
310	Currants, black	Raw	Whole fruit, no stalks	98	77·4	8·7	6·6	0·0	0·15
311	Currants, black	Stewed without sugar	Fruit and juice	127	82·6	6·7	5·1	0·0	0·12
312	Currants, red	Raw	Whole fruit, no stalks	97	82·8	8·2	4·4	0·0	0·18
313	Currants, red	Stewed without sugar	Fruit and juice	126	86·8	6·3	3·4	0·0	0·14
314	Currants, white	Raw	Whole fruit, no stalks	96	83·3	6·8	5·6	0·0	0·20
315	Currants, white	Stewed without sugar	Fruit and juice	125	87·2	5·2	4·3	0·0	0·15

Fruit – *continued*

No.	Food	g. per 100 g.			Calories per 100 g.	mg. per 100 g.									Acid-base balance, m-equiv. per 100 g.	
		Protein (N× 6·25)	Fat	Available carbohydrate (as monosaccharides)		Na	K	Ca	Mg	Fe	Cu	P	S	Cl	Acid	Base
303	Bananas	1·1	Tr.	19·2	77	1·2	348	6·8	41·9	0·41	0·16	28·1	13·0	78·5		7·9
303a	Bananas (weighed with skin)	0·7	Tr.	11·3	45	0·7	206	4·0	24·7	0·24	0·09	16·6	7·7	46·3		4·7
304	Blackberries, raw	1·3	Tr.	6·4	30	3·7	208	63·3	29·5	0·85	0·12	23·8	9·2	22·4		8·4
305	Blackberries, stewed without sugar	1·0	Tr.	4·9	23	2·8	160	48·6	22·6	0·65	0·09	18·3	7·1	17·0		6·5
306	Cherries, eating	0·6	Tr.	11·9	47	2·8	275	15·9	9·6	0·38	0·07	16·8	6·8	<1·0		7·3
306a	Cherries, eating (weighed with stones)	0·5	Tr.	10·4	40	2·4	239	13·8	8·4	0·33	0·06	14·6	5·9	<1·0		6·4
307	Cherries, cooking, raw	0·6	Tr.	11·6	46	4·1	305	20·1	11·6	0·31	0·10	20·8	7·9	<1·0		8·1
307a	Cherries, cooking, raw (weighed with stones)	0·5	Tr.	9·8	39	3·4	256	16·9	9·8	0·26	0·08	17·5	6·6	<1·0		6·8
308	Cherries, stewed without sugar (weighed with stones)	0·5	Tr.	8·9	35	3·2	234	15·5	8·9	0·24	0·08	12·6	6·1	<0·8		6·3
309	Cranberries	0·4	Tr.	3·5	15	1·8	119	14·7	8·4	1·11	0·14	11·2	11·1	<1·0		3·2
310	Currants, black, raw	0·9	Tr.	6·6	29	2·7	372	60·3	17·1	1·27	0·14	43·2	33·1	14·5		8·8
311	Currants, black, stewed without sugar	0·7	Tr.	5·1	22	2·1	286	46·4	13·1	0·98	0·11	33·2	23·8	11·4		6·8
312	Currants, red, raw	1·1	Tr.	4·4	21	2·3	275	35·8	12·8	1·22	0·12	29·5	28·6	14·0		5·9
313	Currants, red, stewed without sugar	0·8	Tr.	3·4	16	1·8	218	27·5	9·8	0·93	0·09	22·7	22·0	10·8		4·5
314	Currants, white	1·3	Tr.	5·6	26	1·5	291	22·4	12·7	0·93	0·14	28·0	23·6	0·7		6·1
315	Currants, white, stewed without sugar	1·0	Tr.	4·3	20	1·2	224	17·3	9·8	0·72	0·11	21·6	18·3	8·2		4·5

Fruit – *continued*

No.	Food	Description	Nature of edible (analysed) material	Edible matter, as eaten, expressed as a percentage of the weight as purchased	Water	Unavailable carbohydrate	Sugar (as monosaccharides)	Starch (as glucose)	Total nitrogen
						g. per 100 g.			
316	Currants, dried	Raw	Whole fruit	100	22·0	6·5	63·1	0·0	0·27
317	Custard apple	Raw	Flesh only, no skin or seeds	71	73·3	3·2	18·1	0·0	0·33
318	Damsons	Raw	Flesh and skin, no stalks or stones	90	77·5	4·1	9·6	0·0	0·08
318a	Damsons (weighed with stones)	Raw	Flesh and skin, no stalks or stones	90	69·8	3·7	8·6	0·0	0·07
319	Damsons (weighed with stones)	Stewed without sugar	Fruit and juice, no stones	120	74·0	3·2	7·4	0·0	0·06
320	Dates.. ..	Dried, as purchased	Flesh and sikn, no stones ..	86	14·6	8·7	63·9	0·0	0·32
320a	Dates (weighed with stones)..	Dried, as purchased	Flesh and sikn, no stones ..	86	12·6	7·5	54·9	0·0	0·28
321	Figs, green	Raw..	Whole fruit, no stalks ..	98	84·6	2·5	9·5	0·0	0·21
322	Figs, dried	Raw	Whole fruit	100	16·8	18·5	52·9	0·0	0·57
323	Figs, dried	Stewed without sugar	Fruit and juice	200	58·4	9·3	26·5	0·0	0·28
324	Fruit salad	Canned in syrup ..	Fruit and syrup, as purchased	100	71·1	1·1	25·0	0·0	0·04
325	Gooseberries, green ..	Raw..	Flesh, skin and pips, no "tops" or "tails"	99	89·9	3·2	3·4	0·0	0·18
326	Gooseberries, green ..	Stewed without sugar	Fruit and juice	130	92·2	2·5	2·6	0·0	0·14
327	Gooseberries, ripe ..	Raw..	Flesh, skin and pips, no "tops" or "tails"	99	83·7	3·5	9·2	0·0	0·09
328	Grapes, black.. ..	Raw..	Flesh only, no skin, pips or stalks	81	80·7	0·4	15·5	0·0	0·09
328a	Grapes, black (whole grapes weighed)	Raw..	Flesh only, no skin, pips or stalks	81	65·2	0·3	13·0	0·0	0·08

Fruit – *continued*

| No. | Food | g. per 100 g. | | | Calories per 100 g. | mg. per 100 g. | | | | | | | | | Acid base-balance, m-equiv. per 100 g. | |
		Protein (N× 6·25)	Fat	Available carbohydrate (as monosaccharides)		Na	K	Ca	Mg	Fe	Cu	P	S	Cl	Acid	Base
316	Currants, dried	1·7	Tr.	63·1	244	19·5	708	95·2	36·2	1·82	0·48	40·4	30·8	15·7		21·8
317	Custard apple	2·1	Tr.	18·1	77	13·8	578	12·0	23·9	0·53	0·15	51·0	26·7	40·0		11·9
318	Damsons, raw	0·5	Tr.	9·6	38	2·2	290	23·5	11·0	0·41	0·08	16·4	6·4	<1·0		8·2
318a	Damsons, raw (weighed with stones)	0·5	Tr.	8·6	34	2·0	261	21·2	9·9	0·37	0·07	14·8	5·8	<1·0		7·4
319	Damsons, stewed without sugar (weighed with stones)	0·4	Tr.	7·4	29	1·7	223	18·1	8·5	0·32	0·06	12·6	4·9	<0·3		6·5
320	Dates	2·0	Tr.	63·9	248	4·8	754	67·9	58·5	1·61	0·21	63·8	51·0	290·0		12·4
320a	Dates (weighed with stones)	1·7	Tr.	54·9	214	4·1	649	58·3	50·3	1·38	0·18	54·8	43·8	249·0		10·7
321	Figs, green	1·3	Tr.	9·5	41	1·6	268	34·2	20·0	0·42	0·06	32·2	12·9	18·4		6·9
322	Figs, dried, raw ..	3·6	Tr.	52·9	214	86·7	1010	284·0	92·3	4·17	0·24	91·5	80·8	166·0		36·1
323	Figs, dried, stewed without sugar	1·8	Tr.	26·5	107	43·4	505	142	46·2	2·09	0·12	45·8	40·4	83·0		18·1
324	Fruit salad, canned in syrup	0·3	Tr.	25·0	94	2·3	116	8·4	7·7	3·45	0·03	9·6	1·8	3·2		3·3
325	Gooseberries, green, raw	1·1	Tr.	3·4	17	1·9	210	28·3	7·1	0·32	0·13	33·9	15·9	6·5		4·1
326	Gooseberries, green, stewed without sugar	0·9	Tr.	2·6	13	1·5	162	21·8	5·5	0·25	0·10	26·1	12·2	5·0		3·1
327	Gooseberries, ripe ..	0·6	Tr.	9·2	37	1·2	170	18·5	8·6	0·58	0·15	19·0	13·5	10·7		3·7
328	Grapes, black	0·6	Tr.	15·5	60	1·7	316	4·2	4·0	0·34	0·08	16·1	7·4	<1·0		7·2
328a	Grapes, black (whole grapes weighed)	0·5	Tr.	13·0	51	1·4	265	3·5	3·4	0·29	0·07	13·5	6·2	<1·0		5·8

Fruit – *continued*

No.	Food	Description	Nature of edible (analysed) material	Edible matter, as eaten, expressed as a percentage of the weight as purchased	g. per 100 g.				
					Water	Unavailable carbohydrate	Sugar (as monosaccharides)	Starch (as glucose)	Total nitrogen
329	Grapes, white	Raw	Flesh and skin, no pips or stalks	95	79·3	0·9	16·1	0·0	0·10
329a	Grapes, white (whole grapes weighed)	Raw	Flesh and skin, no pips or stalks	95	75·5	0·9	15·3	0·0	0·10
330	Grapefruit	Raw	Flesh only, no skin, pith or pips	48	90·7	0·6	5·3	0·0	0·10
330a	Grapefruit (whole fruit weighed)	Raw	Flesh only, no skin, pith or pips	48	43·5	0·3	2·5	0·0	0·05
331	Greengages	Raw	Flesh and skin, no stones or stalks	95	78·2	2·6	11·8	0·0	0·12
331a	Greengages (weighed with stones)	Raw	Flesh and skin, no stones or stalks	95	74·4	2·5	11·2	0·0	0·11
332	Greengages (weighed with stones)	Stewed without sugar	Fruit and juice, no stones	125	77·1	2·0	9·1	0·0	0·09
333	Lemons, whole	Raw	Whole fruit, including skin, no pips	99	85·2	5·2	3·2	0·0	0·12
334	Lemon juice	Raw	Strained juice	36	91·3	0·0	1·6	0·0	0·05
335	Loganberries	Raw	Whole fruit	100	85·0	6·2	3·4	0·0	0·17
336	Loganberries	Stewed without sugar	Fruit and juice	130	88·5	4·8	2·6	0·0	0·13
337	Loganberries	Canned in syrup	Fruit and syrup as purchased	100	66·3	3·3	26·2	0·0	0·10
338	Mandarin oranges	Canned in light syrup	Fruit and syrup as purchased	100	81·0	1·8	16·6	Tr.	0·08
339	Medlars	Raw	Flesh only, no skin or stones	81	74·5	10·2	10·6	0·0	0·08
339a	Medlars (weighed with skin and stones)	Raw	Flesh only, no skin or stones	81	60·2	8·3	8·6	0·0	0·06
340	Melons, Cantaloupe	Raw	Flesh only, no skin or pips	59	93·6	1·0	5·3	0·0	0·16

Fruit – *continued*

No.	Food	g. per 100 g.			Calories per 100 g.	mg. per 100 g.									Acid base-balance, m-equiv. per 100 g.	
		Protein (N×6·25)	Fat	Available carbohydrate (as monosaccharides)		Na	K	Ca	Mg	Fe	Cu	P	S	Cl	Acid	Base
329	Grapes, white	0·6	Tr.	16·1	63	1·6	250	19·1	6·6	0·34	0·10	21·9	9·1	<1·0		6·0
329a	Grapes, white (whole grapes weighed)	0·6	Tr.	15·3	60	1·5	237	18·1	6·3	0·32	0·10	20·8	8·7	<1·0		5·7
330	Grapefruit	0·6	Tr.	5·3	22	1·4	234	17·1	10·4	0·26	0·06	15·6	5·1	1·3		6·4
330a	Grapefruit (whole fruit weighed)	0·3	Tr.	2·5	11	0·7	112	8·2	5·0	0·13	0·03	7·5	2·5	0·6		3·1
331	Greengages	0·8	Tr.	11·8	48	1·4	305	16·8	7·7	0·37	0·08	22·6	3·0	1·0		7·7
331a	Greengages (weighed with stones)	0·8	Tr.	11·2	45	1·3	290	16·0	7·3	0·35	0·08	21·5	2·9	1·0		7·3
332	Greengages, stewed without sugar (weighed with stones)	0·6	Tr.	9·1	37	1·1	235	12·9	5·9	0·28	0·06	17·3	2·3	0·3		5·9
333	Lemons, whole	0·8	Tr.	3·2	15	6·0	163	107·0	11·6	0·35	0·26	20·7	12·3	5·1		8·5
334	Lemon juice	0·3	Tr.	1·6	7	1·5	142	8·4	6·6	0·14	0·13	10·3	2·0	2·6		3·8
335	Loganberries	1·1	Tr.	3·4	17	2·5	257	35·1	25·0	1·37	0·14	24·3	18·1	15·8		7·4
336	Loganberries, stewed without sugar	0·8	Tr.	2·6	13	1·9	198	27·0	19·4	1·05	0·11	18·7	13·9	12·0		5·7
337	Loganberries, canned in syrup	0·6	Tr.	26·2	101	1·2	97	17·6	11·3	2·88	0·04	23·0	3·0	4·6		2·5
338	Mandarins, canned	0·5	Tr.	16·6	64	5·4	99	8·0	6·7	0·19	0·03	7·6	—	2·3		
339	Medlars	0·5	Tr.	10·6	42	6·0	246	30·1	10·5	0·49	0·17	28·0	16·6	3·1	—	6·0
339a	Medlars (weighed with skin and stones)	0·4	Tr.	8·6	34	4·9	200	24·4	8·5	0·40	0·14	22·7	13·5	2·5		4·9
340	Melons, Cantaloupe	1·0	Tr.	5·3	24	13·5	319	19·1	20·1	0·81	0·04	30·4	11·7	<3·5		7·5

Fruit – *continued*

No.	Food	Description	Nature of edible material (analysed) material	Edible matter, as eaten, expressed as a percentage of the weight as purchased	Water	Unavailable carbohydrate	Sugar (as mono-saccharides)	Starch (as glucose)	Total nitrogen
							g. per 100 g.		
340a	Melons, Cantaloupe (weighed with skin)	Raw..	Flesh only, no skin or pips	59	58·6	0·6	3·3	0·0	0·10
341	Melons, yellow	Raw..	Flesh only, no skin or pips	59	94·2	0·9	5·0	0·0	0·10
341a	Melons, yellow (weighed with skin)	Raw..	Flesh only, no skin or pips	59	59·0	0·6	3·1	0·0	0·06
342	Mulberries	Raw..	Whole fruit	100	85·0	1·7	8·1	0·0	0·21
343	Nectarines	Raw..	Flesh and skin, no stones	92	80·2	2·4	12·4	0·0	0·15
343a	Nectarines (weighed with stones)	Raw..	Flesh and skin, no stones	92	74·0	2·2	11·4	0·0	0·14
344	Olives	Bottled in brine	Flesh and skin, no stones	80	76·5	4·4	Tr.	0·0	0·14
344a	Olives (weighed with stones)	Bottled in brine	Flesh and skin, no stones	80	61·1	3·5	Tr.	0·0	0·11
345	Oranges	Raw..	Flesh only, no peel or pips	75	86·1	2·0	8·5	0·0	0·13
345a	Oranges (weighed with peel and pips)	Raw..	Flesh only, no peel or pips	75	64·8	1·5	6·4	0·0	0·10
346	Orange juice	Raw..	Strained juice	46	87·7	0·0	9·4	0·0	0·10
347	Passion fruit	Raw..	Flesh and seeds, no skin	42	73·3	15·9	6·2	0·0	0·44
347a	Passion fruit (weighed with skin)	Raw..	Flesh and seeds, no skin	42	30·8	6·7	2·6	0·0	0·18
348	Peaches, fresh	Raw..	Flesh and skin, no stones	87	86·2	1·4	9·1	0·0	0·10
348a	Peaches, fresh (weighed with stones)	Raw..	Flesh and skin, no stones	87	75·1	1·2	7·9	0·0	0·09
349	Peaches, dried	Raw..	All	100	15·5	14·3	53·0	0·0	0·55
350	Peaches, dried	Stewed without sugar	Fruit and juice	300	71·8	4·7	17·7	0·0	0·18

Fruit – *continued*

No.	Food	Protein (N×6.25)	Fat	Available carbohydrate (as monosaccharides)	Calories per 100 g.	Na	K	Ca	Mg	Fe	Cu	P	S	Cl	Acid	Base
		g. per 100 g.				*mg. per 100 g.*									*Acid-base balance, m-equiv. per 100 g.*	
340a	Melons, Cantaloupe (weighed with skin)	0·6	Tr.	3·3	15	8·5	200	11·9	12·6	0·51	0·03	19·0	7·3	27·2		4·7
341	Melons, yellow	0·6	Tr.	5·0	21	19·5	222	13·8	13·3	0·24	0·04	8·7	6·3	45·0		6·1
341a	Melons, yellow (weighed with skin)	0·4	Tr.	3·1	13	12·2	139	8·6	8·3	0·15	0·03	5·4	3·9	28·2		3·8
342	Mulberries	1·3	Tr.	8·1	36	2·1	257	35·7	15·1	1·57	0·06	47·7	8·8	3·7		6·0
343	Nectarines	0·9	Tr.	12·4	50	9·1	268	3·9	12·6	0·46	0·06	23·9	10·0	4·7		6·2
343a	Nectarines (weighed with stones)	0·8	Tr.	11·4	46	8·4	247	3·6	11·6	0·42	0·06	22·0	9·2	4·3		5·7
344	Olives (in brine)	0·9	11·0	Tr.	106	(2250)	91	61·2	21·8	1·03	0·23	16·8	35·6	(3750)	3·8	
344a	Olives (in brine) (weighed with stones)	0·7	8·8	Tr.	85	(1800)	73	49·0	17·5	0·83	0·18	13·4	28·5	(3000)	3·0	
345	Oranges	0·8	Tr.	8·5	35	2·9	197	41·3	12·9	0·33	0·07	23·7	9·0	3·2		6·1
345a	Oranges (weighed with peel and pips)	0·6	Tr.	6·4	27	2·2	148	31·0	9·7	0·25	0·05	17·8	6·8	2·4		4·6
346	Orange juice	0·6	Tr.	9·4	38	1·7	179	11·5	11·5	0·30	0·05	21·7	4·6	1·2		4·5
347	Passion fruit	2·8	Tr.	6·2	35	28·4	348	15·6	38·6	1·12	0·12	54·2	18·7	36·6		8·5
347a	Passion fruit (weighed with skin)	1·2	Tr.	2·6	15	11·9	146	6·5	16·2	0·47	0·05	22·8	7·8	15·4		3·6
348	Peaches, fresh	0·6	Tr.	9·1	37	2·7	259	4·8	7·9	0·38	0·05	18·5	5·7	<1·0		6·1
348a	Peaches, fresh (weighed with stones)	0·5	Tr.	7·9	32	2·4	225	4·2	6·9	0·33	0·04	16·1	5·0	<1·0		5·3
349	Peaches, dried, raw	3·4	Tr.	53·0	213	6·0	1100	35·6	54·1	6·75	0·63	116·0	240·0	10·5		12·1
350	Peaches, dried, stewed without sugar	1·1	Tr.	17·6	70	2·0	366	11·8	18·0	2·25	0·21	38·7	80·0	3·5		4·0

Fruit – *continued*

No.	Food	Description	Nature of edible (analysed) material	Edible matter, as eaten, expressed as a percentage of the weight as purchased	g. per 100 g.				
					Water	Unavailable carbohydrate	Sugar (as monosaccharides)	Starch (as glucose)	Total nitrogen
351	Peaches	Canned in syrup	Fruit and syrup as purchased	100	74·3	1·0	22·9	0·0	0·06
352	Pears, imported eating	Raw	Flesh only, no skin or core	69	83·0	2·5	10·8	0·0	0·04
352a	Pears, imported eating (weighed with skin and core)	Raw	Flesh only, no skin or core	69	57·2	1·7	7·5	0·0	0·03
353	Pears, English eating	Raw	Flesh only, no skin or core	75	83·4	2·1	10·4	0·0	0·03
353a	Pears, English eating (weighed with skin and core)	Raw	Flesh only, no skin or core	75	62·5	1·6	7·8	0·0	0·02
354	Pears, English cooking	Raw	Flesh only, no skin or core	77	83·0	2·9	9·3	Tr.	0·04
355	Pears, English cooking	Stewed without sugar	Flesh and juice (peeled and cored before cooking)	107	86·9	2·2	7·2	Tr.	0·03
356	Pears	Canned in syrup	Fruit and syrup as purchased	100	76·2	1·7	20·0	0·0	0·06
357	Pineapple, fresh	Raw	Flesh only, no skin or core	53	84·3	1·2	11·6	0·0	0·08
358	Pineapple	Canned in syrup	Fruit and syrup as purchased	100	77·1	0·9	20·2	0·0	0·04
359	Plums, Victoria dessert	Raw	Flesh and skin, no stones or stalks	94	84·1	2·1	9·6	0·0	0·09
359a	Plums, Victoria dessert (weighed with stones)	Raw	Flesh and skin, no stones or stalks	94	79·1	2·0	9·0	0·0	0·08
360	Plums, cooking	Raw	Flesh and skin, no stones or stalks	91	85·1	2·5	6·2	0·0	0·09
360a	Plums, cooking (weighed with stones)	Raw	Flesh and skin, no stones or stalks	91	77·5	2·3	5·6	0·0	0·08
361	Plums, cooking (weighed with stones)	Stewed without sugar	Fruit and juice, no stones	121	88·6	1·9	4·8	0·0	0·07

Fruit – continued

No.	Food	g. per 100 g.			Calories per 100 g.	mg. per 100 g.									Acid base-balance, m-equiv. per 100 g.	
		Protein (N × 6.25)	Fat	Available carbohydrate (as monosaccharides)		Na	K	Ca	Mg	Fe	Cu	P	S	Cl	Acid	Base
351	Peaches, canned in syrup	0.4	Tr.	22.9	87	1.4	151	3.5	6.3	1.93	0.06	10.0	1.0	4.2		3.8
352	Pears, imported eating ..	0.3	Tr.	10.8	42	2.3	129	8.0	9.3	0.19	0.23	9.9	5.6	<1.0		3.6
352a	Pears, imported eating (weighed with skin and core)	0.2	Tr.	7.5	29	1.6	89	5.5	6.4	0.13	0.14	6.8	3.9	<1.0		2.5
353	Pears, English eating ..	0.2	Tr.	10.4	40	2.3	127	6.9	5.1	0.22	0.09	9.5	2.7	<1.0		3.4
353a	Pears, English eating (weighed with skin and core)	0.2	Tr.	7.8	30	1.7	95	5.2	3.8	0.17	0.07	7.1	2.0	<1.0		2.6
354	Pears, cooking, raw ..	0.3	Tr.	9.3	36	2.5	100	7.1	4.2	0.16	0.11	14.6	3.4	1.5		2.2
355	Pears, cooking, stewed without sugar	0.2	Tr.	7.2	27	1.9	77	5.5	3.2	0.12	0.08	11.2	2.6	1.1		1.5
356	Pears, canned in syrup..	0.4	Tr.	20.0	77	1.4	90	5.3	5.9	1.75	0.04	5.3	1.3	2.8		2.6
357	Pineapple, fresh	0.5	Tr.	11.6	46	1.6	247	12.2	16.9	0.42	0.08	7.8	2.6	28.5		7.0
358	Pineapple, canned in syrup	0.3	Tr.	20.2	77	0.5	57	13.4	8.1	1.70	0.05	5.0	2.7	4.2		2.2
359	Plums, Victoria dessert	0.6	Tr.	9.6	38	1.7	188	11.0	7.2	0.36	0.10	16.3	3.5	<1.0		4.8
359a	Plums, Victoria dessert (weighed with stones)	0.6	Tr.	9.0	36	1.5	177	10.4	6.8	0.34	0.09	15.3	3.3	<1.0		4.5
360	Plums, cooking, raw ..	0.6	Tr.	6.2	26	2.0	195	13.7	7.9	0.30	0.09	14.5	4.6	<1.0		5.2
360a	Plums, cooking, raw (weighed with stones)	0.5	Tr.	5.6	23	1.8	177	12.5	7.2	0.27	0.08	13.2	4.2	<1.0		4.7
361	Plums, stewed without sugar (weighed with stones)	0.4	Tr.	4.8	20	1.5	150	10.5	6.1	0.23	0.07	11.2	3.5	<0.3		3.9

Fruit – continued

No.	Food	Description	Nature of edible (analysed) material	Edible matter, as eaten, expressed as a percentage of the weight as purchased	g. per 100 g.				
					Water	Unavailable carbohydrate	Sugar (as monosaccharides)	Starch (as glucose)	Total nitrogen
362	Pomegranate juice	Raw	Juice only	56	85·4	0·0	11·6	0·0	0·03
363	Prunes, dried	Raw	Flesh and skin, no stones	83	23·3	16·1	40·3	0·0	0·39
363a	Prunes, dried (weighed with stones)	Raw	Flesh and skin, no stones	83	19·3	13·4	33·5	0·0	0·32
364	Prunes, dried (weighed with stones)	Stewed without sugar	Fruit and juice, no stones	187	61·6	8·1	20·0	0·0	0·19
365	Quinces	Raw	Flesh only, no skin or core	69	84·2	6·4	6·3	Tr.	0·05
366	Raisins, dried	Raw	Flesh and skin, no stones	92	21·5	6·8	64·4	0·0	0·17
367	Raspberries	Raw	Whole fruit	100	83·2	7·4	5·6	0·0	0·14
368	Raspberries	Stewed without sugar	Fruit and juice	105	87·4	7·0	5·3	0·0	0·13
369	Rhubarb	Raw	Stems only	67	94·2	2·6	1·0	0·0	0·10
370	Rhubarb	Stewed without sugar	Stems and juice	87	95·5	2·0	0·8	0·0	0·08
371	Strawberries	Raw	Flesh and pips, no stalks	97	88·9	2·2	6·2	0·0	0·10
372	Sultanas, dried	Raw	Whole fruit	100	18·3	7·0	64·7	0·0	0·28
373	Tangerines	Raw	Flesh only, no peel or pips	70	86·7	1·9	8·0	0·0	0·14
373a	Tangerines (weighed with peel and pips)	Raw	Flesh only, no peel or pips	70	60·6	1·3	5·6	0·0	0·10

Fruit – *continued*

No.	Food	g. per 100 g.			Calories per 100 g.	mg. per 100 g.									Acid-base balance, m-equiv. per 100 g.	
		Protein (N×6.25)	Fat	Available carbohydrate (as monosaccharides)		Na	K	Ca	Mg	Fe	Cu	P	S	Cl	Acid	Base
362	Pomegranate juice	0.2	Tr.	11.6	44	1.1	204	2.9	3.1	0.15	0.07	7.5	4.2	52.5		3.5
363	Prunes, dried, raw	2.4	Tr.	40.3	161	12.2	864	37.7	26.7	2.90	0.16	83.0	18.5	2.5		20.3
363a	Prunes, dried, raw, (weighed with stones)	2.0	Tr.	33.5	134	10.2	718	31.3	22.2	2.41	0.13	69.0	15.4	2.1		16.9
364	Prunes, stewed without sugar (weighed with stones)	1.2	Tr.	20.2	81	6.1	432	18.9	13.4	1.4	0.08	41.5	9.3	1.3		10.0
365	Quinces	0.3	Tr.	6.3	25	3.2	203	13.9	6.0	0.32	0.13	19.0	5.2	1.9		4.9
366	Raisins, dried	1.1	Tr.	64.4	247	52.2	860	60.6	41.7	1.55	0.24	32.8	23.0	8.5		27.0
367	Raspberries, raw	0.9	Tr.	5.6	25	2.5	224	40.7	21.6	1.21	0.21	28.7	17.3	22.3		6.1
368	Raspberries, stewed without sugar	0.8	Tr.	5.3	23	2.3	213	38.8	20.6	1.15	0.20	27.5	16.5	21.2		5.8
369	Rhubarb, raw	0.6	Tr.	1.0	6	2.2	425	103.0	13.6	0.40	0.13	21.0	8.2	87.0		13.0
370	Rhubarb, stewed without sugar	0.4	Tr.	0.8	5	1.7	326	79.2	10.5	0.38	0.10	16.1	6.3	67.0		10.0
371	Strawberries	0.6	Tr.	6.2	26	1.5	161	22.0	11.7	0.71	0.13	23.0	13.4	17.5		3.5
372	Sultanas, dried	1.7	Tr.	64.7	249	52.7	856	52.2	35.3	1.82	0.35	94.5	44.3	15.5		20.4
373	Tangerines	0.9	Tr.	8.0	34	2.2	155	41.5	11.2	0.27	0.09	16.7	10.3	2.4		5.3
373a	Tangerines (weighed with peel and pips)	0.6	Tr.	5.6	24	1.5	108	29.0	7.8	0.19	0.06	11.7	7.2	1.7		3.7

Nuts

No.	Food	Nature of edible (analysed) material	Edible matter, as eaten, expressed as a percentage of the weight as purchased	Water	Unavailable carbohydrate*	Sugar (as invert sugar)	Starch (as glucose)	Total nitrogen
374	Almonds	Kernel only, no shell	37	4·7	14·3	4·3	0·0	3·27
374a	Almonds (weighed with shells)	Kernel only, no shell	37	1·7	5·3	1·6	0·0	1·21
375	Barcelona nuts	Kernel only, no shell	62	5·7	10·3	3·4	1·8	2·06
375a	Barcelona nuts (weighed with shells)	Kernel only, no shell	62	3·5	6·4	2·1	1·1	1·28
376	Brazil nuts	Kernel only, no shell	45	8·5	9·0	1·7	2·4	2·21
376a	Brazil nuts (weighed with shells)	Kernel only, no shell	45	3·8	4·1	0·8	1·1	0·99
377	Chestnuts	Kernel only, no shell	83	51·7	6·8	7·0	29·6	0·37
377a	Chestnuts (weighed with shells)	Kernel only, no shell	83	42·8	5·7	5·8	24·6	0·31
378	Cob nuts	Kernel only, no shell	36	41·1	6·1	4·7	2·1	1·44
378a	Cob nuts (weighed with shells)	Kernel only, no shell	36	14·8	2·2	1·7	0·8	0·52
379	Coconut, fresh	Kernel only, no shell	70	42·0	13·6	3·7	0·0	0·61
380	Coconut milk	Milk only	15	92·2	—	4·9	0·0	0·06
381	Coconut, desiccated	As purchased	100	Tr.	23·5	6·4	0·0	1·05
382	Peanuts	Kernel only, no shell	69	4·5	8·1	3·1	5·5	4·50
382a	Peanuts (weighed with shells)	Kernel only, no shell	69	3·1	5·6	2·1	3·8	3·10
383	Walnuts	Kernel only, no shell	64	23·5	5·2	3·2	1·8	2·00
383a	Walnuts (weighed with shells)	Kernel only, no shell	64	15·0	3·3	2·0	1·2	1·28

* Undetermined matter, probably unavailable carbohydrate.

Nuts – continued

No.	Food	g. per 100 g.			Calories per 100 g.	mg. per 100 g.									Acid-base balance, m-equiv. per 100 g.	
		Protein (N×6·25)	Fat	Available carbohydrate (as monosaccharides)		Na	K	Ca	Mg	Fe	Cu	P	S	Cl	Acid	Base
374	Almonds	20·5	53·5	4·3	598	5·3	856	247	257	4·23	0·14	442	145	1·7		18·3
374a	Almonds (weighed with shells)	7·6	19·8	1·6	221	2·1	316	92	95	1·56	0·05	164	54	0·6		6·8
375	Barcelona nuts	12·9	64·0	5·2	667	2·5	935	170	202	2·97	0·96	299	176	33·5		18·2
375a	Barcelona nuts (weighed with shells)	8·0	39·6	3·2	413	1·6	580	106	125	1·84	0·60	185	109	20·8		11·3
376	Brazil nuts	13·8	61·5	4·1	644	1·5	760	176	411	2·82	1·10	592	293	61·0		4·5
376a	Brazil nuts (weighed with shells)	6·2	27·6	1·8	289	0·7	342	79	185	1·27	0·50	267	132	27·4		2·0
377	Chestnuts	2·3	2·7	36·6	172	10·9	497	46	33	0·89	0·23	74	29	15·0		11·3
377a	Chestnuts (weighed with shells)	1·9	2·2	30·4	142	9·1	412	38	27	0·74	0·19	61	24	12·4		9·4
378	Cob nuts	9·0	36·0	6·8	398	1·4	345	44	56	1·06	0·21	229	75	5·3	3·9	
378a	Cob nuts (weighed with shells)	3·2	13·0	2·4	143	0·5	124	16	20	0·38	0·08	82	27	2·1	1·4	
379	Coconut, fresh	3·8	36·0	3·7	365	16·5	436	13	52	2·08	0·32	94	44	114·0		4·9
380	Coconut milk	0·4	—	4·9	—	105·0	312	29	30	0·10	0·04	37	24	183·0		7·5
381	Coconut, desiccated	6·6	62·0	6·4	628	28·4	751	22	90	3·59	0·55	162	76	195·0		8·5
382	Peanuts	28·1	49·0	8·6	603	5·6	680	61	181	2·04	0·27	365	377	5·8	11·6	
382a	Peanuts (weighed with shells)	19·4	33·8	5·9	416	3·9	469	42	125	1·41	0·19	252	260	4·7	8·0	
383	Walnuts	12·5	51·5	5·0	549	2·7	687	61	131	2·35	0·31	510	104	23·0	8·4	
383a	Walnuts (weighed with shells)	8·0	33·0	3·2	352	1·7	439	39	84	1·50	0·20	326	67	14·7	5·4	

G

Vegetables

No.	Food	Method and time of cooking	Nature of edible (analysed) material	Edible matter, as eaten, expressed as a percentage of the weight as purchased	g. per 100 g.				
					Water	Unavailable carbohydrate	Sugar (as invert sugar)	Starch (as glucose)	Total nitrogen
384	Artichokes, globe	Boiled 35 minutes	Base of leaves and soft inside parts	41	84·4	—	—	0·0	0·18
384a	Artichokes, globe (weighed as served)	Boiled 35 minutes	Base of leaves and soft inside parts	41	36·3	—	—	0·0	0·08
385	Artichokes, Jerusalem	Boiled 20 minutes	Flesh only	85	80·2	—	—	0·0	0·25
386	Asparagus	Boiled 25 minutes	Soft tips	20	92·4	1·5	1·1	0·0	0·54
386a	Asparagus (weighed as served)	Boiled 25 minutes	Soft tips	20	46·2	0·8	0·6	0·0	0·27
387	Beans, baked	Canned	Contents of can as purchased	100	69·6	5·1	6·1	11·2	0·96
388	Beans, broad	Boiled 30 minutes	Whole beans, without pods	31	83·7	4·2	0·6	6·5	0·66
389	Beans, butter	Raw	Whole beans	100	11·6	21·6	3·6	46·2	3·06
390	Beans, butter	Soaked 24 hours, boiled 2 hours	Whole beans	250	70·5	5·1	1·5	15·6	1·13
391	Beans, French	Cut up and boiled 30 minutes	Flesh and skin of pods and beans	100	95·5	3·2	0·8	0·3	0·12
392	Beans, haricot	Raw	Whole beans	100	11·3	25·4	2·8	42·7	3·42
393	Beans, haricot	Soaked 24 hours, boiled 2 hours	Whole beans	260	69·6	7·4	0·8	15·8	1·06
394	Beans, runner	Raw	Flesh and skin of pods and beans	86	91·6	3·0	2·7	0·2	0·18

Vegetables – *continued*

No.	Food	g. per 100 g.			Calories per 100 g.	mg. per 100 g.									Acid base-balance, m-equiv. per 100 g.	
		Protein (N× 6·25)	Fat	Available carbohydrate (as monosaccharides)		Na	K	Ca	Mg	Fe	Cu	P	S	Cl	Acid	Base
384	Artichokes, globe, boiled	1·1	Tr.	*2·7	15	14·8	327	43·5	27·2	0·49	0·09	39·7	15·5	83·5		7·6
384a	Artichokes, globe, boiled (weighed as served)	0·5	Tr.	*1·2	7	6·4	141	18·7	11·7	0·21	0·04	17·1	6·7	35·9		3·3
385	Artichokes, Jerusalem, boiled	1·6	Tr.	*3·2	19	2·6	420	30·3	11·4	0·41	0·12	33·0	21·6	57·5		8·2
386	Asparagus, boiled	3·4	Tr.	1·1	18	1·7	235	25·8	10·4	0·89	0·20	84·5	46·6	31·4	1·0	
386a	Asparagus, boiled (weighed as served)	1·7	Tr.	0·6	9	0·9	118	12·9	5·2	0·45	0·10	42·3	23·3	15·7	0·5	
387	Beans, baked	6·0	0·4	17·3	93	(591)	344	61·6	36·7	2·05	0·24	184·0	50·7	(≡10)		2·8
388	Beans, broad, boiled	4·1	Tr.	7·1	43	19·6	233	21·2	27·6	0·98	0·43	99·0	27·0	14·2		1·7
389	Beans, butter, raw	19·2	Tr.	49·8	266	61·5	1700	84·8	164·0	5·92	1·22	318·0	109·0	45·5		35·5.
390	Beans, butter, boiled	7·1	Tr.	17·1	93	16·2	398	18·7	33·3	1·67	0·16	86·5	47·2	2·4		6·0
391	Beans, French, boiled	0·8	Tr.	1·1	7	3·4	102	38·6	10·1	0·59	0·10	15·2	8·3	10·7		3·7
392	Beans, haricot, raw	21·4	Tr.	45·5	258	43·2	1160	180·0	183·0	6·65	0·61	309·0	166·0	1·8		25·5
393	Beans, haricot, boiled	6·6	Tr.	16·6	89	15·0	320	64·5	44·5	2·50	0·14	122·0	46·3	1·1		5·0
394	Beans, runner, raw	1·1	Tr.	2·9	15	6·5	276	33·3	23·0	0·74	0·09	25·9	14·1	22·7		7·7

* This vegetable contains inulin.   50 per cent. total carbohydrate taken to be available.

Vegetables – *continued*

No.	Food	Method and time of cooking	Nature of edible (analysed) material	Edible matter, as eaten, expressed as a percentage of the weight as purchased	g. per 100 g.				
					Water	Unavailable carbohydrate	Sugar (as invert sugar)	Starch (as glucose)	Total nitrogen
395	Beans, runner	Cut up and boiled 25 minutes	Flesh and skin of pods and beans	86	93·6	3·0	0·8	0·1	0·12
396	Beetroot	Raw	Flesh only, no skin	82	87·1	3·1	6·0	0·0	0·21
397	Beetroot*	Boiled 2 hours	Flesh only, no skin	80	82·7	2·5	9·9	0·0	0·29
398	Broccoli tops	Boiled 45 minutes	Leaves only, no thick stem	42	90·8	4·2	0·4	0·0	0·50
399	Brussels sprouts	Raw	Inner leaves	58	84·3	3·6	3·6	1·0	0·57
400	Brussels sprouts	Boiled 30 minutes	Inner leaves	94	90·8	4·8	1·1	0·6	0·38
401	Cabbage, red	Raw	Inner leaves	70	89·7	3·4	3·5	0·0	0·27
402	Cabbage, Savoy	Raw	Inner leaves	53	89·9	3·1	3·3	0·0	0·53
403	Cabbage, Savoy	Boiled 30 minutes	Inner leaves	65	95·7	2·5	1·1	0·0	0·21
404	Cabbage, spring	Boiled 30 minutes	Inner leaves	59	96·6	2·2	0·8	0·0	0·18
405	Cabbage, winter	Raw	Inner leaves	60	90·6	2·5	3·8	0·0	0·43
406	Cabbage, winter	Boiled 45 minutes	Inner leaves	71	95·9	2·5	1·2	0·1	0·13
407	Carrageen moss	Dried	Whole moss	100	13·9	71·3	0·4	0·0	1·08
408	Carrots, old	Raw	Flesh only	96	89·8	2·9	5·4	0·0	0·11
409	Carrots, old	Boiled 45 minutes	Flesh only	87	91·5	3·1	4·2	0·1	0·10
410	Carrots, young	Boiled 25 minutes	Flesh only	50	81·1	3·0	4·4	0·1	0·14
411	Carrots	Canned, Smedley's	Edible material only. 6 samples from different shops	—	91·2	3·7	4·4	Tr.	0·11
412	Cauliflower	Raw	Flower and inner leaves	49	89·1	1·5	2·4	0·4	0·55

* weighed cold.

Vegetables – *continued*

No.	Food	Protein (N × 6.25)	Fat	Available carbohydrate (as monosaccharides)	Calories per 100 g.	Na	K	Ca	Mg	Fe	Cu	P	S	Cl	Acid	Base
		g. per 100 g.				*mg. per 100 g.*									*Acid-base balance, m-equiv. per 100 g.*	
395	Beans, runner, boiled	0·8	Tr.	0·9	7	3·3	87	25·6	12·5	0·59	0·03	10·7	9·5	8·8		3·2
396	Beetroot, raw	1·3	Tr.	6·0	28	84·0	303	24·9	15·0	0·37	0·07	32·1	—	59·2	—	
397	Beetroot, boiled	1·8	Tr.	9·9	44	64·0	350	30·0	16·9	0·70	0·14	35·6	22·1	75·5		8·9
398	Broccoli tops, boiled	3·1	Tr.	0·4	14	6·8	103	160·0	13·5	1·52	0·10	54·0	45·0	51·2		4·3
399	Brussels sprouts, raw	3·6	Tr.	4·6	32	9·6	515	28·7	19·6	0·66	0·05	78·4	—	35·2	—	
400	Brussels sprouts, boiled	2·4	Tr.	1·7	16	7·7	247	27·1	10·6	0·63	0·08	44·8	77·8	11·4		0·8
401	Cabbage, red, raw	1·7	Tr.	3·5	20	31·6	302	53·2	16·5	0·57	0·09	32·1	68·0	44·5		5·6
402	Cabbage, Savoy, raw	3·3	Tr.	3·3	26	22·5	263	75·0	19·5	0·90	—	67·7	88·0	22·3		2·6
403	Cabbage, Savoy, boiled	1·3	Tr.	1·1	9	8·1	122	52·5	7·2	0·72	0·07	27·2	30·4	9·4		2·8
404	Cabbage, spring, boiled	1·1	Tr.	0·8	8	12·3	108	30·0	6·3	0·45	0·07	31·8	26·7	6·4		1·4
405	Cabbage, winter, raw	2·2	Tr.	3·8	25	28·4	240	72·3	16·8	1·23		64·1	71·8	39·6		2·7
406	Cabbage, winter, boiled	0·8	Tr.	1·3	8	13·5	144	58·2	7·3	0·47	0·04	16·2	23·4	13·7		4·9
407	Carragen moss, dried	6·8	Tr.	0·4	29	2890	2100	845	630	8·88	0·51	205	5460	1150	113	
408	Carrots, old, raw	0·7	Tr.	5·4	23	95·0	224	48·0	12·0	0·56	0·08	21·0	6·9	68·5		9·0
409	Carrots, old, boiled	0·6	Tr.	4·3	19	50·0	87	36·9	6·4	0·37	0·08	16·7	5·0	31·1		4·4
410	Carrots, young, boiled	0·9	Tr.	4·5	21	22·5	237	28·8	8·4	0·43	0·08	29·5	9·3	27·5		5·9
411	Carrots, canned	0·7	Tr.	4·4	19	(278)	84	26·6	4·6	1·28	0·04	15·1	—	(445)	—	
412	Cauliflower, raw	3·4	Tr.	2·8	25	10·4	408	18·1	16·9	0·58	0·04	75·2	—	35·6	—	

Vegetables – *continued*

No.	Food	Method and time of cooking	Nature of edible (analysed) material	Edible matter, as eaten, expressed as a percentage of the weight as purchased	g. per 100 g.				
					Water	Unavailable carbohydrate	Sugar (as invert sugar)	Starch (as glucose)	Total nitrogen
413	Cauliflower	Boiled 30 minutes	Flower and inner leaves	42	94·9	2·4	1·2	0·0	0·24
414	Celeriac	Boiled 30 minutes	Flesh only	79	90·2	4·9	1·5	0·5	0·26
415	Celery	Raw	Stem only	73	93·5	1·8	1·2	0·1	0·15
416	Celery	Boiled 30 minutes	Stem only	72	95·7	2·2	0·7	0·0	0·10
417	Chicory	Raw	Stem and young leaves	79	96·2	—	—	0·0	0·12
418	Cucumber	Raw	Flesh only	77	96·4	0·4	1·8	0·0	0·10
419	Egg plant	Raw	Flesh only	77	93·4	2·5	2·9	0·2	0·11
420	Endive	Raw	Leaves only	63	93·7	2·2	1·0	0·0	0·28
421	Horseradish	Raw	Flesh of root	45	74·7	8·3	7·3	3·7	0·72
422	Leeks	Raw	Bulb only	36	86·0	3·1	6·0	0·0	0·31
423	Leeks	Boiled 30 minutes	Bulb only	44	90·8	3·9	4·6	0·0	0·28
424	Lentils	Raw	Lentils as purchased	100	12·2	11·7	2·4	50·8	3·80
425	Lentils	Soaked 24 hours, boiled 2 hours	Lentils as purchased	290	71·9	2·4	0·9	17·4	1·08
426	Lettuce	Raw	Inner leaves of long and headed forms	45	95·2	1·4	1·8	0·0	0·17
427	Marrow	Boiled 25 minutes	Flesh only	64	97·8	0·6	1·3	0·1	0·06
428	Mushrooms	Raw	Flesh and stem	75	91·5	2·5	0·0	0·0	0·64*
429	Mushrooms	Fried in dripping	Flesh and stem	61	64·2	—	0·0	0·0	0·90*
430	Mustard and cress	Raw	Leaves and stems	100	92·5	3·7	0·9	0·0	0·26
431	Onions	Raw	Flesh only	97	92·8	1·3	5·2	0·0	0·15
432	Onions	Boiled 30 minutes	Flesh only	85	96·6	1·3	2·7	0·0	0·09

* 60 per cent. of this nitrogen is present as urea.

Vegetables – continued

No.	Food	Protein (N×6.25)	Fat	Available carbohydrate (as monosaccharides)	Calories per 100 g.	Na	K	Ca	Mg	Fe	Cu	P	S	Cl	Acid	Base
		g. per 100 g.				mg. per 100 g.									Acid-base balance, m-equiv. per 100 g.	
413	Cauliflower, boiled	1·5	Tr.	1·2	11	11·4	152	23·0	6·6	0·48	0·06	33·0	29·4	1·6		1·7
414	Celeriac, boiled	1·6	Tr.	2·0	14	28·2	400	46·5	12·0	0·84	0·13	71·0	12·8	23·4		8·8
415	Celery, raw	0·9	Tr.	1·3	9	137·0	278	52·2	9·6	0·61	0·11	31·7	14·9	183·0		8·4
416	Celery, boiled	0·6	Tr.	0·7	5	66·5	132	52·0	8·6	0·43	0·11	19·3	8·3	100·0		5·0
417	Chicory, raw	0·8	Tr.	†1·5	9	7·3	182	18·4	12·6	0·69	0·14	20·9	12·7	25·0		4·1
418	Cucumber, raw	0·6	Tr.	1·8	9	13·0	141	22·8	9·1	0·30	0·09	24·1	11·0	24·5		3·2
419	Egg plant, raw	0·7	Tr.	3·1	15	2·5	238	10·4	9·5	0·39	0·08	12·1	9·0	61·0		4·5
420	Endive, raw	1·8	Tr.	1·0	11	10·1	381	43·9	10·4	2·77	0·09	66·5	25·7	70·5		5·4
421	Horseradish, raw	4·5	Tr.	11·0	60	7·9	579	119·0	35·8	2·03	0·14	70·0	212·0	13·8		5·8
422	Leeks, raw	1·9	Tr.	6·0	30	8·8	314	62·7	10·3	1·12	0·10	43·2	—	42·5	—	
423	Leeks, boiled	1·8	Tr.	4·6	25	6·4	278	60·5	12·5	2·00	0·09	27·5	48·9	42·6		5·5
424	Lentils, raw	23·8	Tr.	53·2	297	36·0	673	38·6	76·5	7·62	0·58	242	122·0	63·5		2·0
425	Lentils, boiled	6·8	Tr.	18·3	96	9·4	217	10·5	20·7	2·20	0·27	80·0	37·3	12·7		0·4
426	Lettuce, raw	1·1	Tr.	1·8	11	3·1	208	25·9	9·7	0·73	0·15	30·2	11·8	39·5		3·8
427	Marrow, boiled	0·4	Tr.	1·4	7	1·2	84	13·6	6·7	0·22	0·03	12·7	5·5	13·9		1·9
428	Mushrooms, raw	*1·8	Tr.	0·0	7	9·1	467	2·9	13·2	1·03	0·64	136·0	33·8	84·5	1·6	
429	Mushrooms, fried	*2·2	22·3	0·0	217	11·0	568	3·5	16·0	1·25	0·78	166·0	73·8	103·0	2·3	
430	Mustard and cress, raw	1·6	Tr.	0·9	10	19·0	337	65·9	27·3	4·54	0·12	65·5	170·0	89·0		0·4
431	Onions, raw	0·9	Tr.	5·2	23	10·2	137	31·2	7·6	0·30	0·08	30·0	50·7	19·5		0·5
432	Onions, boiled	0·6	Tr.	2·7	13	6·6	78	24·4	4·9	0·25	0·07	16·4	23·7	4·9		0·2

* See page 4.   † This vegetable contains inulin.   50 per cent. total carbohydrate taken to be available.

Vegetables – *continued*

No.	Food	Method and time of cooking	Nature of edible (analysed) material	Edible matter, as eaten, expressed as a percentage of the weight as purchased	g. per 100 g.				
					Water	Unavailable carbohydrate	Sugar (as invert sugar)	Starch (as glucose)	Total nitrogen
433	Onions	Cut up and fried in dripping	Flesh only	49	42·0	—	10·1	0·0	0·90
434	Onions, spring	Raw	Flesh of bulb	31	86·8	3·1	8·5	0·0	0·15
435	Parsley	Raw	Leaves	53	78·7	9·1	Tr.	0·0	0·83
436	Parsnips	Raw	Flesh only	74	82·5	4·0	8·8	2·5	0·27
437	Parsnips	Boiled 30 minutes	Flesh only	78	83·2	2·5	2·7	10·8	0·20
438	Peas, fresh†	Raw	Whole peas, no pods	37	78·5	5·2	4·0	6·6	0·92
439	Peas, fresh	Boiled 20 minutes	Whole peas, no pods	37	80·0	5·2	1·8	5·9	0·80
440	Peas, dried	Raw	Whole peas	100	13·3	16·7	2·4	47·6	3·45
441	Peas, dried	Soaked 24 hours, boiled 2 hours	Whole peas	270	70·3	4·8	0·9	18·2	1·11
442	Peas, split, dried	Raw	Peas as purchased	100	12·1	11·9	1·9	54·7	3·54
443	Peas, split, dried	Soaked 24 hours, boiled 2 hours	Peas as purchased	250	67·3	5·1	0·9	21·0	1·33
444	Peas	Canned	Whole peas	100	72·7	4·4	2·3	14·2	0·94
445	Potatoes, old	Raw	Flesh only	86	75·8	2·1	0·5	20·3	0·34
446	Potatoes, old, peel	Raw	Peel only	—	80·0	2·6	0·4	15·5	0·40
447	Potatoes, old	Boiled 30 minutes	Flesh only (peeled before boiling)	86	80·5	1·0	0·4	19·3	0·23
448	Potatoes, old	Boiled and mashed with margarine and milk	Flesh only	94	76·9	0·9	0·6	17·4	0·24
449	Potatoes, old	Baked in skins	Flesh only	68	71·0	2·5	0·6	24·4	0·41
449a	Potatoes, old (weighed with skin)	Baked in skins	Flesh only	68	57·5	2·0	0·5	19·8	0·33

† These values may be used for frozen peas and reconstituted freeze-dried peas.

Vegetables – continued

No.	Food	Protein (N×6·25)	Fat	Available carbohydrate (as monosaccharides)	Calories per 100 g.	Na	K	Ca	Mg	Fe	Cu	P	S	Cl	Acid	Base
433	Onions, fried	1·8	33·3	10·1	355	20·0	267	61·0	14·8	0·59	0·16	59·0	87·8	38·0		1·6
434	Onions, spring, raw	0·9	Tr.	8·5	36	13·0	226	135·0	10·9	1·24	0·13	23·6	50·0	35·5		8·4
435	Parsley, raw	5·2	Tr.	Tr.	21	33·0	1080	325·0	52·2	8·00	0·52	128·0	—	156·0		7·5
436	Parsnips, raw	1·7	Tr.	11·3	49	16·5	342	54·8	22·4	0·57	0·10	69·0	16·5	40·5		6·7
437	Parsnips, boiled	1·3	Tr.	13·5	56	4·1	293	35·5	13·0	0·45	0·10	31·7	14·6	32·7		1·2
438	Peas, fresh, raw*	5·8	Tr.	10·6	64	0·5	342	15·1	30·2	1·88	0·23	104·0	50·0	38·0	—	
439	Peas, fresh, boiled	5·0	Tr.	7·7	49	Tr.	174	12·6	21·4	1·22	0·15	83·3	43·5	7·8	1·4	
440	Peas, dried, raw	21·5	Tr.	50·0	275	37·9	985	60·8	116·0	4·73	0·49	303·0	129·0	60·0		10·3
441	Peas, dried, boiled	6·9	Tr.	19·1	100	12·6	267	24·4	30·3	1·44	0·17	113·0	39·0	9·3		1·2
442	Peas, split, dried, raw	22·1	Tr.	56·6	303	38·3	910	33·0	125·0	5·40	0·58	268·0	166·0	56·0		7·7
443	Peas, split, dried, boiled	8·3	Tr.	21·9	116	14·2	269	10·8	30·2	1·74	0·25	122·0	45·7	10·2	0·5	
444	Peas, canned	5·9	Tr.	16·5	86	(260)	201	25·7	24·4	1·87	0·21	169·0	43·9	(313)	2·9	
445	Potatoes, old, raw	2·1	Tr.	20·8	87	6·5	568	7·7	24·2	0·75	0·15	40·3	34·6	78·5		10·3
446	Potatoes, old, raw, peel	2·5	Tr.	15·9	70	7·0	650	27·0	27·6	2·00	0·25	36·4		95·0	—	
447	Potatoes, old, boiled	1·4	Tr.	19·7	80	3·4	325	4·3	15·0	0·48	0·11	29·0	22·2	40·7		5·3
448	Potatoes, old, mashed	1·5	5·0	18·0	120	(24)	302	11·7	14·4	0·45	0·10	31·6	23·5	(71)		5·1
449	Potatoes, old, baked in skins	2·5	Tr.	25·0	104	7·8	680	9·2	29·0	0·90	0·18	48·3	41·5	94·0		12·4
449a	Potatoes, old, baked in skins (weighed with skins)	2·0	Tr.	20·3	84	6·3	550	7·5	23·5	0·73	0·15	39·1	33·6	76·1		10·0

* See note page 96.

Vegetables – *continued*

No.	Food	Method and time of cooking	Nature of edible (analysed) material	Edible matter, as eaten, expressed as a percentage of the weight as purchased.	Water	Unavailable carbohydrate	Sugar (as invert sugar)	Starch (as glucose)	Total nitrogen
							g. per 100 g.		
450	Potatoes, old	Roast in shallow fat	Flesh only	66	64·3	—	—	—	0·45
451	Potatoes, old, " chips "	Cut in cubes and fried in deep fat	Flesh only	49	47·0	—	—	—	0·61
452	Potatoes, new	Boiled 15 minutes	Flesh only	96	78·8	2·0	0·7	17·6	0·25
453	Potato Crisps (Smith's)		22 samples from different shops	100	4·8	1·4	1·0	48·3	0·95
454	Pumpkin	Raw	Flesh only	81	94·7	0·5	2·7	0·7	0·10
455	Radishes	Raw	Flesh and skin	50	93·3	1·0	2·8	0·0	0·16
456	Salsify	Boiled 45 minutes	Flesh only	63	81·2	—	—	0·0	0·30
457	Seakale	Boiled 20 minutes	Stem only	74	95·6	1·2	0·6	0·0	0·23
458	Spinach	Boiled 15 minutes, without added water	Leaves	42	85·1	6·3	1·2	0·2	0·81
459	Spring greens	Boiled 30 minutes	Leaves	100	93·6	3·8	0·9	0·0	0·27
460	Swedes	Raw	Flesh only	86	91·4	2·7	4·2	0·1	0·18
461	Swedes	Boiled 45 minutes	Flesh only	82	91·6	2·8	3·7	0·1	0·14
462	Sweet potatoes	Boiled 30 minutes	Flesh only	88	72·0	2·3	9·1	11·0	0·17
463	Tomatoes	Raw	Flesh, skin and seeds	100	93·4	1·5	2·8	Tr.	0·14
464	Tomatoes	Fried in dripping	Flesh, skin and seeds	87	86·5	—	3·3	Tr.	0·16
465	Turnips	Raw	Flesh only	84	93·3	2·8	3·8	0·0	0·12
466	Turnips	Boiled 30 minutes	Flesh only	80	94·5	2·2	2·3	0·0	0·11
467	Turnip tops	Boiled 20 minutes	Leaves	45	92·8	3·9	0·0	0·1	0·43
468	Watercress	Raw	Leaves and part of stem	77	91·1	3·3	0·6	0·1	0·46

Vegetables – *continued*

No.	Food	g. per 100 g.			Calories per 100 g.	mg. per 100 g.									Acid-base balance, m-equiv. per 100 g.	
		Protein (N×6·25)	Fat	Available carbohydrate (as monosaccharides)		Na	K	Ca	Mg	Fe	Cu	P	S	Cl	Acid	Base
450	Potatoes, old, roast	2·8	1·0	27·3	123	8·6	745	10·1	32·0	0·99	0·20	53·0	56·3	103·0		12·8
451	Potatoes, old, "chips"	3·8	9·0	37·3	239	11·7	1020	13·8	43·3	1·35	0·27	72·2	44·7	140·0		19·6
452	Potatoes, new, boiled	1·6	Tr.	18·3	75	40·5	330	5·0	19·6	0·46	0·15	33·0	24·3	45·5		7·2
453	Potato Crisps (Smith's)	5·9	37·6	49·3	559	35·2	1350	37·0	47·5	4·08	0·36	125·0	—	267·0	—	—
454	Pumpkin, raw	0·6	Tr.	3·4	15	1·3	309	39·0	8·2	0·39	0·08	19·4	9·5	36·5		7·8
455	Radishes, raw	1·0	Tr.	2·8	15	59·0	240	43·7	11·4	1·88	0·13	27·1	37·5	18·8		7·2
456	Salsify, boiled	1·9	Tr.	*2·8	18	8·4	183	60·0	14·2	1·23	0·12	53·0	25·2	46·0		2·9
457	Seakale, boiled	1·4	Tr.	0·6	8	3·9	50	47·8	10·5	0·60	0·07	33·5	52·0	12·4	1·0	—
458	Spinach, boiled	5·1	Tr.	1·4	26	123·0	490	595·0	59·2	4·00	0·26	93·0	86·5	55·5		39·6
459	Spring greens, boiled	1·7	Tr.	0·9	10	10·3	118	86·0	8·6	1·33	0·08	30·5	28·5	16·1		4·3
460	Swedes, raw	1·1	Tr.	4·3	21	52·2	136	56·4	10·8	0·35	0·05	19·0	39·1	30·5		4·9
461	Swedes, boiled	0·9	Tr.	3·8	18	14·4	102	41·5	7·0	0·29	0·04	18·4	30·5	9·3		2·6
462	Sweet potatoes, boiled	1·1	Tr.	20·1	80	17·8	296	20·5	12·3	0·62	0·15	43·5	14·9	60·0		5·0
463	Tomatoes, raw	0·9	Tr.	2·8	14	2·8	288	13·3	11·0	0·43	0·10	21·3	10·7	51·0		5·6
464	Tomatoes, fried	1·0	5·9	3·3	71	3·3	335	15·4	12·8	0·50	0·12	24·8	9·2	59·0		6·8
465	Turnips, raw	0·8	Tr.	3·8	18	58·0	238	58·8	7·4	0·37	0·07	27·5	22·1	70·0		6·5
466	Turnips, boiled	0·7	Tr.	2·3	11	28·3	160	55·0	6·6	0·35	0·04	19·2	21·2	31·4		5·2
467	Turnip tops, boiled	2·7	Tr.	0·1	11	6·7	78	98·0	10·1	3·08	0·09	45·1	39·0	14·8		2·3
468	Watercress, raw	2·9	Tr.	0·7	15	60·0	314	222·0	17·0	1·62	0·14	52·0	127·0	156·0		7·5

* This vegetable contains inulin.   50 per cent. total carbohydrate taken to be available.

Sugar, Preserves and Sweetmeats

No.	Food	Description and number of samples	Water	Sugar (as invert sugar)	Starch and dextrins (as glucose)	Total nitrogen
						g. per 100 g.
469	Blackcurrant purée	Mixed sample supplied by the makers	57·0	40·0	0·0	0·07
470	Boiled sweets	6 samples from different shops	2·7	86·9	0·4	0·01
471	Bounty Bar	8 samples from different shops	7·6	53·7	4·6	0·77
472	Cherries, glacé	3 samples from different shops	—	55·8	0·0	0·10
473	Chocolate, blended	3 well-known varieties	Tr.	51·5	0·7	1·47
474	Chocolate, milk	2 well-known varieties	Tr.	53·8	0·7	1·39
475	Chocolate, plain	4 well-known varieties	Tr.	49·8	2·7	0·89
476	Chocolates, fancy	8 samples of different brands, mixed, milk and plain	5·7	65·8	7·5	0·66
477	Chutney, apple	Recipe p. 8	45·0	51·9	0·4	0·13
478	Chutney, tomato	Recipe p. 8	58·2	38·5	0·3	0·18
479	Comb honey	2 samples from different shops	20·2	74·4	0·0	0·09
480	Fruit gums (Rowntree's)	8 samples from different shops	12·0	42·6	2·2	0·16
481	Honey, in jars	2 samples from different shops	23·0	76·4	0·0	0·06
482	Ice cream	6 samples from different shops	61·9	19·8	—	0·66
483	Jam, fruit with edible seeds	Blackberry, blackcurrant, gooseberry, raspberry, strawberry. Two samples of each, different makers	29·8	69·0	0·0	0·10

Sugar, Preserves and Sweetmeats – continued

No.	Food	Protein (N× 6·25)	Fat	Available carbohydrate (as monosaccharides)	Calories per 100 g.	Na	K	Ca	Mg	Fe	Cu	P	S	Cl	Acid	Base
		g. per 100 g.				mg. per 100 g.									Acid base-balance, m-equiv. per 100 g.	
469	Blackcurrant purée	0·4	Tr.	40·0	152	11·0	200	34·0	11·8	1·60	0·15	25·0	32·0	13·0		4·3
470	Boiled sweets	Tr.	Tr.	87·3	327	25·1	8	4·8	2·4	0·43	0·09	11·6	—	68·0	—	—
471	Bounty Bar	4·8	26·1	58·3	481	182·0	317	109·0	42·5	1·34	0·47	139·0	—	401		1·7
472	Cherries, glacé	0·6	0·0	55·8	212	64·8	18	44·3	8·2	2·90	1·28	18·0	21·0	71·0		
473	Chocolate, blended	9·2	36·0	52·2	566	(276)	386	253	66·4	2·05	0·48	226·0	—	183·0	—	—
474	Chocolate, milk	8·7	37·6	54·5	588	(275)	349	246	58·9	1·71	0·49	218·0	—	170·0	—	—
475	Chocolate, plain	5·6	35·2	52·5	544	(143)	257	63·0	131·0	2·90	0·81	138·0	—	4·8		
476	Chocolates, fancy	4·1	18·8	73·3	467	60·2	243	91·6	50·7	1·75	0·45	121·0	32·0	177·0		4·6
477	Chutney, apple	0·8	0·1	52·3	201	(170)	217	27·4	17·3	1·01	0·10	33·7	32·0	(251)		5·3
478	Chutney, tomato	1·1	0·1	38·8	151	(130)	278	26·2	17·8	0·93	0·12	36·5	31·1	(215)		
479	Comb honey	0·6	4·6*	74·4	281	7·1	35	7·7	2·0	0·20	0·04	32·3	0·8	26·2	1·1	
480	Fruit gums, (Rowntree's)	1·0	0·0	44·6	171	63·7	363	359	105·0	4·24	1·43	4·4	0·8	156·0		
481	Honey, in jars	0·4	Tr.	76·4	288	10·9	51	5·3	2·2	0·39	0·05	17·0	0·8	17·9		0·6
482	Ice cream	4·1	11·3	19·8	196	79·2	167	137·0	14·9	0·27	0·03	103·0	6·5	149·0		
483	Jam, fruit with edible seeds	0·6	0·0	69·0	261	15·9	112	24·2	10·1	1·47	0·23	17·9	6·5	9·2	—	3·8

* Waxy material, probably not available as fat.   Disregarded in calculating calories.

Sugar, Preserves and Sweetmeats – *continued*

No.	Food	Description and number of samples	g. per 100 g.			Total nitrogen
			Water	Sugar (as invert sugar)	Starch and dextrins (as glucose)	
484	Jam, stone fruit	Apricot, damson, greengage, plum. Two samples of each, different makers	29·6	69·3	0·0	0·06
485	Jelly, packet	8 samples, assorted flavours	29·9	62·5	0·0	1·10
486	Lemon curd	Recipe p. 8	42·1	42·5	0·0	0·52
487	Liquid Glucose, B.P.	1 sample only	20·4	40·2	44·5	Tr.
488	Liquorice Allsorts	6 samples from different shops	6·6	67·2	6·9	0·63
489	Marmalade	4 varieties	28·0	69·5	0·0	0·01
490	Mars Bar	8 samples from different shops	6·9	65·8	0·7	0·84
491	Mincemeat	2 varieties	69·3	25·5	0·0	0·09
492	Pastilles	6 samples of different brands	10·2	61·9	—	0·84
493	Peppermints	Several samples of 6 different makes	0·2	102·2	0·0	0·08
494	Sugar, Demerara	5 samples from different shops	Tr.	99·3*	0·0	0·08
495	Sugar, white	Granulated and loaf	Tr.	99·9*	0·0	Tr.
496	Syrup, golden	3 samples of well-known brand	20·0	79·0	0·0	0·05
497	Toffee, home-made	Recipe p. 8	5·5	90·8	0·0	0·03
498	Toffees, mixed	8 samples of different makes	4·8	70·1	1·0	0·34
499	Treacle, black	3 samples from different shops	28·5	67·2	0·0	0·19

* As sucrose.

Sugar, Preserves and Sweetmeats – continued

Protein, Fat and Available carbohydrate: g. per 100 g. — Na, K, Ca, Mg, Fe, Cu, P, S, Cl: mg. per 100 g. — Acid/Base: Acid-base balance, m-equiv. per 100 g.

No.	Food	Protein (N×6.25)	Fat	Available carbohydrate (as monosaccharides)	Calories per 100 g.	Na	K	Ca	Mg	Fe	Cu	P	S	Cl	Acid	Base
484	Jam, stone fruit	0·4	0·0	69·3	261	12·2	104	12·0	5·4	1·02	0·12	18·2	3·2	3·5	—	2·8
485	Jelly, packet	6·1*	0·0	62·5	259	25·2	25	31·5	4·4	1·74	0·16	7·0	36·6	30·0	—	0·1
486	Lemon curd	3·3	13·9	42·5	302	(63)	67	18·3	5·0	0·72	0·05	62·5	47·0	(84)	3·5	—
487	Liquid Glucose	Tr.	0·0	84·7	318	146·0	3	8·4	2·3	0·51	0·09	10·8	—	193·0	—	—
488	Liquorice Allsorts	3·9	2·2	74·1	315	74·9	216	62·9	38·1	8·05	0·39	29·4	2·1	117·0	—	2·8
489	Marmalade	0·1	0·0	69·5	261	18·2	44	34·7	3·7	0·58	0·12	12·5		7·1	—	—
490	Mars Bars	5·3	18·9	66·5	447	145·0	249	163·0	35·0	1·07	0·31	154·0	28·4	295	—	12·2
491	Mincemeat	0·6	3·3	25·5	129	(208)	560	52·6	20·8	2·12	0·08	15·7	—	(454)	—	—
492	Pastilles	5·2	0·0	62·0	254	77·2	40	39·6	12·3	1·41	0·32	Tr.		118·	—	—
493	Peppermints	0·5	0·7	102·2	391	9·0	Tr.	7·0	3·1	0·20	0·04	Tr.	14·0	21·5	—	3·3
494	Sugar, Demerara	0·5	0·0	104·5*	394	6·2	89	52·6	14·8	0·89	0·06	19·9	Tr.	35·2	—	<0·1
495	Sugar, white	Tr.	0·0	105·0*	394	0·4	2	1·5	0·2	0·04	0·02	Tr.	53·8	Tr.	—	14·2
496	Syrup, golden	0·3	0·0	79·0	297	270	242	26·4	9·5	1·45	0·09	20·0	20·7	41·5	—	5·2
497	Toffee, home-made	0·2	6·2	90·8	399	(115)	91	11·0	4·0	0·55	0·04	9·7		(<0)	—	—
498	Toffees, mixed	2·1	17·2	71·1	435	(318)	205	94·5	25·3	1·52	0·40	64·2		(450)	—	—
499	Treacle, black	1·2	0·0	67·2	257	96·0	1470	495	144	9·17	0·43	30·6	68·5	815	—	49·4

* See p. 4.

Beverages

No.	Food	Description and number of samples	Water	Sugar (as invert sugar)	Starch and dextrins (as glucose)	Total nitrogen	Purine nitrogen
					g. per 100 g.		
500	Bournvita	3 samples from different shops	6·0	60·6	7·0	1·83	—
501	Bovril	3 samples from different shops	—	0·0	0·0	6·05	0·17
502	Cocoa powder	3 varieties	2·5	Tr.	35·0	3·27	—
503	Coffee and chicory essence	6 bottles of a popular brand	37·3	56·4	0·3	0·35	—
504	Coffee, ground, roasted ..	5 samples from different shops	4·1	Tr.	28·5	2·04	0·038
505	Coffee, infusion, 2 minutes	60 g. coffee from mixed sample, boiled in percolator with 900 ml. water and strained	—	Tr.	0·3	0·03	Tr.
506	Coffee, infusion, 5 minutes ..	60 g. coffee from mixed sample, boiled in percolator with 900 ml. water and strained	—	Tr.	0·4	0·04	Tr.
507	Coffee, infusion, 10 minutes	60 g. coffee from mixed sample, boiled in percolator with 900 ml. water and strained	—	Tr.	0·4	0·05	Tr.
508	Coffee, infusion, 20 minutes	60 g. coffee from mixed sample, boiled in percolator with 900 ml water and strained	—	Tr.	0·4	0·05	Tr.
509	Grapefruit squash	6 bottles of a popular brand	60·3	36·2	Tr.	0·02	—
510	Horlick's malted milk	3 samples from different shops	3·0	50·8	20·0*	2·31	—
511	Lemonade	7 bottles of a popular brand	94·6	5·6	0·0	Tr.	—

* Dextrins only

Beverages – *continued*

No.	Food	g. per 100 g.			Calories per 100 g.	mg. per 100 g.									Acid-base balance, m-equiv. per 100 g.	
		Protein	Fat	Available carbohydrate (as monosaccharides)		Na	K	Ca	Mg	Fe	Cu	P	S	Cl	Acid	Base
500	Bournvita	11·4	7·5	67·6	370	360	660	89·0	170	3·3	0·98	411	243	185		4·5
501	Bovril	18·0*	0·7	0·0	80	(4550)	1600	52·0	169	12·1	0·83	1300	362	(6240)		51·0
502	Cocoa powder ..	20·4	25·6	35·0	452	(650)	534	51·2	192	14·3	3·40	685	160	199		0·7
503	Coffee and chicory essence	2·2	0·2	56·7	223	65	745	30·1	39	0·70	0·60	90		85	—	—
504	Coffee, ground, roasted	12·5	15·4	28·5	301	73·5	2020	133·0	235	4·1	0·82	161	110	23·6		63·4
505	Coffee, infusion, 2 min.	0·2	Tr.	0·3	3	0·2	66	2·1	5·5	Tr.	Tr.	1·5		0·4		—
506	Coffee, infusion, 5 min.	0·3	Tr.	0·4	4	0·3	88	3·4	8·3	Tr.	Tr.	2·8		0·6		—
507	Coffee, infusion, 10 min.	0·3	Tr.	0·4	5	0·4	104	3·9	10·5	Tr.	Tr.	4·3		0·6		—
508	Coffee, infusion, 20 min.	0·3	Tr.	0·4	5	0·4	110	4·0	10·8	Tr.	Tr.	4·8		0·5		—
509	Grapefruit squash ..	0·1	Tr.	36·2	136	66·8	66	7·6	3·2	0·14	0·01	24·7		94·3		—
510	Horlick's malted milk	14·4	8·0	70·8	399	690	1128	272	71·0	1·3	1·22	402	167	516		27·4
511	Lemonade	Tr.	0·0	5·6	21	7·4	1	5·3	0·1	Tr.	0·01	Tr.		Tr.		—

* See p. 4. Peptides and amino-acids account for most of the non-protein nitrogen.

H

Beverages – *continued*

g. per 100 g.

No.	Food	Description and number of samples	Water	Sugar (as invert sugar)	Starch and dextrins (as glucose)	Total nitrogen	Purine nitrogen
512	Lemonade, home-made	Recipe, p. 8	—	12·5	0·0	Tr.	—
513	Lemon squash	6 bottles of a popular brand	62·8	33·7	Tr.	0·02	—
514	Lime Juice Cordial	6 bottles of a popular brand	70·5	24·8	Tr.	0·01	—
515	Lucozade	6 bottles from different shops	80·5	7·2	10·7*	Tr.	—
516	Marmite	6 jars from different shops	24·9	—	0·0	6·61	0·27
517	Nescafé	10 tins from different shops	2·7	6·5	4·5*	3·25	1·44
518	Orange squash	6 bottles of a popular brand	60·6	39·8	Tr.	0·04	—
519	Ovaltine	6 samples from different shops	1·1	72·3	Tr.	2·11	0·17
520	Oxo cubes	10 samples from different shops	9·1	—	12·0	6·29	—
521	Pineapple juice	6 cans of different makes	86·1	13·4	Tr.	0·05	—
522	Ribena	Mixed samples taken by makers from 60 batches	36·9	60·9	0·0	0·03	—
523	Tea, Indian	5 samples from different shops	9·3	0·0	0·0	4·08	0·072
524	Tea, Indian, infusion	10 g. tea from mixed sample, infused with 1,000 ml. boiling water 2-10 minutes and strained	—	0·0	0·0	0·01	Tr.
525	Virol	3 samples from different shops	21·5	59·6	0·0	0·55	—

* Dextrins only.

Beverages – *continued*

No.	Food	g. per 100 g.			Calories per 100 g.	mg. per 100 g.									Acid-base balance, m-equiv. per 100 g.	
		Protein	Fat	Available carbohydrate (as monosaccharides)		Na	K	Ca	Mg	Fe	Cu	P	S	Cl	Acid	Base
512	Lemonade, home-made	Tr.	Tr.	12·5	47	Tr.	14	0·8	0·7	Tr.	0·01	1·0	Tr.	Tr.	—	0·4
513	Lemon squash	0·1	Tr.	33·7	126	54·4	68	7·4	2·7	0·13	0·02	6·5	—	76·6	—	—
514	Lime Juice Cordial	0·1	0·0	29·8	112	7·9	49	9·2	3·9	0·29	0·07	4·5	—	3·9	—	—
515	Lucozade	0·0	0·0	17·9	67	33·4	1	6·7	1·7	0·11	0·05	3·2	—	39·0	—	—
516	Marmite	1·4*	Tr.	0·0	6	(4640)	3140	123·0	187·0	6·90	0·97	1900	—	(7460)	—	—
517	Nescafé	11·9	0·0	11·0	90	34·6	5465	149·3	408	5·00	0·09	436	—	56·5	—	—
518	Orange squash	0·3	Tr.	35·8	136	76·1	66	8·6	3·8	0·09	0·02	9·3	—	110·0	—	—
519	Ovaltine	13·2	6·3	72·3	384	167·0	855	134·0	148·0	2·77	1·16	403	—	190·0	—	—
520	Oxo cubes	9·5*	3·4	12·0	116	(10300)	730	180·0	58·6	24·5	0·71	364	—	(16000)	—	—
521	Pineapple juice	0·4	0·1	13·4	53	1·0	136	12·3	11·5	0·73	0·09	9·7	—	38·3	—	—
522	Ribena	0·2	0·0	60·9	229	16·8	140	14·3	6·6	0·50	0·02	13·6	—	17·4	—	—
523	Tea, Indian	14·1	0·0	0·0	58	44·5	2160	426	254	15·2	1·59	628	177	51·8	—	46·5
524	Tea, Indian, infusion	0·1	0·0	0·0	<1	0·4	17	0·3	1·1	Tr.	Tr.	1·0	—	0·4	—	—
525	Virol	3·4	12·0	59·6	349	(374)	360	108·0	61·5	27·0	0·47	266	83	(596)	3·0	—

* See p. 4. Peptides and amino-acids account for most of the non-protein nitrogen in Marmite.

H2

Alcoholic Beverages

No.	Food	Description and number of samples	g. per 100 ml.		
			Alcohol	Solids	Total nitrogen
	Beers				
526	Brown Ale, bottled	6 samples from different brewers	2·24	4·16	0·04
527	Draught Ale, bitter ..	5 samples from different brewers	3·07	3·25	0·04
528	Draught Ale, mild ..	5 samples from different brewers	2·60	2·47	0·03
529	Pale Ale, bottled ..	6 samples from different brewers	3·34	3·28	0·05
530	Stout, bottled	4 samples from different brewers	2·87	5·84	0·05
531	Stout, extra	6 samples of a popular brand	4·26	3·57	0·05
532	Strong Ale	6 samples from different brewers	6·64	8·04	0·11
	Ciders				
533	Cider, dry	3 samples of different brands	3·78	3·68	Tr.
534	Cider, sweet	3 samples of different brands	3·68	5·14	Tr.
535	Cider, vintage	3 samples of a popular brand	10·46	8·93	Tr.
	Wines, Heavy				
536	Port, ruby	1 sample	15·64	12·60	0·02
537	Port, tawny	1 sample	16·13	13·40	0·02
538	Sherry, dry	1 sample	15·69	3·31	0·03
539	Sherry, sweet	1 sample	15·63	9·60	0·05

Alcoholic Beverages – *continued*

No.	Food	g. per 100 g.			Calories per 100 ml.	mg. per 100 ml.									Acid-base balance, m-equiv. per 100 ml.	
		Protein (N × 6.25)	Fat	Available carbohydrate (as monosaccharides)		Na	K	Ca	Mg	Fe	Cu	P	S	Cl	Acid	Base
	Beers															
526	Brown Ale, bottled	0.25	Tr.	2.95	28	16.4	33.4	6.7	5.8	0.03	0.07	11.4	—	36.5	—	—
527	Draught Ale, bitter	0.25	Tr.	2.25	31	12.2	38.4	10.8	8.9	0.01	0.08	13.4	—	32.4	—	—
528	Draught Ale, mild	0.19	Tr.	1.61	25	11.1	32.8	10.4	8.3	0.02	0.05	11.8	—	33.5	—	—
529	Pale Ale, bottled	0.31	Tr.	1.99	32	10.1	48.5	9.4	9.6	0.02	0.04	14.8	—	30.6	—	—
530	Stout, bottled	0.31	Tr.	4.20	37	23.1	44.6	8.4	7.8	0.05	0.08	17.3	—	48.1	—	—
531	Stout, extra	0.31	Tr.	2.09	39	4.1	85.5	4.8	9.4	0.02	0.03	27.5	—	24.2	—	—
532	Strong Ale	0.69	Tr.	6.13	73	14.8	111.0	13.5	19.5	0.03	0.08	40.3	—	56.6	—	—
	Ciders															
533	Cider, dry	Tr.	0.0	2.64	37	6.6	72.0	7.9	3.3	0.49	0.04	3.0	—	6.4	—	—
534	Cider, sweet	Tr.	0.0	4.28	42	6.6	72.0	7.9	3.3	0.49	0.04	3.0	—	6.4	—	—
535	Cider, vintage	Tr.	0.0	7.29	100	2.3	97.0	4.6	3.7	0.31	0.02	9.2	—	5.1	—	—
	Wines, Heavy															
536	Port, ruby	0.13	0.0	11.40	152	-3.8	98.5	4.6	10.1	0.29	0.09	10.6	—	8.1	—	—
537	Port, tawny	0.13	0.0	12.50	160	3.5	96.3	3.8	11.5	0.50	0.11	12.5	—	8.5	—	—
538	Sherry, dry	0.19	0.0	1.36	114	10.3	224.0	7.1	13.0	0.39	0.03	11.1	—	11.9	—	—
539	Sherry, sweet	0.31	0.0	6.88	135	12.8	167.0	6.8	10.6	0.37	0.11	9.6	—	13.7	—	—

Alcoholic Beverages – *continued*

No.	Food	Description and number of samples	g. per 100 ml.		
			Alcohol	*Solids*	*Total nitrogen*
	Table Wines—white				
540	Champagne	1 sample	9·85	3·25	0·04
541	Graves	1 sample	8·83	5·41	0·02
542	Sauternes	1 sample	10·15	9·16	0·03
	Table Wines—red				
543	Australian Burgundy ..	1 sample	10·12	3·08	0·04
544	Beaujolais	1 sample	9·44	1·65	0·03
545	Chianti	1 sample	9·12	1·78	0·02
546	Medoc	1 sample	8·86	2·26	0·03
	Spirits				
547	70% proof	Mean of Brandy, Gin, Rum and Whisky ..	31·46	Tr.	Tr.

Alcoholic Beverages – continued

No.	Food	g. per 100 ml.			Calories per 100 ml.	mg. per 100 ml.									Acid-base balance, m-equiv. per 100 ml.	
		(N × 6·25)	Fat	Available carbohydrate (as monosaccharides)		Na	K	Ca	Mg	Fe	Cu	P	S	Cl	Acid	Base
	Table Wines—white															
540	Champagne	0·25	0·0	1·40	74	3·7	57·0	3·4	6·4	0·50	0·01	7·0	—	7·0	—	—
541	Graves	0·13	0·0	3·37	73	20·9	87·6	14·1	8·7	1·21	0·01	7·6	—	4·3	—	—
542	Sauternes	0·19	0·0	5·89	93	13·4	110·0	14·0	10·8	0·58	0·05	12·6	—	6·8	—	—
	Table Wines—red															
543	Australian Burgundy	0·25	0·0	0·42	72	14·8	176·0	5·6	13·3	0·65	0·10	21·0	—	32·3	—	—
544	Beaujolais	0·19	0·0	0·25	68	8·4	111·0	7·4	10·6	0·75	0·25	8·4	—	14·1	—	—
545	Chianti	0·13	0·0	0·19	65	42·0	69·3	2·9	2·0	0·30	0·07	7·3	—	12·6	—	—
546	Medoc	0·19	0·0	0·27	63	6·6	107·0	7·0	9·2	1·30	0·01	13·2	—	8·3	—	—
	Spirits															
547	70% Proof	Tr.	0·0	Tr.	222	Tr.	Tr.	Tr.	Tr.	Tr.	Tr.	Tr.	—	Tr.	—	—

Condiments

No.	Food	Description and number of samples	g. per 100 g.			
			Water	Sugar (as invert sugar)	Starch	Total nitrogen
548	Curry powder	2 samples from different shops	*	—	—	1·52
549	Ground ginger	3 samples from different shops	*	—	—	1·19
550	Mustard	2 varieties	*	—	—	4·62
551	Pepper	3 samples from different shops	*	—	—	1·40
552	Salt, block	2 samples from different shops	0·2	0·0	0·0	0·0
553	Table salt, " Cerebos "	1 sample	Tr.	0·0	0·0	0·0
554	Table salt, " Saxa "	1 sample	Tr.	0·0	0·0	0·0
555	Vinegar†	4 samples from different shops	—	0·6	0·0	0·07

* The loss of weight at 100° C. cannot be used to determine the amount of water present, since these substances contain volatile essential oils.

† Contains 4·8 ml. acetic acid per cent.

Cakes and Pastries

No.	Food	Description	g. per 100 g.			
			Water	Sugar (as invert sugar)	Starch and dextrins (as glucose)	Total nitrogen
556	Baking powder	6 tins from different shops	6·3	Tr.	37·8	0·91
557	Cherry cake	Recipe, p. 8	10·7	36·3	20·2	0·79
558	Chocolate cakes	Recipe, p. 8	5·4	33·5	27·4	1·46

Condiments – continued

No.	Food	Protein (N× 6·25)	Fat	Available carbohydrate (as monosaccharides)	Calories per 100 g.	Na	K	Ca	Mg	Fe	Cu	P	S	Cl	Acid	Base
		g. per 100 g.				mg. per 100 g.									Acid base-balance, m-equiv. per 100 g.	
548	Curry powder	9·5	10·8	26·1	237	450	1830	637	284	75·00	1·04	270	86	470		86·0
549	Ground ginger	7·4	3·3*	60·0	259	34	910	97	132	17·20	0·45	136	145	40		21·6
550	Mustard	28·9	28·7	20·7	463	5	943	333	256	10·90	0·20	177	1280	62	30·8	
551	Pepper	8·8	6·5†	68·0	309	7	42	127	45	10·20	1·13	130	99	60		28·9
552	Salt, block	0·0	0·0	0·0	0	38,700	Tr.	230	135	0·26	0·39	Tr.	401	59,600	10·7	
553	Table salt, "Cerebos"	0·0	0·0	0·0	0	38,800	Tr.	56	310	0·20	0·10	15	24	59,800		29·1
554	Table salt, "Saxa"	0·0	0·0	0·0	0	38,900	Tr.	2	260	0·15	0·10	Tr.	21	60,000		21·3
555	Vinegar	0·4	0·0	0·6	4	20	89	15	22	0·47	0·04	32	19	47		1·2

* By Soxhlet extraction. The figure for fat obtained by von Lieberman's method is 0·4 per cent. and this has been used for calculating calories.
† By Soxhlet extraction. The figure for fat obtained by von Lieberman's method is 2·0 per cent. and this has been used for calculating calories.

Cakes and Pastries – continued

No.	Food	Protein	Fat	Available carbohydrate (as monosaccharides)	Calories per 100 g.	Na	K	Ca	Mg	Fe	Cu	P	S	Cl	Acid	Base
		g. per 100 g.				mg. per 100 g.									Acid-base balance, m-equiv. per 100 g.	
556	Baking powder	5·2	Tr.	37·8	165	11,800	49	11,300	8·9	Tr.	Tr.	8,430	—	29		—
557	Cherry cake	4·7	24·0	56·5	454	(218)	69	(146)	10·2	(1·22)	0·32	(140)	62·9	(161)	0·2	
558	Chocolate cakes	7·9	25·4	60·9	497	(334)	109	(217)	23·9	(2·26)	0·32	(260)	103·0	(190)		1·6

Cakes and Pastries – *continued*

No.	Food	Description	Water	Sugar (as invert sugar)	Starch and dextrins (as glucose)	Total nitrogen
				g. per 100 g.		
559	Coconut cakes	Recipe, p. 9	14·8	18·2	31·7	1·17
560	Currant buns	20 samples from 4 different shops	28·6	14·0	40·5	1·30
561	Currant cake	Recipe, p. 9	14·6	31·5	28·7	1·03
562	Doughnuts	16 samples from 4 different shops	26·4	15·0	33·8	1·03
563	Dundee cake	4 samples from different shops	15·2	42·0	20·3	0·65
564	Easter biscuits	Recipe, p. 9	11·1	32·5	35·5	1·06
565	Eccles cakes	Recipe, p. 9	9·0	17·5	33·7	1·32
566	Ginger biscuits	Recipe, p. 9	7·9	33·7	37·5	1·00
567	Gingerbread	Recipe, p. 9	19·0	32·7	30·7	0·94
568	Imperial biscuits	Recipe, p. 9	6·1	36·4	35·3	1·00
569	Jam tarts	Recipe, p. 10	19·2	37·9	24·8	0·66
570	Lemon curd tarts	Recipe, p. 10	22·1	18·9	30·7	0·98
571	Mince pies	Recipe, p. 10	30·0	10·1	34·0	0·88
572	Orange cake, plain	Recipe, p. 10	16·9	28·0	25·5	1·06
573	Orange cake, iced	Recipe, p. 10	12·4	45·5	17·4	0·73
574	Pastry, flaky, raw	Recipe, p. 10	30·8	0·7	33·4	0·87
575	Pastry, flaky, baked	Recipe, p. 10	7·3	0·9	44·7	1·17
576	Pastry, short, raw	Recipe, p. 10	20·5	0·9	45·9	1·14
577	Pastry, short, baked	Recipe, p. 10	6·9	1·0	53·9	1·34
578	Plain fruit cake	Recipe, p. 10	21·8	28·4	25·5	0·98
579	Queen cakes	Recipe, p. 10	12·5	31·7	26·6	1·08
580	Rock cakes	Recipe, p. 11	10·4	30·9	34·7	1·02
581	Scones	Recipe, p. 11	21·5	4·2	53·1	1·34
582	Shortbread	Recipe, p. 11	5·0	16·1	48·8	1·06
583	Sponge cake	Recipe, p. 11	30·0	31·4	23·7	1·52
584	Victoria sandwich	Recipe, p. 11	14·9	37·0	20·3	0·92
585	Welsh cheese cakes	Recipe, p. 11	11·7	20·6	39·5	1·17

Cakes and Pastries – continued

No.	Food	g. per 100 g.				mg. per 100 g.									Acid-base balance, m-equiv. per 100 g.	
		Protein	Fat	Available carbohydrate (as monosaccharides)	Calories per 100 g.	Na	K	Ca	Mg	Fe	Cu	P	S	Cl	Acid	Base
559	Coconut cakes	6.9	24.6	49.9	444	(296)	192	(282)	24.4	(1.41)	0.14	(254)	82.7	(158)		7.9
560	Currant buns	7.4	7.6	54.5	305	(101)	182	(90)	22.3	(2.49)	0.03	65.0	73.4	(195)		2.3
561	Currant cake	6.1	18.0	60.2	418	(217)	189	(194)	15.5	(1.29)	0.14	(169)	79.5	(140)		5.5
562	Doughnuts	6.0	15.8	48.8	355	(60)	113	(67)	16.4	(1.92)	0.11	55.0	56.4	(89)		2.1
563	Dundee cake	3.8	15.0	62.3	389	(141)	338	(78)	27.5	(2.20)	0.18	78.5	55.0	(130)		7.4
564	Easter biscuits	6.2	20.7	68.0	473	(242)	138	(144)	15.4	(1.15)	0.12	(123)	—	(271)	—	
565	Eccles cakes	7.8	31.6	51.2	518	(251)	173	(69)	17.9	(0.87)	0.17	58.2	97.0	(410)	1.3	
566	Ginger biscuits	5.9	16.7	71.2	447	(331)	142	(71)	15.2	(1.26)	0.07	75.9	81.3	(141)		8.9
567	Gingerbread	5.5	13.0	63.4	381	(340)	160	(78)	15.4	(1.26)	0.07	81.0	78.1	(126)		10.9
568	Imperial biscuits	5.8	18.8	71.7	468	(183)	78	(94)	11.4	(1.14)	0.11	(110)	—	(165)		—
569	Jam tarts	3.8	15.4	62.7	394	(171)	89	(39)	10.2	(1.08)	0.11	41.5	43.8	(276)	0.6	
570	Lemon curd tarts	5.8	25.0	49.6	442	(229)	69	(48)	11.1	(0.95)	0.08	66.3	65.3	(375)	4.0	
571	Mince pies	5.0	22.3	44.1	393	(301)	252	(64)	17.6	(1.49)	0.09	54.2	65.7	(542)		1.4
572	Orange cake, plain	6.3	25.6	53.5	465	(235)	66	(165)	9.1	(1.11)	0.55	(168)	82.6	(149)	0.3	
573	Orange cake, iced	4.3	23.2	62.9	469	(175)	46	(113)	6.4	(0.78)	0.04	(116)	—	(149)	—	
574	Pastry, flaky, raw	4.9	31.4	34.1	440	(245)	59	(54)	9.7	(0.57)	0.09	51.2	57.4	(404)	2.7	
575	Pastry, flaky, baked	6.7	42.0	45.6	589	(328)	78	(72)	13.0	(0.77)	0.12	68.6	79.5	(541)	3.6	
576	Pastry, short, raw	6.5	28.4	46.8	466	(278)	61	(66)	13.5	(0.95)	0.08	58.9	75.2	(507)	4.7	
577	Pastry, short, baked	7.7	33.4	54.9	548	(326)	72	(77)	15.7	(1.12)	0.10	69.3	90.0	(595)	5.7	
578	Plain fruit cake	5.8	16.3	53.9	378	(358)	200	(293)	15.6	(1.18)	0.10	(246)	85.8	(192)		2.4
579	Queen cakes	6.5	22.5	58.3	455	(229)	146	(181)	13.3	(1.30)	0.10	(172)	74.0	(169)		13.5
580	Rock cakes	6.0	16.0	65.6	419	(328)	240	(330)	20.1	(1.09)	0.15	(259)	85.3	(135)		23.2
581	Scones	7.7	13.2	57.3	369	(587)	162	(636)	21.5	(0.66)	0.08	(480)	69.1	(147)	1.3	
582	Shortbread	6.1	27.2	64.9	521	(86)	93	(81)	15.2	(0.62)	0.06	69.2	123.0	(141)	9.1	
583	Sponge cake	8.9	7.0	55.1	308	79	115	(67)	13.4	(1.61)	0.04	144	—	103		—
584	Victoria sandwich	5.5	25.3	57.3	473	(255)	72	(135)	9.5	(1.17)	0.08	(143)	—	(260)	—	
585	Welsh cheese cakes	6.8	25.4	60.1	489	(188)	60	(177)	11.6	(1.17)	0.09	(123)	82.5	(176)		1.7

Puddings

No.	Food	Description	Water	Sugar (as invert sugar)	Starch and dextrins (as glucose)	Total nitrogen
				g. per 100 g.		
586	Apple dumpling	Recipe, p. 11	58·1	11·6	16·9	0·39
587	Apple pudding	Recipe, p. 12	54·3	14·6	17·0	0·44
588	Apple pie	Recipe, p. 12	60·4	17·9	12·1	0·33
589	Banana custard	Recipe, p. 12	73·3	14·1	4·1	0·40
590	Blancmange	Recipe, p. 12	73·7	12·2	6·6	0·51
591	Bread and butter pudding ..	Recipe, p. 12	67·2	11·4	5·8	0·89
592	Canary pudding	Recipe, p. 12	13·3	26·1	29·4	1·08
593	Castle pudding	Recipe, p. 12	29·6	22·6	24·5	1·03
594	Chocolate mould	Recipe, p. 12	73·3	13·9	6·7	0·53
595	Custard, egg, baked	Recipe, p. 13	77·7	9·9	0·0	0·84
596	Custard, egg, sauce	Recipe, p. 13	75·9	13·4	0·0	0·75
597	Custard, powder, boiled ..	Recipe, p. 13	74·7	12·8	4·7	0·54
598	Custard tart	Recipe, p. 13	48·0	7·8	23·0	0·48
599	Dumpling	Recipe, p. 13	60·2	Tr.	24·0	0·53
600	Gooseberry pie	Recipe, p. 13	61·0	14·2	12·5	0·42
601	Jam omelette	Recipe, p. 13	47·5	27·0	0·0	1·52
602	Jam roll, baked	Recipe, p. 13	20·4	21·0	34·4	0·77

Puddings – continued

No.	Food	g. per 100 g.			Calories per 100 g.	mg. per 100 g.									Acid-base balance m-equiv. per 100 g.	
		Protein	Fat	Available carbohydrate (as monosaccharides)		Na	K	Ca	Mg	Fe	Cu	P	S	C	Acid	Base
586	Apple dumpling	2·2	9·3	28·5	202	(39)	109	(30)	6·9	(0·41)	0·09	32·8	25·8	(67)		0·8
587	Apple pudding	2·6	11·8	31·6	239	(81)	78	(100)	5·2	(0·46)	0·06	(81)	30·2	16		3·3
588	Apple pie	1·9	7·5	30·0	190	(82)	91	(18)	4·0	(0·43)	0·08	25·2	21·4	(56)		0·3
589	Banana custard	2·5	2·6	18·2	103	31	227	84	23·7	0·24	0·09	75·1	24·2	53		4·4
590	Blancmange	3·2	3·7	18·8	118	45	154	117	13·4	0·17	0·04	94·5	28·3	97		2·3
591	Bread and butter pudding	5·5	8·0	17·2	162	(113)	197	(118)	17·3	(0·64)	0·08	124·0	58·6	(190)		0·3
592	Canary pudding	6·4	24·5	55·5	462	(286)	91	(246)	12·5	(0·95)	0·05	(230)	80·6	(142)		4·2
593	Castle pudding, steamed	6·1	20·9	47·1	396	(173)	72	(128)	9·5	(1·03)	0·05	(135)	78·0	(151)	1·5	
594	Chocolate mould	3·1	3·8	20·6	125	56	156	110	15·4	0·32	0·08	96·1	27·2	95		2·5
595	Custard, egg, baked	5·2	5·9	9·9	113	65	175	127	15·2	0·51	0·05	130·0	58·3	123	0·5	
596	Custard, egg, sauce	4·7	5·3	13·4	119	58	156	113	13·7	0·46	0·04	116·0	52·0	110	0·5	
597	Custard, powder, boiled	3·4	3·9	17·5	116	46	160	122	13·9	0·15	0·04	98·0	29·6	100		2·4
598	Custard tart	5·8	16·6	29·8	290	(60)	120	(138)	13·3	(0·71)	0·06	91·3	64·5	(114)		0·6
599	Dumpling	3·0	11·1	24·0	206	(488)	45	(38)	7·3	(0·32)	0·03	(31)	36·8	(626)		3·0
600	Gooseberry pie	2·4	7·5	26·7	180	(81)	143	(34)	7·9	(0·45)	0·10	25·5	29·6	(137)		2·3
601	Jam omelette	9·5	14·6	27·0	276	(121)	139	49	11·7	1·91	0·07	176·0	137·5	(145)	11·8	
602	Jam roll, baked	4·4	19·0	55·4	403	(151)	96	(61)	12·8	(0·84)	0·10	51·6	50·7	(137)		2·8

Puddings – *continued*

No.	Food	Description	g. per 100 g.			
			Water	Sugar (as invert sugar)	Starch and dextrins (as glucose)	Total nitrogen
603	Jelly	Recipe, p. 13 ..	78·6	19·1	0·0	0·34
604	Jelly, milk ..	Recipe, p. 14 ..	72·7	20·9	0·0	0·59
605	Leicester pudding ..	Recipe, p. 14 ..	29·3	29·9	20·6	0·78
606	Mixed fruit pudding	Recipe, p. 14 ..	29·6	22·2	23·5	0·81
607	Pancakes	Recipe, p. 14 ..	43·4	20·5	16·9	0·82
608	Plum pie	Recipe, p. 14 ..	60·4	15·8	12·1	0·36
609	Queen of puddings ..	Recipe, p. 14 ..	54·8	24·6	7·2	0·74
610	Rhubarb pie.. ..	Recipe, p. 14 ..	59·9	16·7	12·5	0·37
611	Rice pudding	Recipe, p. 14 ..	71·4	9·6	6·1	0·59
612	Sago pudding	Recipe, p. 14 ..	72·3	12·0	8·9	0·50
613	Semolina pudding ..	Recipe, p. 15 ..	71·7	12·5	7·7	0·71
614	Suet pudding	Recipe, p. 15 ..	24·6	16·4	27·8	0·87
615	Suet pudding, with raisins	Recipe, p. 15 ..	29·7	23·9	23·5	0·76
616	Swiss apple pudding ..	Recipe, p. 15 ..	50·1	27·0	11·3	0·34
617	Syrup sponge pudding ..	Recipe, p. 15 ..	25·4	35·4	19·7	0·75
618	Tapioca pudding ..	Recipe, p. 15 ..	71·7	12·2	9·2	0·51
619	Treacle tart	Recipe, p. 15 ..	21·0	34·6	28·0	0·62
620	Trifle	Recipe, p. 15 ..	65·2	17·0	5·4	0·54
621	Yorkshire pudding ..	Recipe, p. 16 ..	56·4	3·5	23·5	1·15

Puddings – continued

No.	Food	g. per 100 g.			Calories per 100 g.	mg. per 100 g.									Acid-base balance, m-equiv. per 100 g.	
		Protein	Fat	Available carbohydrate (as monosaccharides)		Na	K	Ca	Mg	Fe	Cu	P	S	C	Acid	Base
603	Jelly	1·9*	0	19·1	82	8	7	10	1·3	0·53	0·06	2·2	11·2	9	—	2·1
604	Jelly, milk	3·5*	1·9	20·9	111	33	87	69	8·4	0·55	0·07	49·4	25·5	58	—	1·4
605	Leicester pudding	4·6	16·1	50·5	358	(217)	75	(140)	10·3	(0·90)	0·07	(133)	—	(156)	—	—
606	Mixed fruit pudding	4·8	14·4	45·7	325	(335)	178	(269)	14·2	(0·94)	0·11	(216)	—	(156)	—	—
607	Pancakes	5·0	15·1	37·4	301	(88)	129	(73)	13·8	(0·52)	0·05	92·8	56·1	(151)	1·8	1·9
608	Plum pie	2·1	7·5	27·9	183	(82)	134	(24)	8·3	(0·43)	0·08	24·3	24·9	(133)	—	0·1
609	Queen of puddings	4·5	8·1	31·8	213	(145)	134	(83)	13·2	(0·84)	0·07	88·7	52·8	(206)	—	7·0
610	Rhubarb pie	2·1	7·5	29·2	188	(82)	274	(79)	11·9	(0·50)	0·10	28·6	24·6	(136)	—	1·6
611	Rice pudding	3·6	7·6	15·7	144	(59)	162	116	14·5	0·12	0·03	109·0	34·0	(112)	—	2·8
612	Sago pudding	3·1	3·7	20·9	127	48	152	119	13·5	0·18	0·04	91·2	27·6	94	—	1·7
613	Semolina pudding	4·3	3·9	20·2	131	50	174	120	17·0	0·19	0·05	104·0	37·9	103	—	—
614	Suet pudding	5·0	19·8	44·2	370	(287)	94	(203)	13·1	(0·83)	0·08	(161)	—	(263)	—	—
615	Suet pudding, with raisins	4·4	16·8	47·4	352	(251)	213	(181)	75·5	(0·95)	0·05	(230)	—	(142)	—	—
616	Swiss apple pudding	1·9	7·6	33·3	222	(113)	126	(25)	9·5	(0·79)	0·11	33·4	18·4	(191)	0·7	—
617	Syrup sponge pudding	4·4	15·4	55·1	368	(265)	110	(138)	11·1	(1·03)	0·06	(127)	—	(·96)	—	—
618	Tapioca pudding	3·2	3·8	21·4	129	49	156	116	13·8	0·98	0·04	95·2	28·4	96	—	2·4
619	Treacle tart	3·5	13·5	62·6	375	(259)	160	(67)	11·7	(1·03)	0·07	46·3	62·9	(341)	—	5·5
620	Trifle	3·3	5·6	22·4	150	36	135	(76)	14·6	(0·85)	0·07	75·0	39·3	67	—	0·9
621	Yorkshire pudding	7·1	9·4	27·0	218	(412)	175	(132)	18·4	(0·68)	0·06	128·0	76·0	(562)	1·2	—

* See p. 4.

Meat and Fish Dishes

No.	Food	Description	Water	g. per 100 g.	
				Total nitrogen	Purine nitrogen
622	Beef steak pudding	Recipe, p. 16	53·3	1·86	—
623	Beef stew	Recipe, p. 16	77·7	1·77	—
624	Curried meat	Recipe, p. 16	69·3	1·31	0·018
625	Fish cakes	Recipe, p. 16	71·2	2·03	0·036
626	Hot pot	Recipe, p. 16	72·1	1·61	0·025
627	Irish stew	Recipe, p. 16	76·0	0·63	0·011
628	Kedgeree	Recipe, p. 17	68·4	1·98	0·022
629	Sausage roll, flaky pastry	Recipe, p. 17	23·0	1·16	—
630	Sausage roll, short pastry	Recipe, p. 17	21·8	1·30	—
631	Shepherd's pie	Recipe, p. 17	78·3	1·65	—
632	Steak and kidney pie	Recipe, p. 17	48·8	2·52	0·049
633	Toad-in-the-hole	Recipe, p. 17	52·5	1·23	—

Meat and Fish Dishes – continued

No.	Food	g. per 100 g.			Calories per 100 g.	mg. per 100 g.									Acid-base balance, m-equiv. per 100 g.	
		Protein	Fat	Available carbohydrate (as glucose)		Na	K	Ca	Mg	Fe	Cu	P	S	Cl	Acid	Base
622	Beef steak pudding	11·1	15·8	18·4	261	(487)	172	(106)	18·1	(2·27)	—	(201)	117	(<26)	5·5	
623	Beef stew	10·7	8·8	3·9	140	(496)	227	17·8	19·5	2·42	0·02	155	118	(<42)	8·4	
624	Curried meat	7·9	11·1	8·7	168	(294)	252	32·7	20·4	4·70	—	101	98	(<36)	2·4	
625	Fish cakes	12·1	13·9	9·8	216	(419)	298	19·6	18·4	0·78	0·14	170	145	(<49)	9·2	
626	Hot pot	9·7	4·6	11·3	125	(577)	464	21·9	25·2	2·33	—	149	117	(<92)	1·9	
627	Irish stew	3·8	11·0	7·8	147	(356)	221	10·3	11·9	0·90	—	57	50	(<59)		0·1
628	Kedgeree	12·1	7·0	9·9	152	(1090)	161	21·0	23·8	1·03	—	169	158	(<10)	11·5	
629	Sausage roll, flaky pastry	7·3	36·0	35·5	498	(406)	111	(13)	13·5	(1·30)	0·07	80	71	(<10)	4·6	
630	Sausage roll, short pastry	8·1	31·2	40·2	474	(450)	125	(15)	15·4	(1·44)	0·07	90	80	(<67)	4·7	
631	Shepherd's pie	9·8	4·2	9·3	114	(351)	194	11·4	16·5	1·73	—	86	111	(<56)	5·3	
632	Steak and kidney pie	15·4	18·9	16·7	302	(471)	243	(10)	20·9	(5·57)	—	213	157	(<06)	14·0	
633	Toad-in-the-hole	7·7	20·3	18·6	290	(699)	163	(67)	16·0	(1·38)	0·07	125	80	(<1050)	3·3	

I

Egg and Cheese Dishes

g . per 100 g.

No.	Food	Description	Water	Sugar (as mono-saccharides)	Starch and dextrins (as glucose)	Total nitrogen
634	Buck rarebit ..	Recipe, p. 17	51·7	1·1	15·9	2·17
635	Cheese omelette	Recipe, p. 17	48·4	Tr.	0·0	2·84
636	Cheese straws ..	Recipe, p. 17	11·2	Tr.	25·9	2·58
637	Cheese pudding	Recipe, p. 18	64·7	3·2	9·0	1·61
638	Macaroni cheese	Recipe, p. 18	63·9	2·6	12·6	1·22
639	Omelette ..	Recipe, p. 18	68·8	Tr.	0·0	1·65
640	Scotch egg ..	Recipe, p. 18	53·1	Tr.	10·3	1·78
641	Scrambled egg	Recipe, p. 18	26·2	0·6	0·6	1·62
642	Welsh rarebit ..	Recipe, p. 18	39·6	1·7	24·7	2·33

Egg and Cheese Dishes – continued

No.	Food	g. per 100 g. Protein	Fat	Available carbohydrate (as monosaccharides)	Calories per 100 g.	mg. per 100 g. Na	K	Ca	Mg	Fe	Cu	P	S	Cl	Acid-base balance, m-equiv. per 100 g. Acid	Base
634	Buck rarebit	13·6	18·0	17·0	287	(676)	122	(275)	27·7	(1·49)	0·06	266	135	(1586)	21·5	
635	Cheese omelette	17·8	30·9	Tr.	360	(1420)	149	316	25·8	2·20	0·06	356	214	(2280)	14·0	
636	Cheese straws	16·4	47·5	25·9	606	(824)	113	(408)	31·2	(0·93)	0·06	328	158	(1320)	7·0	
637	Cheese pudding	9·9	11·1	12·2	190	(457)	165	244	25·4	0·97	0·06	209	—	(740)	—	
638	Macaroni cheese	7·6	12·8	15·2	207	(670)	137	199	25·5	0·35	0·04	162	70	(1060)	13·4	
639	Omelette	10·2	17·0	Tr.	200	(986)	120	50	17·9	2·20	0·03	189	148	(1488)	8·9	
640	Scotch egg	11·1	19·3	10·3	264	(540)	165	35·6	13·9	2·72	0·09	166	126	(741)	12·5	
641	Scrambled egg	10·1	25·2	0·6	278	(1260)	132	61·6	12·0	2·08	0·05	191	144	(1910)	2·1	
642	Welsh rarebit	14·3	21·6	25·4	358	(990)	123	(399)	36·9	(1·04)	0·07	280	127	(1607)		0·1

Sauces and Soups

No.	Food	Description	Water	g. per 100 g. Sugar as mono-saccharides	Starch and dextrins (as glucose)	Total nitrogen
643	Bone and vegetable broth*	Mean of 6 samples, analysed as served in hospital	90·3	1·0	0·1	0·59
644	Bone and vegetable broth (Bickiepegs)*	Mean of 2 samples, analysed as purchased	—	0·3	Tr.	0·71
645	Bread sauce	Recipe, p. 18	76·0	4·0	8·9	0·65
646	Brown sauce, bottled	6 bottles of different brands	64·0	23·1	2·1	0·18
647	Brown sauce	Mean of 2 samples, prepared at Queen Elizabeth College. Recipe, p. 18	76·5	2·0	6·6	0·43
648	Cheese sauce	Recipe, p. 19	70·3	4·0	5·0	1·05
649	Chicken Noodle Soup Mix (Batchelor's)	6 packets from different shops	5·6	6·3	52·6	2·12
650	Egg sauce	Recipe, p. 19	75·4	3·8	4·8	0·79
651	Lentil soup	Mean of 2 samples prepared at Queen Elizabeth College. Recipe, p. 19	77·8	1·9	7·2	0·84
652	Onion sauce	Recipe, p. 19	84·4	3·9	3·2	0·39
653	Potato soup	Recipe, p. 19	81·4	2·5	8·6	0·34
654	Salad Cream (Heinz)	6 bottles from different shops	47·4	10·3	Tr.	0·52
655	Soup, mixed	Mean of 7 samples, analysed as served in hospital	89·9	1·5	2·8	0·32
656	Spaghetti, canned in tomato sauce (Heinz)	6 large cans from different shops	83·1	3·4	8·8	0·30
657	Thick Pea Soup Mix (Batchelor's)	6 packets from different shops	6·7	4·0	56·9	2·90
658	Tomato Ketchup	6 bottles of different brands	64·8	22·9	1·1	0·34
659	Tomato sauce	Mean of 2 samples prepared at Queen Elizabeth College. Recipe, p. 19	81·5	4·8	2·6	0·39
660	Tomato soup, canned (Heinz)	6 large cans from different shops	85·2	7·1	2·3	0·14
661	Vegetable soup, canned (Heinz)	6 large cans from different shops	86·9	3·4	4·7	0·30
662	White sauce, savoury	Recipe, p. 19	75·7	4·4	5·6	0·61
663	White sauce, sweet	Recipe, p. 19	69·3	13·1	5·1	0·56

* See McCance, Sheldon and Widdowson (1934).

Sauces and Soups – *continued*

No.	Food	g. per 100 g.			Calories per 100 g.	mg. per 100 g.									Acid-base balance m-equiv. per 100 g.	
		Protein	Fat	Available carbohydrate (as monosaccharides)		Na	K	Ca	Mg	Fe	Cu	P	S	Cl	Acid	Base
643	Bone and vegetable broth	3·7	4·6	1·1	62	(74)	64	16·9	3·2	0·28	0·04	9·9	—	(75)	—	—
644	Bone and vegetable broth (Bickiepegs)	4·4	—	0·3	—	49	42	10·2	3·9	0·28	0·03	7·0	—	57	—	2·0
645	Bread sauce	4·0	5·1	12·9	112	(325)	153	(104)	15·5	(0·22)	0·04	92·0	33·9	(515)	—	2·0
646	Brown sauce, bottled	1·1	Tr.	25·4	100	(981)	393	43·4	29·1	3·13	0·33	36·0	—	(1546)	—	—
647	Brown sauce	2·7	7·6	8·7	115	(588)	139	20·1	48·6	0·91	0·13	22·2	—	(907)	—	—
648	Cheese sauce	6·6	13·0	9·0	182	(546)	160	203·0	19·2	0·21	0·04	150·0	60·5	(871)	0·5	—
649	Chicken Noodle Soup Mix (Batchelor's)	13·3	6·3	58·9	334	(5631)	160	34·8	40·5	2·84	0·19	165·0	—	(792)	—	—
650	Egg sauce	4·9	10·1	8·6	146	(467)	158	105·0	14·5	0·49	0·04	113·1	54·9	(732)	—	1·5
651	Lentil soup	5·3	4·8	9·1	100	(409)	239	38·8	13·1	0·10	0·11	64·1	—	(66)	—	—
652	Onion sauce	2·4	5·6	7·1	88	(307)	128	76·4	10·8	0·20	0·06	63·1	27·7	(482)	—	2·0
653	Potato soup	2·1	4·4	11·1	92	(328)	95	46·0	15·8	0·39	0·08	52·0	29·4	(542)	0·1	—
654	Salad Cream (Heinz)	3·3	36·0	10·3	387	(838)	80	34·0	20·9	0·81	0·08	90·2	—	(1303)	—	—
655	Soup, mixed	2·0	1·3	4·3	37	(218)	134	33·8	7·2	1·39	0·01	40·0	—	(393)	—	—
656	Spaghetti, canned in tomato sauce (Heinz)	1·9	0·7	12·2	63	(500)	127	21·4	11·3	0·44	0·13	29·8	—	(793)	—	—
657	Thick Pea Soup Mix (Batchelor's)	18·1	7·2	60·9	369	(2389)	610	75·6	60·3	4·62	0·57	342·0	—	(3275)	—	—
658	Tomato Ketchup	2·1	Tr.	24·0	99	(1123)	593	25·2	18·7	1·18	0·40	43·2	—	(1807)	—	—
659	Tomato sauce	2·4	3·9	7·4	74	(384)	462	37·6	12·3	0·08	0·08	42·8	—	(635)	—	—
660	Tomato soup, canned (Heinz)	0·9	3·1	9·4	69	(482)	208	18·5	5·8	0·30	0·11	23·0	—	(793)	—	—
661	Vegetable soup, canned (Heinz)	1·9	0·4	8·1	43	(500)	189	20·5	12·1	0·44	0·13	41·2	—	(774)	—	—
662	White sauce, savoury	3·7	9·7	10·0	143	(523)	161	113·0	14·8	0·15	0·04	96·2	35·6	(828)	—	2·0
663	White sauce, sweet	3·4	8·9	18·2	165	65	148	104·0	13·6	0·14	0·04	88·2	32·7	120	—	1·8

COMPOSITION PER OUNCE

COMPOSITION PER OUNCE
Cereals and Cereal Foods

No.	Food	g. per oz.			Calories per oz.	mg. per oz.									Acid-base balance, m-equiv. per oz.	
		Protein (N × 5·7)	Fat	Available carbohydrate (as monosaccharides)		Na	K	Ca	Mg	Fe	Cu	P	S	Cl	Acid	Base
1	All-Bran, Kellogg's	3·6	1·3	16·5	88	(345)	271	23·4	119·3	3·06	0·13	231·5	51·6	(574)	1·2	—
2	Arrowroot	0·1	Tr.	26·7	101	1·4	5	2·0	2·2	0·55	0·06	7·8	0·5	2·0	0·1	0·05
3	Barley, pearl, raw	2·2	0·5	23·7	102	0·7	35	2·8	5·7	0·19	0·03	58·3	30·5	29·7	5·0	1·6
4	Barley, pearl, boiled	0·7	0·2	7·8	34	0·2	11	1·0	1·9	0·06	0·01	19·9	10·4	10·1	1·7	2·1
5	Bemax	7·9	2·6	12·7	105	2·2	328	15·4	82·0	2·18	0·30	314·0	—	22·8	—	2·0
6	Biscuits, cream crackers	2·7	4·6	19·4	127	(174)	35	(30)	7·0	(0·47)	—	31·2	24·7	(236)		0·4
7	Biscuits, digestive	2·7	5·8	18·7	137	(124)	44	(32)	9·1	(0·57)	0·07	38·0	20·5	(123)		0·3
8	Biscuits, plain mixed	2·1	3·8	21·4	123	(69)	48	(36)	4·1	(0·51)	0·02	11·6	23·7	(74)		
9	Biscuits, rusks	1·7	2·4	23·2	116	(59)	40	(51)	7·7	(0·93)	0·06	22·8	30·5	(49)		
10	Biscuits, sweet, mixed	1·6	8·7	18·9	158	(61)	39	(24)	4·0	(0·34)	0·03	18·8	9·1	(105)		
11	Biscuits, water	3·0	3·5	20·7	126	(134)	40	(34)	5·4	(0·45)	0·04	24·6	28·4	(192)		
12	Bread, Allinson's	2·3	0·6	13·4	65	(132)	74	7·4	25·4	0·82	0·13	68·2	23	(220)	2·0	0·2
13	Bread, brown	2·5	0·6	14·2	68	(156)	65	(27)	17·2	0·69	0·10	50·6	24	(259)	0·9	
14	Bread, currant	1·8	1·0	14·7	71	(47)	71	(34)	7·0	(0·77)	0·03	34·4	16·9	(81)		
15	Bread, Hovis	2·6	0·7	13·5	67	(150)	67	(30)	17·2	0·76	0·10	57·9	25	(231)	0·5	

#	Item	1	2	3	4	5	6	7	8	9	10	11	12	13	14	15
16	Bread, malt	2·4	0·9	14·0	71	(78)	108	(26)	22·0	(1·02)	0·02	71·9	32·6	(149)	1·5	
17	Bread, Procea	3·0	0·7	14·3	72	(138)	40	(40)	7·6	0·50	0·05	30·8	30	(229)	0·6	
18	Bread, white, large loaves	2·2	0·4	14·9	69	(146)	30	(26)	6·4	(0·51)	0·04	22·9	22	(239)	0·6	
19	Bread, white, small loaves	2·4	0·5	15·4	72	(148)	33	(26)	6·7	(0·54)	0·05	25·1	23	(245)	0·9	
20	Bread, white, batch loaves	2·3	0·4	14·7	68	(174)	31	(26)	6·9	(0·52)	0·05	22·9	22	(283)	0·4	
21	Bread, white, dried crumbs	3·3	0·5	22·0	101	(214)	43	(37)	9·6	(0·79)	0·06	34·4	30	(351)	0·9	
22	Bread, white, fried	2·1	10·6	14·6	162	(143)	29	(25)	6·3	(0·50)	0·04	22·4	21	(233)	0·7	
23	Bread, white, toasted	2·7	0·5	18·4	85	(180)	39	(32)	7·9	(0·63)	0·05	28·3	27	(295)	0·7	
24	Cornflakes, Kellogg's	1·9	0·2	25·2	104	(298)	32	2·1	4·7	0·80	0·03	16·5	26·2	(432)	0·6	
25	Cornflour	0·1	0·2	26·2	100	14·7	17	4·4	2·0	0·41	0·04	11·1	0·3	20·2		0·2
26	Custard powder					Take as Cornflour.										
27	Energen rolls	12·5	1·2	13·0	111	6·4	38	13·2	17·8	1·12	0·15	52·9		24·2		
28	Farex	3·7	0·7	20·7	97	(78)	84	251·0	23·9	6·85	0·10	167·0		(94)		
29	Figgerrolls	12·5	1·2	12·8	110	(171)	45	15·0	20·6	1·11	0·14	58·2		(284)		
30	Flour, English (100%)	2·5	0·6	20·8	95	1·0	103	7·0	30·1	0·87	0·18	96·6		10·1		
31	Flour, English (85%)	2·4	0·4	22·5	98	0·8	51	6·1	10·0	0·63	0·10	43·5		12·0		
32	Flour, English (80%)	2·3	0·4	22·9	99	0·6	43	5·5	6·8	0·47	0·08	33·5		12·5		
33	Flour, English (75%)	2·3	0·3	23·2	99	0·6	34	5·4	4·8	0·38	0·06	26·4		12·7		
34	Flour, English (70%)	2·2	0·3	23·3	99	0·6	32	4·3	3·9	0·40	0·06	23·8		12·3		
35	Flour, English (Patent)	2·2	0·2	23·7	100	—	28	7·8	2·5	0·27	0·06	19·3		11·8		
36	Flour, Manitoba (100%)	3·9	0·7	19·7	96	0·9	89	5·3	40·0	1·08	0·17	99·5		10·9		
37	Flour, Manitoba (85%)	3·9	0·5	21·0	99	1·2	41	4·4	17·5	0·77	0·10	53·5		12·6		
38	Flour, Manitoba (80%)	3·8	0·4	21·5	99	0·8	32	3·7	12·7	0·70	0·08	39·5		13·8		
39	Flour, Manitoba (75%)	3·7	0·4	21·7	100	—	25	3·6	8·6	0·65	0·06	31·0		13·6		
40	Flour, Manitoba (70%)	3·6	0·3	21·8	100	0·6	23	3·2	7·6	0·63	0·05	27·6		12·6		
41	Flour, Manitoba (Patent)	3·4	0·3	22·2	100	0·5	20		6·1	0·59	0·04	23·3		12·8		
42	Flour, mixed grist, Basic grade	3·2	0·4	22·0	100	0·8	38	(34)	9·7	(0·55)	0·05	31·4	31	17·6	0·9	
43	Flour, mixed grist, Patent	3·1	0·4	22·2	99	0·8	29	(31)	5·3	(0·47)	0·03	25·2	31	15·9	1·3	
44	Grapenuts	3·3	0·9	21·4	102	(187)	121	13·6	43·4	1·60	0·05	94·6	41·1	(257)	0·4	
45	Macaroni, raw	3·0	0·6	22·6	102	7·3	62	7·5	16·2	0·41	0·02	43·1	27·0	8·9	1·1	
46	Macaroni, boiled	1·0	0·2	7·2	32	2·2	19	2·3	5·0	0·13	0·01	13·2	8·3	2·7	0·3	

Cereals and Cereal Foods – *continued*

No.	Food	Protein (N × 5.7)	Fat	Available carbohydrate (as monosaccharides)	Calories per oz.	Na	K	Ca	Mg	Fe	Cu	P	S	Cl	Acid	Base
		g. per oz.				mg. per oz.									Acid-base balance, m-equiv. per oz.	
47	Oatmeal, raw	3.4	2.5	20.6	115	9.5	104	15.8	32.0	1.17	0.07	108.0	44.0	20.8	3.8	
48	Oatmeal porridge	0.4	0.3	2.3	13	(164)	12	1.8	3.7	0.14	0.01	12.2	5.1	(253)	0.4	
49	Puffed Wheat	4.0	0.6	21.4	102	1.6	122	10.0	35.2	0.93	0.16	94.0	—	19.0	—	|
50	Rice Krispies, Kellogg's	1.6	0.3	24.2	100	(227)	41	1.7	10.3	0.20	0.05	36.4	—	(363)	—	|
51	Rice, polished, raw	1.8	0.3	24.6	102	1.8	32	1.1	3.7	0.13	0.02	28.0	22.4	7.7	2.2	
52	Rice, polished, boiled	0.6	0.1	8.4	35	0.6	11	0.4	1.3	0.04	0.01	9.5	7.6	2.6	0.7	
53	Rye (100%)	2.3	0.6	21.5	95	—	117	8.9	26.1	0.77	—	102.0	—	—	—	
54	Rye (85%)	2.1	0.5	22.8	99	—	58	7.4	12.8	0.56	—	54.8	—	—	—	|
55	Rye (75%)	1.9	0.4	23.4	100	—	49	5.5	7.4	0.49	—	36.7	—	—	—	|
56	Rye (60%)	1.6	0.3	24.4	101	—	40	4.4	4.6	0.38	—	22.2	—	—	—	|
57	Ryvita	2.6	0.6	21.9	98	(175)	133	11.5	25.7	1.06	0.04	83.9	24.7	(266)	0.7	
58	Sago	0.1	0.1	26.7	101	1.0	1	2.8	0.7	0.34	0.01	8.1	0.1	3.6	0.4	
59	Semolina	3.0	0.5	22.0	100	3.4	47	5.2	9.1	0.30	0.04	32.4	26.0	20.2	1.9	
60	Shredded Wheat	2.8	0.8	22.4	103	4.7	86	9.9	34.1	1.27	0.13	81.5	24.6	20.2	1.6	
61	Soya, full fat flour	11.5*	6.7	3.8†	123	—	472	59.3	66.8	1.97	—	169.5	—	—	—	|
62	Soya, low fat flour or grits	14.1*	2.0	4.9†	95	—	575	68.5	81.2	2.60	—	183.0	—	—	—	|
63	Spaghetti	2.8	0.3	23.9	104	1.4	46	6.4	9.9	0.34	0.08	35.2	28	17.9	2.1	
64	Tapioca	0.1	Tr.	27.0	102	1.2	6	2.3	0.6	0.09	0.02	11.1	1.0	3.7	0.3	
65	Vita-Weat	2.4	2.9	22.1	120	(172)	122	12.5	33.4	0.97	0.05	105.8	26.5	(240)	1.2	
66	Weetabix	3.1	0.5	21.9	100	(90)	97	10.1	33.9	1.17	0.14	81.8	—	(142)	—	|

* Total N × 6.25.   † 75 per cent. total carbohydrate taken to be available.

Milk Products and Eggs

No.	Food	g. per oz.			Calories per oz.	mg. per oz.									Acid-base balance, m-equiv. per oz.	
		Protein (N × 6.38)*	Fat	Available carbohydrate (as monosaccharides)		Na	K	Ca	Mg	Fe	Cu	P	S	Cl	Acid	Base
	Milk and milk products															
67	Butter, slightly salted	0·1	24·2	Tr.	226	(63)†		4	0·7	0·05	0·01	7	2·6	(94†)	0·1	—
68	Cheese, Camembert	6·5	6·6	Tr.	88	(399)	31	43	4·9	0·22	0·02	81	—	(659)	—	—
69	Cheese, Cheddar	7·2	9·8	Tr.	120	(174)	33	230	13·3	0·16	0·01	155	65·2	(300)	1·5	—
70	Cheese, Cheshire	7·3	8·7	Tr.	110	(199)	27	176	5·9	0·06	0·01	130	—	(335)	—	—
71	Cheese, cream	0·9	24·5	Tr.	232	(31)	13	8	1·5	0·04	0·01	12	18·2	(42)	1·0	—
72	Cheese, Danish Blue	6·5	8·3	Tr.	103	(402)	53	164	5·8	0·05	0·03	120	—	(679)	—	—
73	Cheese, Edam	6·9	6·5	Tr.	88	(279)	45	210	7·9	0·01	0·01	157	—	(466)	—	—
74	Cheese, Gorgonzola	7·2	8·8	Tr.	112	(347)	49	153	10·7	0·14	0·04	106	50·2	(511)	0·1	—
75	Cheese, Gouda	6·3	7·6	Tr.	96	(299)	35	176	7·0	0·10	0·02	133	—	(485)	—	—
76	Cheese, Gouda, matured	7·4	8·6	Tr.	111	(341)	40	204	7·9	0·13	0·02	152	—	(554)	—	1·0
77	Cheese, Gruyère	10·7	9·5	Tr.	132	(154)	36	306	12·8	0·07	0·08	198	58·5	(235)	—	—
78	Cheese, Norwegian Mysost	3·0	8·1	11·9‡	133	(85)	419	90	17·8	0·12	0·01	117	—	(238)	—	1·4
79	Cheese, Parmesan	9·9	8·4	Tr.	118	(215)	44	346	14·1	0·11	0·10	220	71·0	(375)	—	0·1
80	Cheese, processed	6·5	8·5	Tr.	106	(260)	24	205	13·5	0·16	0·01	136	91·0	(308)	—	—
81	Cheese Spread	5·1	6·5	0·3‡	82	(331)	42	144	7·0	0·20	0·03	124	—	(216)	—	—
82	Cheese, St. Ivel	6·7	8·7	Tr.	108	(161)	19	137	6·6	0·20	0·01	106	52·9	(258)	2·5	—
83	Cheese, Stilton	7·3	11·4	Tr.	135	(326)	46	102	7·7	0·13	0·01	86	64·5	(488)	2·2	—
84	Cheese, Wensleydale	8·2	8·7	Tr.	115	(103)	61	196	7·5	0·09	0·01	150	—	(185)	—	—
85	Cream, double	0·4	13·7	0·6‡	131	7·6	22	14	1·1	0·06	0·04	6	—	13·1	—	—
86	Cream, single	0·7	6·0	0·9‡	62	12·0	35	22	1·7	0·09	0·06	12	—	20·6	—	—
87	Milk, fresh, whole	0·9	1·1	1·4‡	19	14·2	46	34	4·0	0·02	0·01	27	8·3	27·8	—	0·8
88	Milk, fresh, skimmed	1·0	0·1	1·4‡	10	14·8	47	35	4·1	0·02	0·01	28	8·5	28·9	—	0·8

* Eggs. N × 6·25. † Salt-free butter contains approximately 2mg. Na and 3 mg.Cl/oz. Salted butters contain up to 256 mg. Na and 400 mg. Cl/oz.
‡ See p. 4.

Milk Products and Eggs – continued

No.	Food	g. per oz. Protein (N × 6·38)*	Fat	Available carbohydrate (as monosaccharides)	Calories per oz.	mg. per oz. Na	K	Ca	Mg	Fe	Cu	P	S	Cl	Acid-base balance, m-equiv. per oz. Acid	Base
89	Milk, condensed, whole, sweetened	2·3	3·4	15·9	100	40·7	116	97	10·2	0·05	0·02	68	23·5	81·0		2·4
90	Milk, condensed, whole, unsweetened	2·2	2·5	3·5‡	45	45·8	143	82	9·9	0·05	0·03	72	21·3	79·0		2·4
91	Milk, condensed, skimmed, sweetened	2·8	0·1	17·0	76	51·0	142	109	10·7	0·08	0·01	77	26·8	88·0		3·1
92	Milk, dried, skimmed	9·8	0·1	14·0‡	93	170·0	378	359	31·5	0·15	0·40§	298	85·0	321·0		4·1
93	Milk, dried, whole	7·7	8·4	11·0‡	150	113·0	363	272	31·8	0·18	0·05	215	66·1	222·0		6·1
94	Human milk, transitional	0·5	1·0	2·0‡	19	13·7	19	7	0·7	0·02	0·01	4	—	24·4	—	—
94a	Human milk, mature	0·3	1·5	1·9‡	22	4·2	15	8	0·9	0·01	—	4	—	18·0	—	—
95	Milk, substitute, low Na "Edosol"	8·4	7·5	10·6‡	145	12·2	210	240	4·9	0·16	0·03	172	—	58·8	—	—
96	Milk, substitute, low Ca "Locasol"	6·3	5·7	14·7‡	134	61·9	172	13	16·2	0·43	0·03	97	—	68·2	—	
97	Ostermilk No. 1	5·2	5·0	16·4‡	129	80·9	254	191	16·3	(1·15)	0·02	143	—	157·0	—	
97a	Yoghurt, low fat	1·4	0·5	1·4‡	15	17·4	50	46	4·3	0·01	—	34	—	33·5	—	
98	Eggs, fresh, whole	3·4	3·5	Tr.	46	38·4	39	16	3·5	0·72	0·01	62	49·1	45·2	4·6	
99	Egg white	2·6	Tr.	Tr.	11	54·7	42	2	3·0	0·03	0·01	9	51·9	48·4	1·4	
100	Egg yolk	4·6	8·7	Tr.	99	14·2	35	37	4·2	1·74	0·01	141	46·7	40·4	9·4	
101	Eggs, dried	12·3	12·3	Tr.	165	147·0	137	54	11·7	2·23	0·05	227	179·0	168·5	17·0	
102	Eggs, fried	4·0	5·5	Tr.	68	62·4	50	18	3·9	0·72	0·01	73	58·4	56·5	4·7	
103	Eggs, poached	3·5	3·3	Tr.	45	31·5	34	15	3·2	0·65	0·01	68	51·3	44·0	5·6	

* Eggs N × 6·25.   § Most of this copper was probably derived from the manufacturing machinery.
‡ See p. 4.

Fats and Oils

No.	Food	Protein (N × 6.25)	Fat	Carbohydrate	Calories per oz.	Na	K	Ca	Mg	Fe	Cu	P	S	Cl	Acid	Base
		g. per oz.				mg. per oz.									Acid-base balance, m-equiv. per oz.	
104	Cod liver oil	—	28·3	0·0	264	Tr.	Tr.	Tr.	Tr.	Tr.	Tr.	Tr.	Tr.	Tr.	—	—
105	Compound cooking fat	—	28·2	0·0	262	Tr.	Tr.	Tr.	Tr.	Tr.	Tr.	Tr.	Tr.	Tr.	—	—
106	Dripping, beef	Tr.	28·1	0·0	262	1·4	1	0·2	Tr.	0·06	—	4	3	0·6	0·3	
107	Lard	Tr.	28·1	0·0	262	0·6	Tr.	0·2	0·4	0·03	0·01	1	7	1·1	0·5	
108	Margarine	Tr.	24·2	0·0	226	(90)	1	1·2	0·3	0·09	0·01	Tr.	3·4	(141)	0·4	
109	Olive oil	Tr.	28·3	0·0	264	Tr.	Tr.	0·1	0·1	0·02	0·02	Tr.	Tr.	Tr.		<0·1
110	Suet	0·3	28·1	0·0	262	6·0	4	1·7	0·3	0·11	0·01	2	6	5·1	0·2	

Meat, Poultry and Game

No.	Food	Protein	Fat	Carbohydrate (as glucose)	Calories per oz.	Na	K	Ca	Mg	Fe	Cu	P	S	Cl	Acid	Base
		g. per oz.				mg. per oz.									Acid-base balance, m-equiv. per oz.	
	Bacon, Raw—															
111	Danish Wilts., average	4·0	10·6	0·0	115	(348)	71	3·8	4·1	0·37	0·05	35	46	(530)	2·1	
112	Danish Wilts., fore end	4·2	9·0	0·0	101	(385)	75	4·1	4·4	0·30	0·06	39	48	(588)	3·0	
113	Danish Wilts., middle	3·7	12·7	0·0	133	(329)	64	3·8	3·9	0·37	0·05	34	43	(501)	1·4	
114	Danish Wilts., gammon	4·3	8·0	0·0	92	(342)	81	3·6	4·2	0·48	0·05	32	51	(533)	2·8	
115	English Wilts.	3·6	14·0	0·0	144	(277)	76	3·8	3·5	0·25	0·08	27	41	(428)	1·9	
116	English Midland	3·0	17·4	0·0	174	(236)	80	2·0	3·0	0·28	0·16	26	34	(370)	1·6	
117	Bacon, back, fried	7·0	15·2	0·0	169	(793)	147	3·3	7·3	0·80	—	65	85	(1180)	3·7	

Meat, Poultry and Game – continued

No.	Food	Protein	Fat	Carbohydrate (as glucose)	Calories per oz.	Na	K	Ca	Mg	Fe	Cu	P	S	Cl	Acid	Base
		g. per oz.				mg. per oz.									Acid-base balance, m-equiv. per oz.	
118	Bacon, collar, fried	7·8	9·9	0·0	124	(866)	140	6·6	7·3	1·11	—	67	94	(1360)	6·4	
119	Bacon, gammon, fried	8·9	9·6	0·0	126	(662)	181	7·1	9·3	0·80	—	86	109	(1200)	11·6	
120	Bacon, streaky, fried	6·8	13·1	0·0	149	(880)	131	14·9	7·1	0·91	—	68	85	(1350)	4·8	
121	Beef, corned	6·3	4·3	0·0	66	(392)	33	3·6	8·2	2·78	—	34	60	(590)	3·9	
122	Beef, frozen, raw	5·8	2·1	0·0	43	21·0	100	2·3	7·1	1·05	0·05	57	61	21·0	3·9	
123	Beef, silverside, boiled	7·9	5·7	0·0	86	(417)	82	6·6	5·7	1·05	0·05	69	83	(660)	7·1	
124	Beef, sirloin, roast, lean only	7·6	3·5	0·0	64	19·9	101	1·8	7·1	1·50	0·05	81	80	21·0	6·6	
125	Beef, sirloin, roast, lean and fat	6·0	9·1	0·0	109	17·6	82	1·6	5·7	1·31	0·05	67	64	18·2	5·4	
126	Beef steak, raw	5·5	3·0	0·0	50	19·6	95	1·5	6·9	1·22	—	78	57	19·9	5·2	
127	Beef steak, fried	5·8	5·8	0·0	78	22·7	106	1·5	7·1	1·70	—	73	62	25·6	4·9	
128	Beef steak, grilled	7·2	6·1	0·0	86	19·0	105	2·6	7·2	1·48	—	86	76	18·2	6·6	
129	Beef steak, stewed	8·7	2·4	0·0	58	10·8	43	0·9	6·0	1·45	—	65	93	11·0	8·2	
130	Beef, topside, boiled	9·5	2·3	0·0	61	13·1	63	1·0	7·4	2·36	—	70	98	13·9	8·2	
131	Beef, topside, roast, lean only	7·6	4·3	0·0	71	21·6	105	1·8	8·0	1·34	0·07	81	79	17·6	6·3	
132	Beef, topside, roast, lean and fat	6·9	6·8	0·0	91	20·4	96	1·7	7·2	1·25	0·07	75	72	16·8	5·8	
133	Brain, calf, boiled	3·4	1·6	0·0	29	41·8	77	4·6	3·8	0·57	—	101	38	47·4	5·8	
134	Brain, sheep, boiled	3·3	1·9	0·0	31	48·3	76	3·1	5·1	0·63	—	96	37	40·9	5·8	
135	Chicken, muscle, raw	6·6	0·6	0·0	33	13·0	115	1·7	8·2	0·21	—	70	76	17·0	5·5	
136	Chicken, boiled	7·4	2·9	0·0	58	27·8	108	3·0	7·5	0·60	—	77	83	17·6	5·9	
136a	Chicken, boiled (weighed with bone)	4·8	1·9	0·0	38	18·1	70	2·0	4·9	0·39	—	50	54	11·4	3·8	

No.	Food														
137	Chicken, roast	8·4	2·1	0·0	54	22·7	101	4·1	6·5	0·74	—	77	92	25·4	7·2
137a	Chicken, roast (weighed with bone)	4·5	1·1	0·0	29	12·2	55	2·2	3·5	0·40	—	42	50	15·4	3·9
138	Duck, roast	6·5	6·7	0·0	89	55·3	90	5·4	6·8	1·64	—	66	112	44·9	6·9
138a	Duck, roast (weighed with bone)	3·5	3·6	0·0	48	29·8	49	2·9	3·7	0·88	—	36	61	24·2	3·7
139	Goose, roast	8·0	6·4	0·0	92	41·2	115	3·0	8·8	1·32	—	76	91	45·1	6·2
139a	Goose, roast (weighed with bone)	4·6	3·7	0·0	53	23·8	67	1·7	5·1	0·77	—	44	53	26·1	3·6
140	Grouse, roast	8·6	1·5	0·0	49	27·3	132	8·5	11·6	2·16	—	96	97	38·0	7·3
140a	Grouse, roast (weighed with bone)	5·7	1·0	0·0	32	18·0	87	5·6	7·6	1·42	—	63	64	25·0	4·8
141	Guinea fowl, roast	9·2	2·3	0·0	60	38·6	122	5·5	8·2	2·64	—	83	103	50·9	7·5
141a	Guinea fowl, roast (weighed with bone)	4·9	1·2	0·0	32	20·4	65	2·9	4·3	1·40	—	44	55	27·0	4·0
142	Ham, York, raw	4·3	13·9	0·0	146	(320)	98	4·0	4·4	0·34	—	30	50	(503)	2·2
143	Ham, boiled, lean only	6·6	3·8	0·0	62	(595)	129	4·8	6·7	0·74	—	69	80	(950)	6·3
144	Ham, boiled, lean and fat	4·6	11·2	0·0	123	(422)	91	3·6	4·9	0·71	0·03	54	56	(665)	4·6
145	Ham or Pork, chopped	4·3	8·5	Tr.	97	(438)	63	3·4	4·7	0·44	0·07	39	—	(602)	—
146	Hare, roast	8·9	2·0	0·0	55	15·0	115	8·0	8·5	2·78	0·05	96	99	30·6	8·5
146a	Hare, roast (weighed with bone)	6·1	1·4	0·0	37	10·2	78	5·4	5·8	1·89	—	65	67	20·8	5·8
147	Hare, stewed	8·3	2·3	0·0	55	11·4	60	5·9	6·3	3·07	—	71	91	21·0	8·0
147a	Hare, stewed (weighed with bone)	6·1	1·7	0·0	40	8·3	44	4·3	4·6	2·24	—	51	66	15·3	5·8
148	Heart, pig, raw	4·9	0·8	0·0	27	23·7	85	1·6	5·6	1·38	—	50	56	32·0	3·2
149	Heart, sheep, roast	7·1	4·2	0·0	68	43·5	105	2·7	9·9	2·30	—	111	84	35·5	7·8
150	Kidney, ox, raw	4·8	1·5	0·0	34	69·5	66	4·0	5·2	4·25	—	74	46	72·7	4·3
151	Kidney, ox, stewed	7·3	1·6	0·0	45	46·5	47	5·9	6·3	2·02	—	111	69	40·9	8·6
152	Kidney, sheep, raw	4·8	0·9	0·0	28	71·0	72	3·8	4·5	3·32	—	72	47	83·8	4·5
153	Kidney, sheep, fried	7·9	2·6	0·0	57	74·0	86	4·7	7·6	4·12	—	123	78	82·0	8·8
154	Liver, raw	4·7	2·3	0·0	41	24·4	92	2·4	5·9	3·95	1·65	89	68	28·4	8·8
155	Liver, pig, raw	5·6	2·1	0·0	43	24·1	91	1·4	6·6	3·70	—	105	65	29·0	6·7
156	Liver, calf, fried	8·3	4·1	0·7	74	34·6	116	2·5	6·8	6·15	—	164	122	34·1	7·0
157	Liver, ox, fried	8·4	4·5	1·1	81	26·1	110	2·4	7·5	5·89	—	156	116	23·3	14·0
158	Luncheon meat, canned	3·2	7·8	1·4	95	(248)	59	5·0	2·7	0·32	0·02	47	—	(341)	13·3

Meat, Poultry and Game – continued

No.	Food	g. per oz.			Calories per oz.	mg. per oz.									Acid-base balance, m-equiv. per oz.	
		Protein	Fat	Carbohydrate (as glucose)		Na	K	Ca	Mg	Fe	Cu	P	S	Cl	Acid	Base
159	Meat paste	5·6	3·6	1·2	61	(267)	59	7·5	6·2	1·05	0·03	38	37	(426)	2·7	
160	Mutton chop, raw, lean only	5·3	3·4	0·0	53	25·9	100	3·6	7·7	0·48	0·05	55	59	23·8	3·4	
160a	Mutton chop, raw, lean only (weighed with fat and bone)	2·0	1·3	0·0	20	9·7	37	1·3	2·9	0·17	0·02	20	22	8·8	1·3	
161	Mutton chop, raw, lean and fat	3·9	14·9	0·0	154	21·3	70	3·6	5·3	0·28	0·05	49	42	19·8	3·0	
161a	Mutton chop, raw, lean and fat (weighed with bone)	3·1	11·5	0·0	119	16·5	54	2·8	4·1	0·23	0·03	38	33	15·3	2·4	
162	Mutton chop, grilled, lean only	7·5	5·0	0·0	77	36·0	114	5·9	8·5	0·71	0·05	68	81	31·2	4·8	
162a	Mutton chop, grilled, lean only (weighed with fat and bone)	3·5	2·3	0·0	36	17·0	53	2·8	4·0	0·34	0·03	32	38	14·8	2·3	
163	Mutton chop, grilled, lean and fat	5·7	12·8	0·0	142	29·0	87	5·1	6·5	0·68	0·05	58	60	25·5	4·0	
163a	Mutton chop, grilled, lean and fat (weighed with bone)	4·3	9·7	0·0	108	21·8	65	3·8	4·9	0·51	0·04	44	46	19·3	3·0	
164	Mutton chop, fried, lean only	6·5	7·2	1·6	97	33·0	99	4·4	7·4	0·88	0·04	63	71	38·0	4·7	
164a	Mutton chop, fried, lean only (weighed with fat and bone)	2·4	2·7	0·6	36	12·5	37	1·6	2·8	0·34	0·01	24	27	14·2	1·8	

No.	Item														
165	Mutton chop, fried, lean and fat	4·4	17·1	0·7	178	24·4	69	4·0	5·1	0·74	0·03	52	47	26·1	3·6
165a	Mutton chop, fried, lean and fat (weighed with bone)	3·6	13·9	0·6	146	19·9	56	3·2	4·2	0·60	0·03	43	38	21·3	2·9
166	Mutton, leg, boiled	7·3	4·7	0·0	74	18·2	78	1·0	7·8	1·45	0·07	68	80	19·0	6·4
167	Mutton, leg, roast	7·1	5·8	0·0	83	20·1	98	1·2	7·5	1·22	—	69	77	17·6	5·7
168	Mutton, scrag and neck, stewed	6·9	6·9	0·0	92	18·8	53	14·2	7·6	1·93	—	63	74	23·3	5·7
168a	Mutton, scrag and neck, stewed (weighed with bone)	5·2	5·2	0·0	69	14·1	40	10·6	5·7	1·45	—	47	55	17·4	4·3
169	Partridge, roast	10·0	2·0	0·0	60	28·4	116	13·0	10·2	2·19	—	89	113	28·1	7·9
169a	Partridge, roast (weighed with bone)	6·0	1·2	0·0	36	17·0	69	7·8	6·1	1·31	—	53	68	16·8	4·7
170	Pemmican (Bovril)	12·8	12·4	0·0	167	(462)	290	83·0	19·1	3·36	0·08	148	—	(681)	—
171	Pheasant, roast	8·8	2·6	0·0	61	29·6	117	14·0	9·9	2·38	—	88	87	30·7	6·1
171a	Pheasant, roast (weighed with bone)	5·5	1·7	0·0	38	18·7	74	8·8	6·3	1·50	—	55	55	19·3	3·9
172	Pigeon, boiled	6·2	4·0	0·0	62	21·0	85	5·0	8·9	2·78	—	100	69	21·3	7·3
172a	Pigeon, boiled (weighed with bone)	2·7	1·7	0·0	27	9·2	37	2·2	3·9	1·22	—	44	30	9·4	3·2
173	Pigeon, roast	7·6	3·8	0·0	66	29·8	116	4·6	9·6	5·51	—	114	86	28·1	8·3
173a	Pigeon, roast (weighed with bone)	3·3	1·7	0·0	29	13·1	51	2·0	4·2	2·42	—	50	38	12·4	3·6
174	Pork, raw	6·3	0·7	0·0	33	12·8	113	1·2	7·4	0·39	—	63	73	14·0	4·9
175	Pork, leg, roast	7·0	6·6	0·0	90	18·8	88	1·5	6·4	0·48	—	103	72	23·6	8·1
176	Pork, loin, roast, lean only	6·7	5·7	0·0	81	19·6	100	2·1	6·7	0·74	0·03	59	69	28·7	4·8
177	Pork, loin, roast, lean and fat	5·5	11·5	0·0	129	17·0	82	2·1	5·1	0·65	0·03	53	57	21·8	4·2
178	Pork, loin, salt, smoked, lean only	6·7	4·5	0·0	69	(511)	85	7·8	6·9	0·65	—	62	69	(880)	7·8
179	Pork chops, grilled, lean only	7·2	6·7	0·0	92	21·6	99	2·6	5·9	0·82	0·03	60	74	32·1	5·3

K

Meat, Poultry and Game – continued

No.	Food	g. per oz.			Calories per oz.	mg. per oz.									Acid-base balance, m-equiv. per oz.	
		Protein	Fat	Carbohydrate (as glucose)		Na	K	Ca	Mg	Fe	Cu	P	S	Cl	Acid	Base
179a	Pork chops, grilled, lean only (weighed with bone)	3·0	2·8	0·0	38	8·8	40	1·1	2·4	0·34	0·01	25	30	13·2	2·2	
180	Pork chops, grilled, lean and fat	5·3	14·3	0·0	155	16·8	73	2·4	4·2	0·68	0·03	51	54	20·4	4·0	
180a	Pork chops, grilled, lean and fat (weighed with bone)	4·4	11·9	0·0	128	13·9	61	2·0	3·5	0·56	0·02	42	45	16·9	3·4	
181	Rabbit, stewed	7·6	2·2	0·0	51	9·1	60	3·2	6·1	0·54	0·06	57	70	12·2	5·7	
181a	Rabbit, stewed (weighed with bone)	3·9	1·1	0·0	26	4·6	30	1·6	3·1	0·28	0·03	29	36	6·2	2·9	
182	Sausage, beef, fried	3·9	5·2	4·5	81	(321)	72	6·0	4·7	1·16	0·05	48	46	(503)	3·7	
183	Sausage, pork, raw	2·5	8·2	2·8	97	(218)	45	4·3	3·3	0·72	0·03	31	21	(305)	0·7	
184	Sausage, pork, fried	3·3	7·1	3·6	93	(284)	58	5·6	4·2	0·94	0·04	40	27	(397)	1·0	
185	Sausage, black	1·5	6·4	4·2	81	(255)	37	8·8	4·3	5·55	0·07	8	49	(374)	1·2	
186	Sausage, breakfast	2·5	5·8	4·8	82	(250)	48	6·2	4·7	0·54	0·02	24	22	(369)	0·6	
187	Sweetbreads, stewed	6·4	2·6	0·0	51	19·6	66	4·1	4·4	0·46	—	169	53	21·0	11·7	
188	Tongue, ox, pickled	5·4	6·8	0·7	88	(532)	43	8·8	4·6	0·85	—	65	57	(851)	6·7	
189	Tongue, sheep's, stewed	5·1	6·8	0·0	84	22·5	31	3·2	3·7	0·97	—	56	53	22·7	5·3	
190	Tripe, stewed	5·1	0·9	0·0	29	20·4	3	(36)	2·2	0·45	—	38	41	8·5	2·3	
191	Turkey, roast	8·6	2·2	0·0	56	36·9	104	10·9	8·0	1·08	—	91	66	34·9	5·5	
191a	Turkey, roast (weighed with bone)	5·1	1·3	0·0	34	22·1	62	6·5	4·8	0·65	—	55	40	21·0	3·3	
192	Veal, fillet, raw	5·7	0·8	0·0	31	30·4	101	2·2	7·1	0·65	—	73	63	19·3	4·6	
193	Veal, frozen, raw	5·3	1·0	0·0	31	27·0	105	2·9	7·1	0·51	0·04	57	59	27·8	3·5	
194	Veal, cutlet, fried	8·6	2·3	1·3	61	30·1	120	2·8	9·3	0·74	—	81	93	32·6	6·7	
195	Veal, fillet, roast	8·7	3·3	0·0	66	27·5	122	4·1	7·9	1·22	—	101	94	32·1	8·1	
196	Venison, roast	9·5	1·8	0·0	56	24·4	103	8·2	9·5	2·22	—	81	91	25·3	6·8	

Fish

No.	Food	g. per oz.			Calories per oz.	mg. per oz.									Acid-base balance, m-equiv. per oz.	
		Protein	Fat	Carbo-hydrate (as glucose)		Na	K	Ca	Mg	Fe	Cu	P	S	Cl	Acid	Base
197	Bass, steamed	5·5	1·5	0·0	36	21·3	93	13·3	7·6	0·20	—	62	66	24·1	4·2	
197a	Bass, steamed (weighed with bones)	2·9	0·8	0·0	19	11·3	49	7·1	4·0	0·11	—	33	35	12·8	2·2	
198	Bloaters, grilled	6·4	4·9	0·0	73	(200)	126	35·0	12·7	0·62	—	101	88	(322)	21·1	
198a	Bloaters, grilled (weighed with bones and skin)	4·7	3·7	0·0	54	(148)	94	25·9	9·4	0·46	—	75	65	(238)	15·6	
199	Bream, Red, steamed	5·6	1·1	0·0	34	33·8	98	7·9	8·5	0·11	—	61	69	39·2	4·2	
199a	Bream, Red, steamed (weighed with bones)	2·9	0·6	0·0	17	17·6	51	4·1	4·4	0·06	—	32	36	20·2	2·2	
200	Bream, Sea, steamed	5·1	0·9	0·0	29	32·1	80	9·9	7·6	0·17	—	68	62	34·5	4·7	
200a	Bream, Sea, steamed (weighed with bones)	3·3	0·6	0·0	19	20·8	52	6·4	4·9	0·11	—	44	40	22·4	3·0	
201	Brill, steamed	5·8	1·0	0·0	33	26·7	75	4·3	8·8	0·20	0·04	65	61	35·5	5·0	
201a	Brill, steamed (weighed with bones and skin)	3·9	0·7	0·0	22	18·2	51	2·9	6·0	0·14	0·03	45	42	24·1	3·4	
202	Catfish, steamed	5·8	1·1	0·0	34	30·6	90	3·9	7·6	0·17	—	60	61	30·6	4·1	
202a	Catfish, steamed (weighed with bones)	4·9	0·9	0·0	28	26·0	76	3·3	6·4	0·14	—	51	52	26·0	3·5	
203	Catfish, fried	5·3	3·0	1·8	57	34·0	92	5·4	7·3	0·65	—	65	57	42·5	4·2	
203a	Catfish, fried (weighed with bones)	5·0	2·8	1·7	53	32·0	86	5·1	6·9	0·61	—	61	53	40·0	3·9	
204	Cockles	3·1	0·1	Tr.	14	(1000)	12	36·1	14·5	7·39	—	58	91	(1480)	4·4	
205	Cod, steamed	5·1	0·3	0·0	23	28·4	102	4·2	5·9	0·14	0·03	69	60	34·0	4·6	
205a	Cod, steamed (weighed with bones and skin)	4·1	0·2	0·0	19	23·0	83	3·4	4·7	0·11	0·02	56	49	27·5	3·7	
206	Cod, fried, as purchased	5·6	2·9	2·1	58	29·0	104	22·7	6·9	0·15	0·02	57	—	71·6	—	
207	Cod, fried	5·9	1·3	0·8	40	45·8	97	14·1	7·6	0·28	0·03	74	69	41·1	4·4	

K2

Fish – *continued*

No.	Food	g. per oz.			Calories per oz.	mg. per oz.									Acid-base balance, m-equiv. per oz.	
		Protein	Fat	Carbohydrate (as glucose)		Na	K	Ca	Mg	Fe	Cu	P	S	Cl	Acid	Base
207a	Cod, fried (weighed with bones)	5·4	1·2	0·7	36	41·5	88	12·8	6·9	0·25	0·03	68	63	37·4	4·0	
208	Cod, grilled	7·7	1·5	0·0	45	31·2	116	8·8	10·2	0·28	—	78	92	36·9	6·2	
208a	Cod, grilled (weighed with bones and skin)	6·5	1·3	0·0	39	26·6	99	7·5	8·7	0·24	—	66	78	31·5	5·3	
209	Cod roe, fried	5·8	3·4	0·9	59	36·0	73	4·8	3·0	0·45	—	143	68	53·2	11·0	
210	Cod roe, baked in vinegar	6·8	0·9	0·0	34	20·7	38	3·7	2·3	0·65	—	114	77	49·1	11·4	
211	Conger, steamed	6·5	0·5	0·0	31	28·1	99	8·5	8·1	0·14	—	63	76	23·3	4·6	
211a	Conger, steamed (weighed with bones and skin)	4·9	0·4	0·0	23	21·0	74	6·4	6·1	0·11	—	47	57	17·5	3·5	
212	Conger, fried	5·3	5·7	1·8	81	30·6	100	6·9	8·3	0·28	—	70	63	44·3	4·8	
212a	Conger, fried (weighed with bones)	4·7	5·0	1·6	72	27·0	88	6·1	7·3	0·25	—	62	55	38·9	4·2	
213.	Crab, boiled	5·4	1·5	0·0	36	104·0	77	8·3	13·6	0·37	—	99	132	162·0	11·2	
213a	Crab, boiled (weighed with shell)	1·1	0·3	0·0	7	20·7	15	1·7	2·7	0·07	—	20	26	32·4	2·2	
214	Dabs, fried	5·5	4·1	2·8	71	36·0	80	36·9	8·3	0·28	0·02	71	74	69·5	5·0	
214a	Dabs, fried (weighed with bones)	4·4	3·2	2·2	56	28·8	64	29·5	6·7	0·23	0·02	57	59	55·6	4·0	
215	Dogfish, fried	5·1	7·1	1·7	94	46·2	70	3·6	5·7	0·37	—	76	60	57·5	5·8	
215a	Dogfish, fried (weighed with bone)	4·6	6·5	1·6	85	42·0	63	3·2	5·2	0·34	—	69	54	52·2	5·3	
216	Eels, elvers, raw	3·6	0·6	0·0	20	19·0	65	146·5	8·8	1·14	Tr.	125	40	15·8	0·5	
217	Eels, silver, raw	4·1	7·9	0·0	90	21·8	61	3·6	4·1	0·23	0·01	55	46	19·7	3·9	
217a	Eels, silver, raw (weighed with bones and skin)	2·7	5·2	0·0	60	14·5	40	2·4	2·7	0·14	0·01	36	30	13·0	2·6	
218	Eels, silver, stewed	5·0	9·2	0·0	106	20·7	57	4·1	4·2	0·28	—	57	57	18·1	4·8	

No.	Food													
219	Eels, yellow, raw	4·7	3·2	0·0	49	25·3	76	5·3	5·4	0·20	0·01	63	53	16·2	4·1
219a	Eels, yellow, raw (weighed with bones and skin)	3·2	2·1	0·0	33	17·1	51	3·5	3·6	0·14	0·01	44	36	10·9	2·7
220	Fillet, smoked, steamed	5·5	0·3	0·0	25	(306)	76	5·6	12·4	0·28	—	63	71	(440)	4·2
221	Fish paste	4·2	2·7	1·9	49	(420)	87	41·5	8·6	1·70	0·02	60	53	(677)	2·9
222	Flounder, steamed	5·5	0·5	0·0	27	32·6	90	15·6	7·1	0·37	—	84	66	42·0	5·6
222a	Flounder, steamed (weighed with bones and skin)	3·1	0·3	0·0	15	18·2	50	8·8	4·0	0·21	—	47	37	23·5	3·1
223	Flounder, fried	4·8	3·7	1·8	61	36·9	80	21·1	6·4	0·31	—	62	58	56·8	4·0
223a	Flounder, fried (weighed with bones)	3·3	2·5	1·3	42	25·5	55	14·6	4·4	0·22	—	43	40	39·1	2·7
224	Gurnet, grey, steamed	6·0	1·5	0·0	38	33·2	87	3·7	6·8	0·23	—	56	70	33·2	4·5
224a	Gurnet, grey, steamed (weighed with bones and skin)	4·8	1·2	0·0	31	26·9	70	3·0	5·5	0·18	—	45	57	26·9	3·6
225	Gurnet, red, steamed	6·0	1·3	0·0	37	52·9	99	5·9	8·8	0·20	—	68	72	40·0	4·2
225a	Gurnet, red, steamed (weighed with bones and skin)	4·3	0·9	0·0	26	37·5	70	4·2	6·2	0·14	—	49	51	28·4	3·0
226	Haddock, fillets, raw	4·5	0·2	0·0	20	35·5	86	9·0	6·4	0·28	—	61	63	44·5	4·4
227	Haddock, fresh, steamed	6·2	0·2	0·0	28	34·4	92	15·5	7·9	0·20	0·04	66	86	22·5	5·0
227a	Haddock, fresh, steamed (weighed with bones and skin)	4·7	0·2	0·0	21	26·2	70	11·8	6·0	0·15	0·03	51	66	16·3	3·8
228	Haddock, fresh, fried	5·8	2·4	1·0	50	50·2	99	32·4	8·7	0·34	—	70	81	51·3	4·0
228a	Haddock, fresh, fried (weighed with bones)	5·3	2·2	0·9	46	46·3	91	29·8	8·0	0·31	—	64	75	47·1	3·7
229	Haddock, smoked, steamed	6·3	0·3	0·0	28	(346)	83	16·3	7·2	0·28	—	71	72	(540)	5·6
229a	Haddock, smoked, steamed (weighed with bones and skin)	4·1	0·2	0·0	18	(225)	54	10·6	4·7	0·18	—	46	47	(350)	3·6
230	Hake, steamed	5·2	0·9	0·0	30	33·5	88	4·5	7·6	0·17	0·03	62	55	27·0	3·6
230a	Hake, steamed (weighed with bones and skin)	4·2	0·7	0·0	24	26·8	70	3·6	6·1	0·14	0·03	50	44	21·5	2·9
231	Hake, fried	5·5	3·2	1·5	58	43·5	84	7·3	8·2	0·26	0·05	74	56	28·0	4·2
231a	Hake, fried (weighed with bones)	5·2	3·0	1·4	55	40·8	79	6·9	7·7	0·24	0·05	69	53	55·7	3·9

Fish – *continued*

No.	Food	g. per oz.			Calories per oz.	mg. per oz.									Acid-base balance, m-equiv. per oz.	
		Protein	Fat	Carbohydrate (as glucose)		Na	K	Ca	Mg	Fe	Cu	P	S	Cl	Acid	Base
232	Halibut, steamed	6·4	1·1	0·0	37	31·5	97	3·7	6·6	0·17	0·02	72	72	22·7	5·3	
232a	Halibut, steamed (weighed with bones and skin)	4·9	0·8	0·0	28	23·8	74	2·8	5·0	0·13	0·01	55	54	17·3	4·0	
233	Herring, raw	4·7	5·1	0·0	67	36·9	90	28·7	9·0	0·43	—	77	54	34·6	3·3	
234	Herring, fried in oatmeal	6·2	4·3	0·4	67	28·7	118	11·0	9·9	0·54	—	96	74	35·5	6·2	
234a	Herring, fried in oatmeal (weighed with bones)	5·4	3·8	0·4	59	25·2	104	9·7	8·7	0·48	—	85	65	31·2	5·5	
235	Herring, baked in vinegar	4·8	3·7	0·0	54	17·6	66	16·6	6·2	0·45	—	93	58	33·7	6·8	
235a	Herring, baked in vinegar (weighed with bones)	4·4	3·4	0·0	50	16·2	61	15·2	5·7	0·42	—	85	53	31·0	6·2	
236	Herring roe, fried	6·6	4·5	1·3	74	24·6	68	4·5	2·3	0·43	—	260	69	34·9	18·8	
237	John Dory, steamed	5·6	0·4	0·0	27	39·5	81	6·5	8·2	0·17	—	71	67	40·5	5·1	
237a	John Dory, steamed (weighed with bones and skin)	3·5	0·2	0·0	17	24·4	50	4·0	5·1	0·11	—	44	41	25·2	3·2	
238	Kippers, baked	6·6	3·2	0·0	57	(281)	148	18·4	13·5	0·40	—	121	80	(433)	6·9	
238a	Kippers, baked (weighed with bones and skin)	3·6	1·7	0·0	31	(152)	80	9·9	7·3	0·22	—	65	43	(234)	3·8	
239	Lemon sole, steamed	5·6	0·3	0·0	26	32·6	79	6·3	5·7	0·17	0·03	70	69	33·2	3·4	
239a	Lemon sole, steamed (weighed with bones and skin)	4·0	0·2	0·0	18	23·2	56	4·5	4·0	0·12	0·03	50	49	23·5	2·4	
240	Lemon sole, fried	4·4	3·7	2·6	62	38·6	71	26·9	5·1	0·31	0·05	68	54	35·2	3·5	
240a	Lemon sole, fried (weighed with bones)	3·5	2·9	2·1	49	30·5	56	21·3	4·0	0·25	0·04	54	42	27·8	2·8	
41	Ling, steamed	6·4	0·2	0·0	28	34·0	105	5·0	10·4	0·14	—	63	76	28·1	4·2	

No.	Food														
241a	Ling, steamed (weighed with bones and skin)	4·8	0·2	0·0	21	25·5	79	3·8	7·9	0·11	—	47	57	21·0	3·2
242	Ling, fried	4·8	3·5	1·8	59	41·1	89	11·3	9·1	0·23	—	65	58	44·5	3·6
242a	Ling, fried (weighed with bones)	4·3	3·1	1·6	52	36·6	79	10·0	8·1	0·20	—	58	51	39·6	3·2
243	Lobster, boiled	6·0	1·0	0·0	34	92·3	73	17·5	9·7	0·23	—	81	146	149·0	10·9
243a	Lobster, boiled (weighed with shell)	2·2	0·3	0·0	12	33·2	26	6·3	3·5	0·09	—	29	53	53·6	3·9
244	Mackerel, fried	5·7	3·2	0·0	53	43·5	118	8·1	9·9	0·34	0·06	80	60	32·4	5·6
244a	Mackerel, fried (weighed with bones and skin)	4·2	2·3	0·0	39	31·8	86	5·9	7·2	0·25	0·04	58	44	23·6	2·6
245	Megrim, raw	4·9	0·3	0·0	22	34·4	76	17·5	8·3	0·34	—	53	58	34·6	3·0
246	Megrim, steamed	5·9	0·4	0·0	28	27·2	61	21·6	7·9	0·26	—	62	70	33·8	4·9
246a	Megrim, steamed (weighed with bones and skin)	3·9	0·3	0·0	18	18·2	41	14·4	5·3	0·17	—	41	47	22·7	3·3
247	Megrim, fried	5·5	3·3	2·7	64	50·1	71	17·8	8·8	0·17	—	62	67	52·0	4·0
247a	Megrim, fried (weighed with bones)	4·7	2·8	2·3	54	42·6	61	15·2	7·5	0·14	—	53	57	44·3	3·4
248	Monkfish, steamed ..	6·2	0·3	0·0	28	38·3	101	3·0	8·4	0·14	—	61	73	38·6	4·5
248a	Monkfish, steamed (weighed with bones)	5·0	0·2	0·0	23	31·0	82	2·4	6·8	0·11	—	49	59	31·2	3·6
249	Monkfish, fried ..	4·8	2·3	1·7	48	46·5	114	3·2	9·0	0·34	—	58	58	55·9	3·2
249a	Monkfish, fried (weighed with bones)	4·1	2·0	1·5	41	40·0	98	2·8	7·7	0·29	—	50	50	48·0	2·7
250	Mullet, grey, steamed ..	6·1	1·1	0·0	36	26·6	78	4·0	8·5	0·57	—	73	72	21·3	5·7
250a	Mullet, grey, steamed (weighed with bones and skin)	3·9	0·7	0·0	23	17·0	50	2·6	5·4	0·37	—	47	46	14·3	3·6
251	Mullet, red, steamed ..	6·1	1·2	0·0	36	33·5	103	8·3	9·3	0·26	—	80	73	28·6	5·3
251a	Mullet, red, steamed (weighed with bones)	4·0	0·8	0·0	24	22·1	68	5·5	6·2	0·17	—	53	49	19·0	3·5
252	Mussels, raw	3·3	0·5	Tr.	19	82·0	90	25·0	6·5	1·65	—	67	104	131·0	6·9
253	Mussels, boiled	4·8	0·6	Tr.	25	59·8	26	56·0	7·1	3·84	—	94	99	89·5	8·1
253a	Mussels, boiled (weighed with shells)	1·4	0·2	Tr.	7	17·9	8	16·8	2·1	1·16	—	28	30	35·5	2·4
254	Oysters, raw	2·9	0·3	Tr.	14	143·0	73	52·9	11·9	1·70	—	76	71	231·0	4·1

Fish – *continued*

No.	Food	g. per oz.			Calories per oz.	mg. per oz.									Acid-base balance, m-equiv. per oz.	
		Protein	Fat	Carbohydrate (as glucose)		Na	K	Ca	Mg	Fe	Cu	P	S	Cl	Acid	Base
254a	Oysters, raw (weighed with shells)	0·3	Tr.	Tr.	2	17·2	9	6·3	1·4	0·20	—	9	9	27·8	0·5	
255	Pilchards, canned (fish only)	6·2	3·1	0·0	54	(169)	87	65·8	11·8	0·88	0·06	84	70	(257)	3·5	
256	Pilchards, canned (whole contents of can)	5·4	4·4	0·0	63	(163)	82	54·0	10·8	0·74	0·05	77	60	(247)	2·8	
257	Plaice, raw	4·3	0·5	0·0	22	27·2	100	4·7	6·2	0·23	—	62	61	23·6	4·0	
258	Plaice, steamed	5·1	0·5	0·0	26	34·0	79	10·7	6·8	0·17	—	70	71	31·8	5·2	
258a	Plaice, steamed (weighed with bones and skin)	2·8	0·3	0·0	14	18·4	43	5·8	3·7	0·09	—	38	38	17·2	2·8	
259	Plaice, fried	5·1	4·1	2·0	66	35·3	62	12·7	6·9	0·23	0·04	71	71	49·4	6·1	
259a	Plaice, fried (weighed with bones)	3·1	2·5	1·2	40	21·5	38	7·8	4·2	0·14	0·03	43	43	30·1	3·7	
260	Pollack, steamed	5·5	0·2	0·0	25	27·0	124	3·6	9·3	0·14	—	57	68	32·4	3·5	
260a	Pollack, steamed (weighed with bones and skin)	4·8	0·2	0·0	21	23·2	107	3·1	8·0	0·12	—	49	58	27·8	3·0	
261	Pollack, fried	4·7	2·0	1·9	45	46·0	95	36·4	12·9	0·79	—	69	56	78·1	2·8	
261a	Pollack, fried (weighed with bones)	4·3	1·8	1·7	41	42·3	87	33·5	11·8	0·73	—	63	52	72·0	2·6	
262	Pollan, steamed	5·1	0·6	0·0	27	19·6	106	23·3	6·5	0·26	—	82	63	20·2	4·5	
262a	Pollan, steamed (weighed with bones and skin)	3·1	0·4	0·0	16	11·9	65	14·2	4·0	0·16	—	50	38	12·3	2·7	
263	Pollan, fried	5·3	3·5	0·5	56	18·2	111	56·8	7·4	0·34	—	104	65	18·2	4·2	
263a	Pollan, fried (weighed with bones)	3·8	2·5	0·3	40	13·1	80	40·8	5·3	0·25	—	75	47	13·1	3·0	
264	Prawns	6·0	0·5	0·0	30	(451)	74	41·2	11·9	0·31	—	99	104	(725)	8·7	
264a	Prawns (weighed with shells)	2·3	0·2	0·0	11	(172)	28	15·6	4·5	0·12	—	38	40	(275)	3·3	
265	Saithe, steamed	6·4	0·2	0·0	28	27·5	99	5·3	8·8	0·17	—	71	76	23·6	5·2	

1·1
0·9

No.	Food														
265a	Saithe, steamed (weighed with bones and skin)	5·4	0·1	0·0	24	23·5	84	4·5	7·5	0·14	—	61	64	20·1	4·4
266	Salmon, fresh, steamed	5·4	3·7	0·0	57	30·4	95	8·2	8·1	0·23	—	86	54	18·2	2·6
266a	Salmon, fresh, steamed (weighed with bones and skin)	4·4	3·0	0·0	46	24·7	77	6·6	6·6	0·18	—	70	44	14·8	5·7
267	Salmon, canned	5·6	1·7	0·0	39	(152)	91	18·8	8·5	0·37	0·01	81	67	(246)	5·7
268	Sardines, canned	5·8	6·4	0·0	84	(223)	123	116·0	11·7	1·13	0·01	194	80	(342)	7·5
269	Scallops, steamed	6·4	0·4	Tr.	30	75·3	135	32·7	10·9	0·85		96	162	116·0	-0·3
270	Shrimps	6·3	0·7	0·0	32	(1090)	114	91·0	29·8	0·51	0·23	77	96	(1660)	0·5
270a	Shrimps (weighed with shells)	2·1	0·2	0·0	11	(360)	38	30·0	9·8	0·17	0·08	25	32	(550)	0·2
271	Skate, fried	4·3	4·7	2·1	69	51·8	67	5·5	6·6	0·34	—	68	61	75·7	5·5
271a	Skate, fried (weighed with bones)	3·5	3·9	1·8	57	42·9	56	4·6	5·5	0·28	—	56	50	62·8	4·6
272	Smelts, fried	7·1	8·8	1·4	116	42·0	147	195·0	16·6	0·94	—	152	86	39·2	
272a	Smelts, fried (weighed with heads)	6·0	7·5	1·2	98	35·7	124	166·0	14·2	0·80	—	129	73	33·3	
273	Sole, steamed	5·0	0·4	0·0	24	31·2	68	32·1	8·0	0·20	—	77	67	37·5	4·8
273a	Sole, steamed (weighed with bones and skin)	3·0	0·2	0·0	14	18·7	41	19·3	4·8	0·12	—	46	40	22·5	2·9
274	Sole, fried	5·7	5·2	1·5	78	54·5	67	37·2	7·9	0·40	—	74	75	54·9	4·4
274a	Sole, fried (weighed with bones)	5·0	4·6	1·3	68	48·0	59	32·7	7·0	0·15	—	65	66	48·3	3·9
275	Sprats, fresh, fried	6·3	10·8	0·0	126	37·5	116	201·0	13·0	1·28	—	180	81	51·6	2·4
275a	Sprats, fresh, fried (weighed with heads)	5·6	9·5	0·0	111	33·0	102	176·0	11·4	1·12	—	158	71	45·4	2·1
276	Sprats, smoked, grilled	7·1	6·6	0·0	91	(240)	137	124·0	11·4	1·62	—	161	78	(378)	4·8
276a	Sprats, smoked, grilled (weighed with heads)	6·3	5·9	0·0	81	(213)	122	110·0	10·1	1·44	—	143	70	(336)	4·3
277	Stockfish, boiled	9·1	0·3	0·0	40	(112)	9	6·4	9·9	0·51	—	46	106	(90)	8·7
277a	Stockfish, boiled (weighed with bones and skin)	7·6	0·2	0·0	33	(93)	7	5·3	8·2	0·42	—	38	88	(153)	7·2
278	Sturgeon, steamed	7·0	1·6	0·0	44	30·6	67	4·3	5·3	0·57	—	75	83	39·2	7·4
278a	Sturgeon, steamed (weighed with bone)	4·8	1·1	0·0	30	20·8	46	2·9	3·6	0·39	—	51	56	26·6	5·0

Fish – continued

No.	Food	g. per oz.			Calories per oz.	mg. per oz.									Acid-base balance, m-equiv. per oz.	
		Protein	Fat	Carbohydrate (as glucose)		Na	K	Ca	Mg	Fe	Cu	P	S	Cl	Acid	Base
279	Torsk, steamed	6·4	0·2	0·0	28	21·0	110	7·7	7·5	0·28	—	80	79	28·7	6·2	
279a	Torsk, steamed (weighed with bones and skin)	3·8	0·1	0·0	16	12·4	65	4·5	4·4	0·17	—	47	47	16·9	3·7	
280	Torsk, fried	5·5	1·2	2·2	42	26·4	106	18·4	7·1	0·17	—	85	67	43·5	5·5	
280a	Torsk, fried (weighed with bones and skin)	3·9	0·9	1·6	30	18·8	75	13·0	5·0	0·12	—	60	47	30·9	3·9	
281	Trout, steamed	6·3	1·3	0·0	38	25·0	106	10·2	8·8	0·28	—	77	62	19·9	4·3	
281a	Trout, steamed (weighed with bones and skin)	4·2	0·9	0·0	25	16·5	70	6·7	5·8	0·19	—	51	41	13·1	2·8	
282	Trout, Sea, steamed	6·0	1·4	0·0	37	58·7	89	3·5	8·6	0·28	—	82	74	74·1	6·3	
282a	Trout, Sea, steamed (weighed with bones and skin)	4·7	1·1	0·0	29	46·3	70	2·8	6·8	0·22	—	65	58	58·6	4·9	
283	Turbot, steamed	5·9	0·5	0·0	28	25·6	72	3·8	6·8	0·14	—	53	70	40·3	5·2	
283a	Turbot, steamed (weighed with bones and skin)	3·9	0·3	0·0	19	16·9	48	2·5	4·5	0·09	—	35	46	26·6	3·4	
284	Whelks	5·1	0·5	Tr.	26	(75)	90	15·3	45·4	1·76	—	64	127	(166)	6·6	
284a	Whelks (weighed with shells)	0·8	0·1	Tr.	4	(11)	13	2·3	6·8	0·26	—	10	19	(25)	1·0	
285	Whitebait, fried	5·2	13·5	1·5	152	63·9	32	244·0	14·3	1·45	—	243	77	92·3	6·1	
286	Whiting, steamed	5·7	0·3	0·0	26	36·1	85	11·9	8·0	0·28	—	54	87	26·4	4·6	
286a	Whiting, steamed (weighed with bones and skin)	3·8	0·2	0·0	17	24·5	58	8·1	5·4	0·19	—	36	59	17·9	3·2	
287	Whiting, fried	4·9	2·9	2·0	55	56·5	90	13·6	9·2	0·20	—	73	76	55·1	4·8	
287a	Whiting, fried (weighed with bones and skin)	4·4	2·6	1·8	49	50·9	81	12·2	8·3	0·18	—	66	68	49·7	4·3	
288	Winkles, boiled in salt water	4·3	0·4	Tr.	21	(325)	44	38·7	102·0	4·26	—	62	107	(511)		0·6

No.	Food	g. per oz.			Calories per oz.	mg. per oz.									Acid-base balance, m-equiv. per oz.	
		Protein (N × 6.25)	Fat	Available carbohydrate (as monosaccharides)		Na	K	Ca	Mg	Fe	Cu	P	S	Cl	Acid	Base
288a	Winkles, boiled in salt water (weighed with shells)	0·8	0·1	Tr.	4	(62)	8	7·3	19·3	0·81	—	12	20	(97)		0·1
289	Winkles, boiled in fresh water	5·0	0·7	Tr.	27	75·8	60	46·9	118·0	4·86	—	79	127	142·0	<0·1	
289a	Winkles, boiled in fresh water (weighed with shells)	0·7	0·1	Tr.	4	11·4	9	7·0	17·6	0·73	—	12	19	21·3	<0·1	
290	Witch, steamed	5·4	0·3	0·0	25	38·6	86	8·6	6·8	0·26	—	66	72	34·9	4·8	
290a	Witch, steamed (weighed with bones and skin)	3·2	0·2	0·0	15	23·2	52	5·2	4·1	0·15	—	40	43	20·9	2·9	
291	Witch, fried	5·0	4·0	2·2	66	50·0	85	14·8	6·9	0·23	—	53	67	53·1	3·4	
291a	Witch, fried (weighed with bones and skin)	4·2	3·4	1·9	56	42·0	71	12·4	5·8	0·19	—	45	56	44·5	2·9	

Fruit

No.	Food	g. per oz.			Calories per oz.	mg. per oz.									Acid-base balance, m-equiv. per oz.	
		Protein (N × 6.25)	Fat	Available carbohydrate (as monosaccharides)		Na	K	Ca	Mg	Fe	Cu	P	S	Cl	Acid	Base
292	Apples, imported, eating ..	0·1	Tr.	3·5	13	0·8	33	1·0	1·4	0·08	0·04	1·9	1·1	Tr.		0·9
292a	Apples, imported, eating (weighed with skin and core)	0·1	Tr.	2·6	10	0·5	25	0·8	1·1	0·06	0·03	1·4	0·8	Tr.		0·7
293	Apples, English eating ..	0·1	Tr.	3·3	13	0·6	34	1·0	1·2	0·08	0·02	2·4	2·2	0·5		0·7
293a	Apples, English eating (weighed with skin and core)	0·1	Tr.	2·6	10	0·5	27	0·8	1·0	0·07	0·02	1·9	1·7	0·5		0·6
294	Apples, cooking, raw ..	0·1	Tr.	2·7	10	0·6	35	1·0	0·8	0·08	0·03	4·6	0·8	1·3		0·7

Fruit – *continued*

No.	Food	g. per oz.			Calories per oz.	mg. per oz.									Acid-base balance, m-equiv. per oz.	
		Protein (N × 6·25)	Fat	Available carbohydrate (as monosaccharides)		Na	K	Ca	Mg	Fe	Cu	P	S	Cl	Acid	Base
295	Apples, cooking, baked	0·1	Tr.	2·8	11	0·6	36	1·0	0·9	0·09	0·03	4·8	0·9	1·4		0·7
295a	Apples, cooking, baked (weighed with skin)	0·1	Tr.	2·3	9	0·5	29	0·8	0·7	0·07	0·02	3·8	0·7	1·1		0·5
296	Apples, cooking, stewed without sugar	0·1	Tr.	2·1	9	0·1	27	0·8	0·6	0·06	0·01	3·5	0·6	1·0		0·5
297	Apricots, fresh	0·2	Tr.	1·9	8	Tr.	91	4·9	3·5	0·11	0·03	6·1	1·7	Tr.		2·4
297a	Apricots, fresh (weighed with stones)	0·2	Tr.	1·7	7	Tr.	84	4·5	3·2	0·10	0·03	5·6	1·6	Tr.		2·2
298	Apricots, fresh, stewed without sugar	0·1	Tr.	1·5	6	<0·2	69·9	3·7	2·7	0·10	0·03	4·6	1·3	<0·2		1·8
299	Apricots, dried, raw	1·4	Tr.	12·3	52	16·0	535	26·3	18·6	1·16	0·08	33·5	46·6	9·8		11·9
300	Apricots, dried, stewed without sugar	0·4	Tr.	4·1	17	5·3	178	8·8	6·2	0·40	0·03	10·5	15·5	3·3		3·9
301	Apricots, canned in syrup	0·1	Tr.	7·9	30	0·3	73	3·4	2·0	0·20	0·01	3·7	0·3	0·4		2·0
302	Avocado pears	0·3	2·3	0·7	25	4·6	112	4·4	8·3	0·15	0·06	8·8	5·5	1·7		3·0
303	Bananas	0·3	Tr.	5·5	22	0·3	99	1·9	11·9	0·12	0·05	8·0	3·7	22·3		2·3
303a	Bananas (weighed with skin)	0·2	Tr.	3·2	13	0·2	58	1·1	7·0	0·07	0·03	4·7	2·2	13·1		1·3
304	Blackberries, raw	0·4	Tr.	1·8	8	1·1	59	18·0	8·4	0·24	0·03	6·8	2·6	6·3		2·4
305	Blackberries, stewed without sugar	0·3	Tr.	1·4	6	0·8	45	13·8	6·4	0·18	0·03	5·2	2·0	4·8		1·8
306	Cherries, eating	0·2	Tr.	3·4	13	0·8	78	4·5	2·7	0·11	0·02	4·8	1·9	Tr.		2·1

No.	Food														
306a	Cherries, eating (weighed with stones)	0·1	Tr.	3·0	11	0·7	68	3·9	2·4	0·09	0·02	4·2	1·7	Tr.	1·8
307	Cherries, cooking, raw	0·2	Tr.	3·3	13	1·2	87	5·7	3·3	0·09	0·03	5·9	2·2	Tr.	2·3
307a	Cherries, cooking, raw (weighed with stones)	0·1	Tr.	2·8	11	1·0	73	4·8	2·8	0·07	0·02	5·0	1·9	Tr.	1·9
308	Cherries, stewed without sugar (weighed with stones)	0·1	Tr.	2·5	10	0·9	66	4·4	2·5	0·07	0·02	3·8	1·7	Tr.	1·8
309	Cranberries	0·1	Tr.	1·0	4	0·5	34	4·2	2·4	0·32	0·04	3·2	3·2	Tr.	0·9
310	Currants, black, raw	0·3	Tr.	1·9	8	0·8	106	17·2	4·9	0·36	0·04	12·3	9·4	4·2	2·5
311	Currants, black, stewed without sugar	0·2	Tr.	1·4	6	0·6	81	13·2	3·7	0·28	0·03	9·4	6·8	3·2	1·9
312	Currants, red, raw	0·3	Tr.	1·2	6	0·7	78	10·2	3·6	0·35	0·03	8·4	8·1	4·0	1·7
313	Currants, red, stewed without sugar	0·2	Tr.	1·0	4	0·5	62	7·8	2·5	0·26	0·03	6·4	6·3	3·1	1·3
314	Currants, white	0·4	Tr.	1·6	7	0·4	83	6·4	3·6	0·26	0·04	8·0	6·7	3·0	1·7
315	Currants, white, stewed without sugar	0·3	Tr.	1·2	6	0·3	64	4·9	2·8	0·20	0·03	6·1	5·2	2·3	1·3
316	Currants, dried	0·5	Tr.	18·0	69	5·5	201	27·1	10·3	0·52	0·14	11·4	8·8	4·5	6·2
317	Custard apple	0·6	Tr.	5·1	22	3·9	164	3·4	6·8	0·15	0·04	14·5	7·6	11·4	3·4
318	Damsons, raw	0·1	Tr.	2·7	11	0·6	82	6·7	3·1	0·12	0·02	4·7	1·8	Tr	2·3
318a	Damsons, raw (weighed with stones)	0·1	Tr.	2·4	9	0·6	74	6·0	2·8	0·11	0·02	4·2	1·6	Tr.	2·1
319	Damsons, stewed without sugar (weighed with stones)	0·1	Tr.	2·1	8	0·5	63	5·1	2·4	0·09	0·02	3·6	1·4	T-.	1·8
320	Dates	0·6	Tr.	18·1	70	1·4	215	19·2	16·6	0·46	0·06	18·1	14·5	82·4	3·6
320a	Dates (weighed with stones)	0·5	Tr.	15·6	61	1·2	185	16·6	14·3	0·39	0·05	15·6	12·4	7·0	3·0
321	Figs, green	0·4	Tr.	2·7	12	0·5	76	9·7	5·7	0·12	0·02	9·1	3·7	5·2	2·0
322	Figs, dried, raw	1·0	Tr.	15·0	61	24·6	288	80·5	26·2	1·18	0·07	26·0	22·9	47·1	10·2

Fruit – *continued*

No.	Food	g. per oz.			Calories per oz.	mg. per oz.									Acid-base balance, m-equiv. per oz.	
		Protein (N × 6.25)	Fat	Available carbohydrate (as monosaccharides)		Na	K	Ca	Mg	Fe	Cu	P	S	Cl	Acid	Base
323	Figs, dried, stewed without sugar	0·5	Tr.	7·5	30	12·3	143	40·3	13·1	0·59	0·04	13·1	11·5	23·6		5·1
324	Fruit salad, canned in syrup	0·1	Tr.	7·1	27	0·7	33	2·4	2·2	0·98	0·01	2·7	0·5	0·9		0·9
325	Gooseberries, green, raw ..	0·3	Tr.	1·0	5	0·5	60	8·0	2·0	0·09	0·04	9·6	4·5	1·9		1·2
326	Gooseberries, green, stewed without sugar	0·3	Tr.	0·7	4	0·4	46	6·2	1·6	0·07	0·03	7·4	3·5	1·4		0·2
327	Gooseberries, ripe	0·2	Tr.	2·6	10	0·3	48	5·2	2·4	0·16	0·04	5·4	3·8	3·0		1·0
328	Grapes, black	0·2	Tr.	4·4	17	0·5	90	1·2	1·1	0·10	0·02	4·6	2·1	Tr.		2·0
328a	Grapes, black (whole grapes weighed)	0·1	Tr.	3·7	14	0·4	75	1·0	1·0	0·08	0·02	3·8	1·8	Tr.		1·7
329	Grapes, white	0·2	Tr.	4·6	18	0·5	71	5·4	1·9	0·10	0·03	6·2	2·6	Tr.		1·7
329a	Grapes, white (whole grapes weighed)	0·2	Tr.	4·4	17	0·4	67	5·2	1·8	0·09	0·03	5·9	2·5	Tr.		1·6
330	Grapefruit	0·2	Tr.	1·5	6	0·4	66	4·9	3·0	0·07	0·02	4·4	1·5	0·4		1·8
330a	Grapefruit (whole fruit weighed)	0·1	Tr.	0·7	3	0·2	32	2·3	1·4	0·04	0·01	2·1	0·7	0·2		0·9
331	Greengages..	0·2	Tr.	3·4	14	0·4	87	4·8	2·2	0·11	0·02	6·4	0·9	0·3		2·2
331a	Greengages (weighed with stones)	0·2	Tr.	3·2	13	0·4	82	4·5	2·1	0·10	0·02	6·1	0·8	0·3		2·1
332	Greengages, stewed without sugar (weighed with stones)	0·2	Tr.	2·6	11	0·3	66	3·7	1·7	0·08	0·02	4·9	0·7	0·2		1·7

No.	Food															
333	Lemons, whole	0·2	Tr.	0·9	4	1·7	46	30·5	3·3	0·10	0·07	5·9	3·5	1·5		2·4
334	Lemon juice	0·1	Tr.	0·5	2	0·4	40	2·4	1·9	0·04	0·04	2·9	0·6	0·7		1·1
335	Loganberries	0·3	Tr.	1·0	5	0·7	73	10·0	7·1	0·39	0·04	6·9	5·1	4·5		2·1
336	Loganberries, stewed without sugar	0·2	Tr.	0·7	4	0·5	56	7·7	5·5	0·30	0·03	5·3	3·9	3·4		1·6
337	Loganberries, canned in syrup	0·2	Tr.	7·4	29	0·3	28	5·0	3·2	0·82	0·01	6·5	0·9	1·3	—	0·7
338	Mandarins, canned	0·1	0·0	4·7	18	1·5	28	2·3	1·9	0·05	Tr.	2·2	—	Tr.		
339	Medlars	0·1	Tr.	3·0	12	1·7	70	8·6	3·0	0·14	0·05	8·0	4·7	0·3		1·7
339a	Medlars (weighed with skin and stone)	0·1	Tr.	2·4	10	1·4	57	6·9	2·4	0·11	0·04	6·5	3·8	0·7		1·4
340	Melons, Cantaloupe	0·3	Tr.	1·5	7	3·8	90	5·4	5·7	0·23	0·01	8·6	3·3	12·4		2·1
340a	Melons, Cantaloupe (weighed with skin)	0·2	Tr.	0·9	4	2·4	57	3·4	3·6	0·14	0·01	5·4	2·1	7·7		1·3
341	Melons, yellow	0·2	Tr.	1·4	6	5·5	63	3·9	3·8	0·07	0·01	2·5	1·8	12·8		1·7
341a	Melons, yellow (weighed with skin)	0·1	Tr.	0·9	4	3·5	39	2·4	2·4	0·04	0·01	1·5	1·1	8·0		1·1
342	Mulberries	0·4	Tr.	2·3	10	0·6	73	10·2	4·3	0·45	0·02	13·5	2·5	1·1		1·7
343	Nectarines	0·3	Tr.	3·5	14	2·6	76	1·1	3·6	0·13	0·02	6·8	2·8	·3		1·8
343a	Nectarines (weighed with stones)	0·2	Tr.	3·2	13	2·4	70	1·0	3·3	0·12	0·02	6·3	2·6	·2		1·6
344	Olives (in brine)	0·3	3·1	Tr.	30	(639)	26	17·4	6·2	0·29	0·07	4·8	10·1	(1060)	1·1	
344a	Olives (in brine) (weighed with stones)	0·2	2·5	Tr.	24	(510)	21	14·0	5·0	0·23	0·05	3·8	8·1	(355)	0·9	
345	Oranges	0·2	Tr.	2·4	10	0·8	56	11·7	3·7	0·09	0·02	6·7	2·6	0·9		1·7
345a	Oranges (weighed with peel and pips)	0·2	Tr.	1·8	8	0·6	42	8·8	2·8	0·07	0·01	5·1	1·9	0·7		1·3
346	Orange juice	0·2	Tr.	2·7	11	0·5	51	3·3	3·3	0·09	0·01	6·2	1·3	0·3		1·3
347	Passion fruit	0·8	Tr.	1·8	10	8·1	99	4·4	11·0	0·32	0·03	15·4	5·3	10·4		2·4
347a	Passion fruit (weighed with skin)	0·3	Tr.	0·7	4	3·4	42	1·8	4·6	0·13	0·01	6·5	2·2	4·4		1·0

Fruit – *continued*

No.	Food	g. per oz.			Calories per oz.	mg. per oz.									Acid-base balance, m-equiv. per oz.	
		Protein (N × 6.25)	Fat	Available carbohydrate (as monosaccharides)		Na	.K	Ca	Mg	Fe	Cu	P	S	Cl	Acid	Base
348	Peaches, fresh	0.2	Tr.	2.6	11	0.8	74	1.4	2.3	0.11	0.01	5.3	1.6	Tr.		1.7
348a	Peaches, fresh (weighed with stones)	0.2	Tr.	2.3	9	0.7	64	1.2	2.0	0.09	0.01	4.6	1.4	Tr.		1.5
349	Peaches, dried, raw ..	1.0	Tr.	15.0	61	1.7	314	10.1	15.4	1.92	0.18	33.0	68.1	3.0		3.4
350	Peaches, dried, stewed without sugar	0.3	Tr.	5.0	20	0.6	104	3.4	5.1	0.64	0.06	11.0	22.7	1.0		1.1
351	Peaches, canned in syrup..	0.1	Tr.	6.5	25	0.4	43	1.0	1.8	0.55	0.02	2.8	0.3	1.2		1.1
352	Pears, imported eating ..	0.1	Tr.	3.1	12	0.7	37	2.3	2.6	0.05	0.06	2.8	1.6	Tr.		1.0
352a	Pears, imported eating (weighed with skin and core)	0.1	Tr.	2.1	8	0.5	25	1.6	1.8	0.04	0.04	1.9	1.1	Tr.		0.7
353	Pears, English eating ..	0.1	Tr.	3.0	11	0.7	36	2.0	1.5	0.06	0.03	2.7	0.8	Tr.		1.0
353a	Pears, English eating (weighed with skin and core)	0.1	Tr.	2.2	9	0.5	27	1.5	1.1	0.05	0.02	2.0	0.6	Tr.		0.7
354	Pears, cooking, raw ..	0.1	Tr.	2.6	10	0.7	28	2.0	1.2	0.05	0.03	4.2	1.0	0.4		0.6
355	Pears, cooking, stewed without sugar	0.1	Tr.	2.0	8	0.5	22	1.6	0.9	0.03	0.02	3.2	0.7	0.3		0.5
356	Pears, canned in syrup ..	0.1	Tr.	5.7	22	0.4	26	1.5	1.7	0.50	0.01	1.5	0.4	0.8		0.7
357	Pineapple, fresh	0.1	Tr.	3.3	13	0.5	70	3.5	4.8	0.12	0.02	2.2	0.7	8.1		2.0
358	Pineapple, canned in syrup	0.1	Tr.	5.7	22	0.1	16	3.8	2.3	0.48	0.01	1.4	0.8	1.2		0.6

No.															
359	Plums, Victoria dessert	0·2	Tr.	2·7	11	0·5	53	3·1	2·0	0·10	0·03	4·6	1·0	Tr.	1·4
359a	Plums, Victoria dessert (weighed with stones)	0·2	Tr.	2·6	10	0·5	50	2·9	1·9	0·10	0·03	4·3	0·9	Tr.	1·3
360	Plums, cooking, raw	0·2	Tr.	1·8	7	0·6	55	3·9	2·2	0·09	0·03	4·1	1·3	Tr.	1·5
360a	Plums, cooking, raw (weighed with stones)	0·2	Tr.	1·6	7	0·5	50	3·6	2·0	0·08	0·02	3·7	1·2	Tr.	1·3
361	Plums, stewed without sugar (weighed with stones)	0·1	Tr.	1·4	6	0·4	43	3·0	1·7	0·07	0·02	3·2	1·0	0·2	1·1
362	Pomegranate juice	0·1	Tr.	3·3	13	0·3	58	0·8	0·9	0·04	0·02	2·1	1·2	14·9	1·0
363	Prunes, dried, raw	0·7	Tr.	11·4	46	3·5	246	10·7	7·6	0·82	0·05	23·5	5·3	0·7	5·8
363a	Prunes, dried, raw (weighed with stones)	0·6	Tr.	9·5	38	2·9	204	8·9	6·3	0·68	0·04	19·6	4·4	0·5	4·8
364	Prunes, stewed without sugar (weighed with stones)	0·3	Tr.	4·8	19	1·5	102	4·4	3·2	0·34	0·02	9·8	2·2	0·3	2·4
365	Quinces	0·1	Tr.	1·3	7	0·9	58	4·0	1·7	0·09	0·04	5·4	1·5	0·5	1·4
366	Raisins, dried	0·3	Tr.	18·3	70	14·9	244	17·2	11·8	0·44	0·07	9·3	6·5	2·4	7·6
367	Raspberries, raw	0·3	Tr.	1·6	7	0·7	64	11·6	6·2	0·34	0·06	8·2	4·9	6·3	1·7
368	Raspberries, stewed without sugar	0·2	Tr.	1·5	7	0·7	60	11·0	5·9	0·33	0·06	7·8	4·7	6·0	1·6
369	Rhubarb, raw	0·2	Tr.	0·3	2	0·6	121	29·2	3·9	0·11	0·04	6·0	2·3	24·7	3·7
370	Rhubarb, stewed without sugar	0·1	Tr.	0·2	1	0·5	93	22·4	3·0	0·08	0·03	4·6	1·8	19·1	2·8
371	Strawberries	0·2	Tr.	1·8	7	0·4	46	6·3	3·3	0·20	0·04	6·5	3·8	5·0	1·0
372	Sultanas, dried	0·5	Tr.	18·4	71	15·0	243	14·9	10·0	0·52	0·10	26·8	12·6	4·4	5·8
373	Tangerines	0·3	Tr.	2·3	10	0·6	44	11·8	3·2	0·08	0·03	4·7	2·9	0·7	1·5
373a	Tangerines (weighed with peel and pips)	0·2	Tr.	1·6	7	0·4	31	8·3	2·2	0·05	0·02	3·3	2·0	0·5	1·1

L

Nuts

| No. | Food | g. per oz. | | | Calories per oz. | mg. per oz. | | | | | | | | | Acid-base balance, m-equiv. per oz. | |
		Protein (N × 6·25)	Fat	Available carbohydrate (as monosaccharides)		Na	K	Ca	Mg	Fe	Cu	P	S	Cl	Acid	Base
374	Almonds	5·8	15·2	1·2	170	1·6	243	70·0	73·0	1·20	0·04	126	41	0·5		5·2
374a	Almonds (weighed with shells)	2·2	5·6	0·5	63	0·6	90	26·0	27·0	0·44	0·01	47	15	0·2		1·9
375	Barcelona nuts	3·7	18·2	1·5	189	0·7	266	48·2	57·2	0·84	0·27	85	50	9·5		5·2
375a	Barcelona nuts (weighed with shells)	2·3	11·3	0·9	117	0·4	165	30·0	35·5	0·52	0·17	53	31	5·9		3·2
376	Brazil nuts	3·9	17·3	1·2	183	0·4	216	50·0	117·0	0·80	0·31	168	83	17·3		1·3
376a	Brazil nuts (weighed with shells)	1·8	7·8	0·5	82	0·2	97	22·4	52·6	0·36	0·14	76	37	7·8		0·6
377	Chestnuts	0·7	0·8	10·4	49	3·1	141	13·1	9·4	0·25	0·07	21	8	4·3		3·2
377a	Chestnuts (weighed with shells)	0·5	0·6	8·6	40	2·6	117	10·8	7·8	0·21	0·05	17	7	3·5		2·7
378	Cob nuts	2·6	10·2	1·9	113	0·4	98	12·5	15·9	0·30	0·06	65	21	1·7	1·1	
378a	Cob nuts (weighed with shells)	0·9	3·7	0·7	41	0·1	35	4·5	5·7	0·11	0·02	23	8	0·6	0·4	
379	Coconut, fresh	1·1	10·2	1·1	104	4·7	124	3·7	14·8	0·59	0·09	27	13	32·4		1·4
380	Coconut milk	0·1	—	1·4	—	29·8	89	8·2	8·5	0·03	0·01	11	7	52·0		2·1
381	Coconut, desiccated	1·9	17·6	1·8	178	8·1	214	6·4	25·5	1·02	0·16	46	22	55·8		2·4
382	Peanuts	8·0	13·9	2·4	171	1·6	193	17·3	51·3	0·58	0·08	104	107	1·9	3·3	
382a	Peanuts (weighed with shells)	5·5	9·6	1·7	118	1·1	133	11·9	35·5	0·40	0·05	72	74	1·3	2·3	
383	Walnuts	3·6	14·6	1·4	156	0·8	195	17·3	37·2	0·67	0·09	145	30	6·5	2·4	
383a	Walnuts (weighed with shells)	2·3	9·4	0·9	100	0·5	124	11·1	23·8	0·43	0·06	93	19	4·2	1·5	

Vegetables

No.	Food	Protein (N × 6.25)	Fat	Available carbohydrate (as monosaccharides)	Calories per oz.	Na	K	Ca	Mg	Fe	Cu	P	S	Cl	Acid	Base
		g. per oz.				mg. per oz.									Acid-base balance, m-equiv. per oz.	
384	Artichokes, globe, boiled ..	0·3	Tr.	0·8*	4	4·2	93	12·4	7·7	0·14	0·03	11·3	4·4	23·7		2·2
384a	Artichokes, globe, boiled (weighed as served)	0·1	Tr.	0·3*	2	1·8	40	5·3	3·3	0·06	0·01	4·9	1·9	10·2		0·9
385	Artichokes, Jerusalem, boiled	0·5	Tr.	0·9*	5	0·7	119	8·6	3·2	0·12	0·03	9·4	6·1	16·4		2·3
386	Asparagus, boiled	1·0	Tr.	0·3	5	0·5	67	7·3	3·0	0·25	0·06	24·0	13·2	8·9	0·3	
386a	Asparagus, boiled (weighed as served)	0·5	Tr.	0·2	3	0·3	34	3·7	1·5	0·13	0·03	12·0	6·6	4·5	0·1	
387	Beans, baked	1·7	0·1	4·9	26	(168)	98	17·4	10·4	0·58	0·07	52·1	14·4	(230)		0·8
388	Beans, broad, boiled	1·2	Tr.	2·0	12	5·6	66	6·0	7·8	0·28	0·12	28·1	7·7	4·0		0·5
389	Beans, butter, raw ..	5·5	Tr.	14·2	76	17·4	485	24·1	46·5	1·68	0·35	90·4	31·1	12·2		10·1
390	Beans, butter, boiled	2·0	Tr.	4·9	26	4·6	113	5·3	9·5	0·47	0·05	24·5	13·4	0·7		1·7
391	Beans, French, boiled	0·2	Tr.	0·3	2	1·0	29	11·0	2·9	0·17	0·03	4·3	2·4	3·0		1·1
392	Beans, haricot, raw	6·1	Tr.	12·9	73	12·3	329	51·1	52·0	1·89	0·17	87·8	47·3	0·5		7·2
393	Beans, haricot, boiled	1·9	Tr.	4·7	25	4·3	91	18·3	12·6	0·71	0·04	34·6	13·1	0·3		1·4
394	Beans, runner, raw	0·3	Tr.	0·8	4	1·8	78	9·5	6·5	0·21	0·03	7·4	4·0	6·5		2·2
395	Beans, runner, boiled	0·2	Tr.	0·3	2	0·9	25	7·3	3·6	0·17	0·01	3·0	2·7	2·5		0·9
396	Beetroot, raw ..	0·4	Tr.	1·7	8	23·9	86	7·1	4·3	0·11	0·02	9·1		16·8	—	—
397	Beetroot, boiled	0·5	Tr.	2·8	13	18·2	99	8·5	4·8	0·20	0·04	10·1	6·3	21·5		2·5
398	Broccoli tops, boiled	0·9	Tr.	0·1	4	1·9	29	45·4	3·8	0·43	0·03	15·3	12·8	14·5		1·2
399	Brussels sprouts, raw ..	1·0	Tr.	1·3	9	2·7	146	8·2	5·6	0·19	0·01	22	—	10·0	—	—
400	Brussels sprouts, boiled ..	0·7	Tr.	0·5	5	2·2	70	7·7	3·0	0·18	0·02	12·7	22·0	3·2		0·2

* This vegetable contains inulin. 50 per cent. total carbohydrate taken to be available.

L2

Vegetables – *continued*

No.	Food	Protein (N × 6·25)	Fat	Available carbohydrate (as monosaccharides)	Calories per oz.	Na	K	Ca	Mg	Fe	Cu	P	S	Cl	Acid	Base
		g. per oz.				*mg. per oz.*									*Acid-base balance, m-equiv. per oz.*	
401	Cabbage, red, raw	0·5	Tr.	1·0	6	9·0	86	15·1	4·7	0·16	0·03	9·1	19·3	12·6		1·6
402	Cabbage, Savoy, raw	0·9	Tr.	0·9	7	6·4	75	21·3	5·5	0·26	—	19·2	25·0	6·3		0·7
403	Cabbage, Savoy, boiled	0·4	Tr.	0·3	3	2·3	35	14·9	2·0	0·20	0·02	7·7	8·6	2·7		0·8
404	Cabbage, spring, boiled	0·3	Tr.	0·2	2	3·5	31	8·5	1·8	0·13	0·02	9·0	7·6	1·8		0·4
405	Cabbage, winter, raw	0·8	Tr.	1·1	7	8·1	68	20·6	4·8	0·35	—	18·2	20·3	11·2		0·8
406	Cabbage, winter, boiled	0·2	Tr.	0·4	3	3·8	41	16·6	2·1	0·13	0·01	4·6	6·7	3·9		1·4
407	Carrageen moss, dried	1·9	Tr.	0·1	8	823	596	240	179	2·52	0·15	58·3	1550	327	32·0	
408	Carrots, old, raw	0·2	Tr.	1·5	6	27·0	64	13·6	3·4	0·16	0·02	6·0	2·0	19·5		2·6
409	Carrots, old, boiled	0·2	Tr.	1·2	5	14·2	25	10·4	1·8	0·11	0·02	4·7	1·4	8·8		1·3
410	Carrots, young, boiled	0·3	Tr.	1·3	6	6·4	67	8·2	2·4	0·12	0·02	8·4	2·6	7·8		1·7
411	Carrots, canned	0·2	Tr.	1·3	5	(79)	24	7·6	1·3	0·36	0·01	4·3	—	(126)		—
412	Cauliflower, raw	1·0	Tr.	0·8	7	3·0	116	5·1	4·8	0·16	0·01	21·0	8·4	9·5	—	0·5
413	Cauliflower, boiled	0·4	Tr.	0·3	3	3·2	43	6·5	1·9	0·14	0·02	9·4	3·6	3·3	—	2·5
414	Celeriac, boiled	0·5	Tr.	0·6	4	8·0	114	13·2	3·4	0·24	0·04	20·2	4·2	6·6		2·4
415	Celery, raw	0·3	Tr.	0·4	3	38·9	79	14·8	2·7	0·17	0·03	9·0	2·4	52·0		1·4
416	Celery, boiled	0·2	Tr.	0·2	1	18·9	38	14·8	2·4	0·12	0·03	5·5	3·6	28·4		1·2
417	Chicory, raw	0·2	Tr.	0·4*	3	2·1	52	5·2	3·6	0·20	0·04	5·9	3·1	7·1		0·9
418	Cucumber, raw	0·2	Tr.	0·5	3	3·7	40	6·5	2·6	0·09	0·03	6·9	2·6	6·9		1·3
419	Egg plant, raw	0·2	Tr.	0·9	4	0·7	68	3·0	2·7	0·11	0·02	3·4		17·3		1·5
420	Endive, raw	0·5	Tr.	0·3	3	2·9	108	12·4	3·0	0·79	0·03	18·9	7·3	20·0		1·7
421	Horseradish, raw	1·3	Tr.	3·1	17	2·2	164	33·8	10·2	0·58	0·04	19·9	60·2	5·3		1·5
422	Leeks, raw	0·5	Tr.	1·7	9	2·5	89	17·8	2·9	0·32	0·03	12·0	—	12·0	—	1·5
423	Leeks, boiled	0·5	Tr.	1·3	7	1·8	79	17·2	3·6	0·57	0·03	7·8	13·9	12·1		1·5
424	Lentils, raw	6·8	Tr.	15·1	84	10·2	192	11·0	21·7	2·17	0·17	69·0	34·8	18·0		0·6

No.	Food														
425	Lentils, boiled	1.9	Tr.	5.2	27	2.7	62	3.0	5.9	0.63	0.08	22.7	10.6	3.6		0.1
426	Lettuce, raw	0.3	Tr.	0.5	3	0.9	59	7.4	2.8	0.21	0.04	8.6	3.4	11.2		1.1
427	Marrow, boiled	0.5†	Tr.	0.4	2	0.3	24	3.9	1.9	0.06	0.01	3.6	1.6	3.9		0.5
428	Mushrooms, raw	0.6†	Tr.	0.0	2	2.6	133	0.8	3.8	0.29	0.18	38.6	9.6	24.0		0.1
429	Mushrooms, fried	0.5	6.4	0.0	62	3.1	161	1.0	4.6	0.36	0.22	47.2	20.9	29.3	0.5	
430	Mustard and cress, raw	0.3	Tr.	0.3	3	5.4	96	18.7	7.8	1.29	0.03	18.6	48.2	25.3	0.7	0.1
431	Onions, raw	0.2	Tr.	1.5	7	2.9	39	8.9	2.2	0.09	0.02	8.5	14.4	5.5		0.1
432	Onions, boiled	0.5	Tr.	0.8	4	1.9	22	6.9	1.4	0.07	0.02	4.7	6.7	1.4		0.5
433	Onions, fried	0.3	9.5	2.9	101	5.7	76	17.4	4.2	0.17	0.05	16.8	24.9	10.8		2.4
434	Onions, spring, raw	1.5	Tr.	2.4	10	3.7	64	38.4	3.1	0.35	0.04	6.7	14.2	10.1		
435	Parsley, raw	0.5	Tr.	Tr.	6	9.4	307	92.2	14.8	2.27	0.15	36.3		44.3		2.1
436	Parsnips, raw	0.4	Tr.	3.2	14	47.0	97	15.6	6.4	0.16	0.03	19.6	4.7	11.5		1.9
437	Parsnips, boiled	1.6	Tr.	3.8	16	1.2	83	10.1	3.7	0.13	0.03	9.0	4.1	9.3		0.3
438	Peas, fresh, raw‡	1.4	Tr.	3.0	18	0.1	97	4.3	8.6	0.53	0.07	29.5	14.2	10.8		
439	Peas, fresh, boiled	6.1	Tr.	2.2	14	Tr.	49	3.6	6.1	0.35	0.04	23.6	12.4	2.2	0.4	2.9
440	Peas, dried, raw	2.0	Tr.	14.2	78	10.8	280	17.2	33.0	1.34	0.14	86.0	36.7	17.0		0.3
441	Peas, dried, boiled	6.3	Tr.	5.4	28	3.6	76	6.9	8.6	0.41	0.05	32.1	11.1	2.6		2.2
442	Peas, split, dried, raw	2.3	Tr.	16.1	86	10.9	258	9.4	35.5	1.54	0.16	76.1	47.1	15.9		
443	Peas, split, dried, boiled	1.7	Tr.	6.2	33	4.0	76	3.1	8.6	0.49	0.07	34.6	13.0	2.9	0.1	2.9
444	Peas, canned	0.6	Tr.	4.7	24	(74)	57	7.3	6.9	0.53	0.06	48.0	12.4	(90)	0.8	
445	Potatoes, old, raw	0.7	Tr.	5.9	25	1.9	161	2.2	6.9	0.21	0.04	11.4	9.8	22.3		1.6
446	Potatoes, old, raw, peel	0.4	Tr.	4.5	20	2.0	184	7.7	7.8	0.57	0.07	10.3		26.9	—	1.4
447	Potatoes, old, boiled	0.4	Tr.	5.6	23	1.0	92	1.2	4.3	0.14	0.03	8.2	6.3	11.6		3.5
448	Potatoes, old, mashed	0.7	1.4	5.1	34	(7)	86	3.3	4.1	0.13	0.03	9.3	6.4	(20)		2.8
449	Potatoes, old, baked in skins	0.6	Tr.	7.1	30	2.2	193	2.6	8.3	0.25	0.05	13.7	11.8	26.8		
449a	Potatoes, old, baked in skins (weighed with skins)		Tr.	5.8	24	1.8	156	2.1	6.7	0.20	0.04	11.1	9.5	21.7		
450	Potatoes, old, roast	0.8	0.3	7.8	35	2.4	211	2.9	9.1	0.28	0.06	15.1	16.0	29.3		3.6
451	Potatoes, old, " chips "	1.1	2.6	10.6	68	3.3	290	3.9	12.3	0.38	0.08	20.6	12.7	39.8		5.6
452	Potatoes, new, boiled	0.5	Tr.	5.2	21	11.5	94	1.4	5.6	0.13	0.04	9.4	6.9	12.9		2.0
453	Potato crisps (Smith's)	1.7	10.2	14.0	159	10	383	10.5	13.5	1.16	0.10	36.0	2.7	76.0	—	
454	Pumpkin, raw	0.2	Tr.	1.0	4	0.4	88	11.1	2.3	0.11	0.02	5.5	10.4	10.4		2.2
455	Radishes, raw	0.3	Tr.	0.8	4	16.8	68	12.4	3.2	0.54	0.04	7.7	10.6	5.3		2.0
456	Salsify, boiled	0.5	Tr.	0.8*	5	2.4	52	17.0	4.0	0.35	0.03	15.0	7.2	13.0		0.8
457	Seakale, boiled	0.4	Tr.	0.2	2	1.1	14	13.6	3.0	0.17	0.02	9.5	14.8	3.5	0.3	

* This vegetable contains inulin.   50 per cent. total carbohydrate taken to be available.   † See p. 4.   ‡ See note p. 96.

Vegetables – continued

No.	Food	g. per oz. Protein (N × 6.25)	g. per oz. Fat	g. per oz. Available carbohydrate (as monosaccharides)	Calories per oz.	mg. per oz. Na	mg. per oz. K	mg. per oz. Ca	mg. per oz. Mg	mg. per oz. Fe	mg. per oz. Cu	mg. per oz. P	mg. per oz. S	mg. per oz. Cl	Acid-base balance, m-equiv. per oz. Acid	Acid-base balance, m-equiv. per oz. Base
458	Spinach, boiled	1·4	Tr.	0·4	7	34·9	139	169·0	16·8	1·14	0·07	26·4	24·6	15·8		11·2
459	Spring greens, boiled	0·5	Tr.	0·3	3	2·9	34	24·4	2·4	0·38	0·02	8·7	8·1	4·6		1·2
460	Swedes, raw	0·3	Tr.	1·2	6	14·8	39	16·0	3·1	0·10	0·01	5·4	11·1	8·7		1·4
461	Swedes, boiled	0·3	Tr.	1·1	5	4·1	29	11·8	2·0	0·08	0·01	5·2	8·7	2·6		0·8
462	Sweet potatoes, boiled	0·3	Tr.	5·7	23	5·1	84	5·8	3·5	0·18	0·04	12·4	4·2	17·0		1·4
463	Tomatoes, raw	0·3	Tr.	0·8	4	0·8	82	3·8	3·1	0·12	0·03	6·1	3·0	14·5		1·6
464	Tomatoes, fried	0·3	1·7	0·9	20	0·9	95	4·4	3·6	0·14	0·03	7·1	2·6	16·8		1·9
465	Turnips, raw	0·2	Tr.	1·1	5	16·5	68	16·7	2·1	0·11	0·02	7·8	6·3	19·9		1·8
466	Turnips, boiled	0·2	Tr.	0·7	3	8·0	45	15·6	1·9	0·10	0·01	5·4	6·0	8·9		1·5
467	Turnip tops, boiled	0·8	Tr.	Tr.	3	1·9	22	27·8	2·9	0·88	0·03	12·8	11·1	4·2		0·6
468	Watercress, raw	0·8	Tr.	0·2	4	17·0	89	63·0	4·8	0·46	0·04	14·8	36·1	44·4		2·1

Sugar, Preserves and Sweetmeats

No.	Food	g. per oz.			Calories per oz.	mg. per oz.									Acid-base balance, m-equiv. per oz.	
		Protein (N × 6·25)	Fat	Available carbohydrate (as monosaccharides)		Na	K	Ca	Mg	Fe	Cu	P	S	C'	Acid	Base
469	Blackcurrant purée	0·1	Tr.	11·4	43	3·1	57	9·7	3·4	0·45	0·04	7·1	9·1	3·7		1·2
470	Boiled sweets	Tr.	Tr.	24·8	93	7·1	2	1·4	0·7	0·12	0·03	3·3	—	19·5	—	—
471	Bounty Bar	1·4	7·4	16·6	137	51·7	90	30·9	12·1	0·38	0·13	39·5	—	114·0	—	—
472	Cherries, glacé	0·2	0·0	15·8	60	18·4	5	12·6	2·3	0·82	0·36	4·1	6·0	20·2		0·5
473	Chocolate, blended	2·6	10·2	14·9	161	(78)	110	72·0	18·8	0·58	0·14	64·0	—	52·0	—	—
474	Chocolate, milk	2·5	10·7	15·5	167	(78)	99	69·9	16·7	0·49	0·14	62·0	—	43·2	—	—
475	Chocolate, plain	1·6	10·0	14·9	155	(41)	73	17·9	37·2	0·82	0·23	39·2	—	14	—	—
476	Chocolates, fancy	1·2	5·3	20·8	133	17·1	69	26·0	14·4	0·50	0·13	34·4	—	50·3	—	—
477	Chutney, apple	0·2	Tr.	14·8	57	(48)	62	7·8	5·1	0·29	0·03	9·6	9·1	(7)		1·3
478	Chutney, tomato	0·3	Tr.	11·0	43	(37)	79	7·4	5·1	0·26	0·03	10·4	8·8	(E1)		1·5
479	Comb honey	0·2	Tr.	21·2	80	2·0	10	2·2	0·6	0·06	0·01	9·2	0·2	·5	0·3	
480	Fruit gums (Rowntrees)	0·3	0·0	12·7	49	18·1	103	102·0	29·8	1·20	0·41	1·2	—	44·3		
481	Honey, in jars	0·1	Tr.	21·7	82	3·1	15	1·5	0·6	0·11	0·01	4·8	0·2	5·1		0·2
482	Ice cream	1·2	3·2	5·6	56	22·5	47	38·9	4·2	0·08	0·08	29·3	—	42·3	—	
483	Jam, fruit with edible seeds	0·2	0·0	19·6	74	4·5	32	6·9	2·9	0·42	0·07	5·1	1·8	2·6		1·1
484	Jam, stone fruit	0·1	0·0	19·7	74	3·5	30	3·4	1·5	0·29	0·03	5·2	0·9	1·0		0·8

* See note p. 101.

Sugar, Preserves and Sweetmeats – *continued*

No.	Food	g. per oz.			Calories per oz.	mg. per oz.									Acid-base balance, m-equiv. per oz.	
		Protein (N × 6.25)	Fat	Available carbohydrate (as monosaccharides)		Na	K	Ca	Mg	Fe	Cu	P	S	Cl	Acid	Base
485	Jelly, packet	1.7*	0.0	17.7	73	7.2	7	8.9	1.3	0.49	0.05	2.0	10.4	8.5	—	<0.1
486	Lemon curd	0.9	3.9	12.0	86	(18)	19	5.2	1.4	0.20	0.01	17.8	13.4	(24)	1.0	—
487	Liquid glucose B.P.	Tr.	0.0	24.1	90	41.5	1	2.4	0.7	0.14	0.03	3.1	—	54.8	—	—
488	Liquorice Allsorts	1.1	0.6	21.0	90	21.3	61	17.9	10.8	2.30	0.11	8.3	0.6	33.2	—	0.8
489	Marmalade	Tr.	0.0	19.8	74	5.2	12	9.9	1.1	0.16	0.03	3.6	—	2.0	—	—
490	Mars Bar	1.5	5.4	18.9	127	41.2	71	46.3	9.9	0.30	0.09	43.7	8.1	83.8	—	3.5
491	Mincemeat	0.2	0.9	7.2	37	(59)	159	14.9	5.9	0.60	0.02	4.5	—	(129)	—	—
492	Pastilles	1.5	0.0	17.6	73	21.9	11	11.2	3.5	0.40	0.09	Tr.	—	33.5	—	—
493	Peppermints	0.1	0.2	29.0	111	2.6	Tr.	2.0	0.9	0.06	0.01	Tr.	—	6.1	—	0.9
494	Sugar, Demerara	0.1	0.0	29.6*	112	1.8	25	4.9	4.2	0.25	0.02	5.7	4.0	10.0	—	<0.1
495	Sugar, white	Tr.	0.0	29.7*	112	0.1	1	0.4	0.1	0.01	0.01	Tr.	Tr.	Tr.	—	<0.1
496	Syrup, golden	0.1	0.0	22.4	84	76.6	69	7.5	2.7	0.41	0.03	5.7	15.3	11.8	—	4.1
497	Toffee, home made	0.1	1.8	25.6	113	(33)	26	3.1	1.1	0.16	0.01	2.8	5.9	(11)	—	1.5
498	Toffees, mixed	0.6	4.9	20.2	123	(90)	58	26.8	7.2	0.43	0.01	18.2	—	(136)	—	—
499	Treacle, black	0.3	0.0	19.1	73	27.2	416	140.5	40.9	2.60	0.12	8.7	19.5	231.0	—	14.0

* See p. 4.

Beverages

No.	Food	g. per oz. Protein	g. per oz. Fat	g. per oz. Available carbohydrate (as monosaccharides)	Calories per oz.	mg. per oz. Na	mg. per oz. K	mg. per oz. Ca	mg. per oz. Mg	mg. per oz. Fe	mg. per oz. Cu	mg. per oz. P	mg. per oz. S	mg. per oz. Cl	Acid-base balance, m-equiv. per oz. Acid	Acid-base balance, m-equiv. per oz. Base
500	Bournvita	3·2	2·1	19·2	105	102·0	188	25·3	43·2	0·94	0·28	116·7	69·0	52·5	—	1·3
501	Bovril	5·1*	0·2	0·0	23	(1290)	454	14·8	48·0	3·44	0·24	369·0	103·0	(1770)	—	14·5
502	Cocoa powder	5·8	6·6	9·9	128	(185)	152	14·6	54·5	4·06	0·97	194·0	45·5	56·5	—	0·2
503	Coffee and chicory essence	0·6	Tr.	16·1	63	18·6	212	8·5	11·1	0·19	0·17	25·4	—	24·1	—	—
504	Coffee, ground, roasted	3·6	4·4	8·1	85	20·8	575	37·8	66·8	1·16	0·23	45·7	31·3	6·7	—	18·0
505	Coffee, infusion, 2 min.	0·1	Tr.	0·1	1	Tr.	19	0·6	1·6	Tr.	Tr.	0·4	—	Tr.	—	—
506	Coffee, infusion, 5 min.	0·1	Tr.	0·1	1	Tr.	25	1·0	2·4	Tr.	Tr.	0·8	—	Tr.	—	—
507	Coffee, infusion, 10 min.	0·1	Tr.	0·1	1	Tr.	30	1·1	3·0	Tr.	Tr.	1·2	—	Tr.	—	—
508	Coffee, infusion, 20 min.	0·1	Tr.	0·1	1	Tr.	31	1·1	3·1	Tr.	Tr.	1·4	—	Tr	—	—
509	Grapefruit squash	Tr.	Tr.	10·3	39	18·9	19	2·2	0·9	0·04	Tr.	7·0	—	26·8	—	7·8
510	Horlick's malted milk	4·1	2·3	20·1	113	196·0	321	77·2	20·0	0·37	0·35	114·0	47·5	16·0	—	—
511	Lemonade	Tr.	0·0	1·6	6	2·1	4	1·5	Tr.	Tr.	Tr.	0·3	Tr.	Tr.	—	—
512	Lemonade, home-made	Tr.	Tr.	3·5	13	Tr.	19	0·2	0·2	Tr.	Tr.	1·8	Tr.	Tr.	—	0·1
513	Lemon squash	Tr.	Tr.	9·6	36	15·4	19	2·1	0·8	0·03	0·02	1·2	—	21·8	—	—
514	Lime Juice Cordial	0·0	0·0	8·5	32	2·2	14	2·6	1·1	0·08	0·03	0·9	—	1·1	—	—
515	Lucozade	0·0	0·0	5·1	19	9·5	Tr.	1·9	0·5	0·03	0·01		—	11·1	—	—
516	Marmite	0·4*	Tr.	0·0	2	(1318)	891	34·9	53·1	1·96	0·28	540·0	—	(2120)	—	—
517	Nescafé	3·4*	0·0	3·1	25	9·8	1550	42·3	116·0	1·42	0·03	124·0	—	15·1	—	—
518	Orange squash	0·1	Tr.	10·2	39	21·6		2·4	1·1	0·03	Tr.	2·6	—	31·2	—	—
519	Ovaltine	3·8	1·8	20·6	109	47·4	243	38·1	42·0	0·79	0·33	114·0	—	54·0	—	—
520	Oxo cubes	2·7*	1·0	3·4	33	(2922)	207	51·1	166·0	6·96	0·21	103·0	—	(4550)	—	—
521	Pineapple juice	0·1	Tr.	3·8	15	0·3	38	3·5	3·3	0·21	0·03	2·8	—	0·8	—	—
522	Ribena	0·1	0·0	17·3	65	4·8	40	4·1	1·9	0·14	Tr.	3·9	—	4·9	—	—
523	Tea, Indian	4·4	0·0	0·0	17	12·6	612	121·0	72·0	4·32	0·45	178·0	50·2	14·7	—	13·2
524	Tea, Indian, infusion	Tr.	0·0	0·0	<1	Tr.	5	0·1	0·3	0·3	Tr.	0·3	—	Tr.	—	—
525	Virol	1·3	3·4	16·9	99	(106)	102	30·6	17·4	7·66	0·13	75·5	23·5	(169)	0·9	—

* See pp. 4 and 105.

Alcoholic Beverages

No.	Food	Alcohol	Protein (N × 6·25)	Fat	Available carbohydrate (as monosaccharides)	Calories per oz.	Na	K	Ca	Mg	Fe	Cu	P	S	Cl	Acid	Base
	Beers																
526	Brown Ale, bottled	0·64	0·07	Tr.	0·84	8	4·7	9·5	1·9	1·7	0·01	0·02	3·2	—	10·4	—	—
527	Draught Ale, bitter	0·87	0·07	Tr.	0·64	9	3·4	10·9	3·1	2·5	Tr.	0·02	3·8	—	9·2	—	—
528	Draught Ale, mild	0·74	0·05	Tr.	0·46	7	3·2	9·3	3·0	2·4	Tr.	0·01	3·3	—	9·5	—	—
529	Pale Ale, bottled..	0·95	0·09	Tr.	0·56	9	2·9	13·8	2·7	2·8	Tr.	0·01	4·2	—	8·7	—	—
530	Stout, bottled ..	0·81	0·09	Tr.	1·19	10	6·6	12·6	2·4	2·2	0·01	0·02	4·9	—	13·6	—	—
531	Stout, extra ..	1·21	0·09	Tr.	0·59	11	1·2	24·2	1·4	2·7	Tr.	Tr.	7·8	—	6·9	—	—
532	Strong Ale ..	1·88	0·20	Tr.	1·74	21	4·2	31·6	3·8	5·5	0·01	0·02	11·4	—	16·1	—	—
	Ciders																
533	Cider, dry ..	1·07	Tr.	—	0·75	10	1·9	20·4	2·3	1·0	0·14	0·01	0·09	—	1·8	—	—
534	Cider, sweet ..	1·05	Tr.	—	1·21	12	1·9	20·4	2·3	1·0	0·14	0·01	0·09	—	1·8	—	—
535	Cider, vintage ..	2·97	Tr.	—	2·07	28	0·7	27·6	1·3	1·1	0·09	Tr.	2·6	—	1·4	—	—
	Wines, heavy																
536	Port, ruby ..	4·44	—	—	3·24	43	1·1	28·0	1·3	2·9	0·08	0·03	3·0	—	2·3	—	—
537	Port, tawny ..	4·58	—	—	3·55	45	1·0	27·4	1·1	3·3	0·14	0·03	3·5	—	2·3	—	—
538	Sherry, dry ..	4·46	—	—	0·39	33	2·9	63·6	2·0	3·7	0·11	0·01	3·2	—	3·4	—	—
539	Sherry, sweet ..	4·44	—	—	1·95	38	3·6	47·5	1·9	3·0	1·1	0·03	2·7	—	3·9	—	—
	Table wines, white																
540	Champagne ..	2·80	—	—	0·40	21	1·1	16·2	1·0	1·8	0·14	Tr.	2·0	—	2·0	—	—
541	Graves ..	2·52	—	—	0·95	21	5·9	24·9	4·0	2·5	0·34	Tr.	2·2	—	1·2	—	—
542	Sauternes ..	2·88	—	—	1·67	26	3·8	31·2	4·0	3·1	0·16	0·01	3·6	—	1·9	—	—

g. per oz. (Alcohol, Protein, Fat, Available carbohydrate); *mg. per oz.* (Na–Cl); *Acid-base balance, m-equiv. per oz.* (Acid, Base)

No.	Food	Alcohol	Protein	Fat	Carbohydrate	Calories per oz.	Na	K	Ca	Mg	Fe	Cu	P	S	Cl	Acid	Base
	Table wines, red																
543	Australian Burgundy	2·87	—	—	0·11	20	4·2	50·0	1·6	3·8	0·18	0·03	5·9	—	9·2	—	—
544	Beaujolais	2·68	—	—	0·07	19	2·4	31·5	2·1	3·0	0·21	0·07	2·4	—	4·0	—	—
545	Chianti	2·59	—	—	0·05	18	11·9	19·7	0·9	0·6	0·08	0·02	2·1	—	3·6	—	—
546	Medoc	2·52	—	—	0·08	18	1·9	30·4	2·0	2·6	0·37	Tr.	3·7	—	2·4	—	—
	Spirits																
547	70% proof	8·91	—	—	Tr.	63	Tr.	Tr.	Tr.	Tr.	Tr.	Tr.	Tr.	—	Tr.	—	—

Condiments

No.	Food	Protein. (N × 6.25)	Fat	Available carbohydrate (as monosaccharides)	Calories per oz.	Na	K	Ca	Mg	Fe	Cu	P	S	Cl	Acid	Base
		g. per oz.				*mg. per oz.*									*Acid-base balance, m-equiv. per oz.*	
548	Curry powder	2·7	3·1	7·4	67	128	520	181	81	21·30	0·30	77	24	134		24·4
549	Ground ginger	2·1	0·9*	17·0	74	10	258	28	38	4·90	0·13	39	41	1		6·1
550	Mustard	8·2	8·1	5·9	132	1	268	95	73	3·10	0·06	50	364	8	8·8	
551	Pepper	2·5	1·8*	19·3	88	2	12	36	13	2·90	0·32	37	28	17		8·2
552	Salt, block	0·0	0·0	0·0	0	11,000	Tr.	65	10	0·07	0·11	Tr.	114	6,900	3·0	
553	Table salt, "Cerebos"	0·0	0·0	0·0	0	11,000	Tr.	16	88	0·06	0·03	4	7	17,000		8·3
554	Table salt, "Saxa"	0·0	0·0	0·0	0	11,000	Tr.	Tr.	74	0·04	0·03	Tr.	6	17,000		6·0
555	Vinegar	0·1	0·0	0·2	1	6	25	4	6	0·13	0·01	9	5	13		0·3

* See note p. 113.

Cakes and Pastries

No.	Food	Protein (g. per oz.)	Fat (g. per oz.)	Available carbohydrate (as monosaccharides) (g. per oz.)	Calories per oz.	Na (mg. per oz.)	K	Ca	Mg	Fe	Cu	P	S	Cl	Acid (m-equiv. per oz.)	Base
556	Baking powder	1·5	Tr.	10·7	47	3,350	14	3,200	2·5	Tr.	Tr.	2390	—	8·2	—	—
557	Cherry cake	1·3	6·8	16·1	129	(62)	20	(42)	2·8	(0·35)	0·09	(40)	18·0	(46)	<0·1	0·5
558	Chocolate cakes	2·3	7·2	17·3	141	(95)	40	(62)	6·7	(0·64)	0·09	(74)	29·0	(54)	—	2·2
559	Coconut cakes	2·0	7·0	14·2	126	(84)	55	(80)	6·9	(0·40)	0·04	(72)	23·0	(45)	—	0·7
560	Currant buns	2·1	2·2	15·4	87	(29)	52	(26)	6·3	(0·71)	0·02	18·4	20·8	(55)	—	1·6
561	Currant cake	1·7	5·1	17·1	119	(62)	54	(55)	4·4	(0·37)	0·04	(48)	23·0	(40)	—	0·6
562	Doughnuts	1·7	4·5	13·8	101	(17)	32	(19)	4·7	(0·55)	0·03	15·6	16·0	(25)	—	2·1
563	Dundee cake	1·1	4·3	17·7	110	(40)	96	(22)	7·8	(0·62)	0·05	22·3	15·6	(51)	—	—
564	Easter biscuits	1·8	5·9	19·3	134	(69)	39	(41)	4·3	(0·33)	0·03	(35)	—	(77)	—	—
565	Eccles cakes	2·2	8·9	14·5	147	(71)	49	(20)	5·0	(0·25)	0·05	17·0	28·0	(116)	—	2·5
566	Ginger biscuits	1·7	4·7	20·2	127	(94)	40	(20)	4·3	(0·36)	0·02	21·6	23·1	(40)	0·4	3·1
567	Gingerbread	1·6	3·7	18·0	108	(97)	45	(22)	4·4	(0·36)	0·02	23·0	22·2	(36)	—	—
568	Imperial biscuits	1·7	5·3	9·7	133	(52)	22	(27)	3·2	(0·32)	0·03	(31)	—	(47)	—	—
569	Jam tarts	1·1	4·4	17·8	112	(49)	25	(11)	2·8	(0·31)	0·03	11·8	12·0	(78)	0·2	—
570	Lemon curd tarts	1·6	7·1	14·1	125	(65)	20	(14)	3·1	(0·27)	0·02	18·8	19·0	(106)	1·1	—
571	Mince pies	1·4	6·3	12·5	111	(85)	72	(18)	4·9	(0·42)	0·03	15·4	19·0	(154)	—	0·2
572	Orange cake, plain	1·8	7·3	15·2	132	(67)	19	(47)	2·6	(0·31)	0·16	(48)	23·4	(53)	0·1	—
573	Orange cake, iced	1·2	6·6	17·9	133	(50)	13	(32)	1·8	(0·22)	0·01	(33)	—	(42)	—	—
574	Pastry, flaky, raw	1·4	8·9	12·9	125	(70)	17	(15)	2·7	(0·16)	0·03	14·5	16·3	(115)	0·8	—
575	Pastry, flaky, baked	1·9	11·9	13·3	167	(93)	22	(20)	3·6	(0·22)	0·03	19·5	22·6	(154)	1·0	—
576	Pastry, short, raw	1·9	8·1	15·6	132	(79)	17	(19)	3·8	(0·27)	0·02	16·7	21·4	(144)	1·3	—
577	Pastry, short, baked	2·2	9·5	15·4	157	(93)	20	(22)	4·4	(0·32)	0·03	19·7	35·6	(169)	1·6	—
578	Plain fruit cake	1·7	4·6	15·3	107	(102)	57	(83)	4·4	(0·34)	0·03	(70)	24·4	(55)	—	0·7
579	Queen cakes	1·8	6·4	16·6	129	(65)	42	(51)	3·7	(0·37)	0·03	(49)	—	(48)	—	—

No.	Food	Protein (g.)	Fat (g.)	Available carbohydrate (as monosaccharides) (g.)	Calories per oz.	Na	K	Ca	Mg	Fe	Cu	P	S	Cl	Acid	Base
580	Rock cakes	1·7	4·5	18·6	119	(93)	68	(94)	5·7	(0·31)	0·04	(74)	21·0	(38)		3·8
581	Scones	2·2	3·7	16·3	105	(167)	46	(181)	6·1	(0·19)	0·02	(136)	24·2	(42)		6·6
582	Shortbread	1·7	7·7	18·4	148	24	26	(23)	4·3	(0·18)	0·02	19·6	19·5	(40)		
583	Sponge cake	2·5	2·0	15·6	87	23	33	(19)	3·9	(0·46)	0·01	41·2	34·9	29		
584	Victoria sandwich	1·6	7·2	16·3	134	(72)	21	(38)	2·6	(0·33)	0·02	(41)	—	(74)	0·4	—
585	Welsh cheese cakes	1·9	7·2	17·1	139	(53)	17	(50)	3·2	(0·33)	0·03	(35)	23·4	(50)	2·6	0·5

Puddings

No.	Food	Protein (g.)	Fat (g.)	Available carbohydrate (as monosaccharides) (g.)	Calories per oz.	Na	K	Ca	Mg	Fe	Cu	P	S	Cl	Acid	Base
586	Apple dumpling	0·6	3·6	8·1	57	(11)	31	(2)	1·9	(0·12)	0·03	9·3	7·3	(20)	0·1	0·9
587	Apple pudding	0·7	3·1	7·5	68	(23)	22	(28)	1·4	(0·13)	0·02	(23)	8·6	5		0·1
588	Apple pie	0·5	2·1	8·5	54	(23)	26	(5)	1·1	(0·12)	0·03	7·1	6·1	(39)		1·2
589	Banana custard	0·7	0·7	5·2	29	9	64	23·9	6·7	0·07	0·02	21·3	6·9	26		0·7
590	Blancmange	0·9	1·1	5·3	34	13	44	33·1	3·8	0·05	0·01	26·8	8·0	28		0·1
591	Bread and butter pudding	1·6	2·3	4·9	46	(32)	56	(34)	4·9	(0·18)	0·02	35·4	16·4	(54)		1·2
592	Canary pudding	1·8	6·9	15·8	131	(81)	26	(70)	3·5	(0·27)	0·01	(65)	22·8	(40)		
593	Castle pudding	1·7	5·9	13·4	112	(49)	21	(36)	2·6	(0·29)	0·01	(38)	22·2	(46)	0·4	0·7
594	Chocolate mould	0·9	1·1	5·8	35	16	44	31·2	4·3	0·09	0·03	27·3	7·7	27		
595	Custard, egg, baked	1·5	1·7	2·8	32	19	50	36·1	3·9	0·14	0·01	37·1	16·6	35	0·2	
596	Custard, egg, sauce	1·3	1·5	3·8	34	17	44	32·1	4·0	0·13	0·01	33·0	14·7	31	0·2	
597	Custard, powder, boiled	0·9	1·1	5·0	33	13	46	34·7	3·7	0·04	0·01	27·9	8·4	28		0·7
598	Custard tart	1·6	4·7	8·8	82	(17)	34	(39)	2·1	(0·20)	0·02	25·9	18·3	(32)		0·2
599	Dumpling	0·9	3·2	6·8	59	(139)	13	(2)	2·2	(0·09)	0·01	(9)	10·5	(177)		0·4
600	Gooseberry pie	0·7	2·1	7·6	51	(23)	41	(10)		(0·13)	0·03	7·2	8·4	(39)		0·7

g. per oz.: Protein, Fat, Available carbohydrate. mg. per oz.: Na, K, Ca, Mg, Fe, Cu, P, S, Cl. Acid-base balance, m-equiv. per oz.: Acid, Base.

Puddings – continued

No.	Food	g. per oz.			Calories per oz.	mg. per oz.									Acid-base balance, m-equiv. per oz.	
		Protein	Fat	Available carbohydrate (as monosaccharides)		Na	K	Ca	Mg	Fe	Cu	P	S	Cl	Acid	Base
601	Jam omelette	2·7	4·1	7·7	78	(34)	39	13·9	3·3	0·54	0·02	50·0	39·0	(41)	3·4	0·1
602	Jam roll, baked	1·3	5·4	15·7	115	(49)	27	(4)	3·5	(0·20)	0·03	14·6	14·4	(39)		0·1
603	Jelly	0·6*	0·0	5·4	23	2	2	2·7	0·4	0·15	0·02	0·7	3·2	3		<0·1
604	Jelly, milk	1·0*	0·5	5·9	31	9	25	19·7	2·4	0·16	0·02	14·1	7·2	16		0·4
605	Leicester pudding	1·3	4·6	14·3	102	(62)	21	(40)	2·9	(0·26)	0·02	(38)	—	(56)	—	—
606	Mixed fruit pudding	1·4	4·1	12·9	92	(95)	51	(76)	4·0	(0·27)	0·03	(61)	—	(56)	—	—
607	Pancakes	1·4	4·3	10·6	85	(25)	37	(21)	4·0	(0·15)	0·01	26·4	15·9	(43)	0·5	
608	Plum pie	0·6	2·1	7·9	52	(23)	38	(7)	2·3	(0·12)	0·02	6·9	7·1	(4)		0·5
609	Queen of puddings	1·3	2·3	9·0	60	(41)	38	(23)	3·7	(0·24)	0·02	25·2	15·0	(59)		Tr.
610	Rhubarb pie	0·6	2·1	8·3	53	(23)	78	(22)	3·3	(0·14)	0·03	8·1	7·0	(53)		2·0
611	Rice pudding	1·0	2·2	4·5	42	(17)	46	32·9	4·1	0·03	0·01	30·9	9·7	(32)		0·5
612	Sago pudding	0·9	1·1	5·9	36	14	43	32·8	3·9	0·05	0·01	25·9	7·8	27		0·8
613	Semolina pudding	1·2	1·1	5·7	37	14	49	34·0	4·8	0·06	0·01	29·7	107·0	29		0·5
614	Suet pudding	1·4	5·6	12·6	105	(82)	27	(58)	3·7	(0·24)	0·02	(46)	—	(75)	—	—
615	Suet pudding, with raisins	1·3	4·8	13·4	100	(71)	61	(51)	5·0	(0·27)	0·03	(40)	—	(61)	—	—
616	Swiss apple pudding	0·6	2·2	10·9	63	(32)	36	(7)	2·7	(0·22)	0·03	9·4	5·2	(54)	0·2	
617	Syrup sponge pudding	1·3	4·4	15·6	104	(75)	31	(39)	3·1	(0·29)	0·02	(36)	—	(56)	—	—
618	Tapioca pudding	0·9	1·1	6·1	37	14	44	32·9	3·3	0·28	0·01	27·0	8·1	27		0·7
619	Treacle tart	1·0	3·8	17·8	107	(73)	45	(5)	3·9	(0·29)	0·01	13·1	17·8	(68)		1·0
620	Trifle	0·9	1·6	6·4	43	10	38	(22)	4·1	(0·24)	0·02	21·3	11·2	19		0·3
621	Yorkshire pudding	2·0	2·7	7·7	63	(117)	49	(29)	5·2	(0·19)	0·02	36·4	21·1	(188)	0·8	

* See p. 4.

Meat and Fish Dishes

No.	Food	g. per 100 g. Protein	g. per 100 g. Fat	g. per 100 g. Available Carbohydrate (as glucose)	Calories per oz.	Na	K	Ca	Mg	Fe	Cu	P	S	Cl	Acid	Base
622	Beef steak pudding	3·2	4·5	5·2	74	(138)	49	(30)	5·1	(0·64)	—	(57)	33·4	(178)	1·6	
623	Beef stew	3·0	2·5	1·1	40	(141)	65	5·0	5·5	0·69	0·01	44·0	33·7	(211)	2·4	
624	Curried meat	2·3	3·2	2·5	48	(84)	72	9·3	5·8	1·39	—	28·7	27·9	(124)	0·7	
625	Fish cakes	3·5	4·0	2·8	61	(119)	85	5·6	5·2	0·22	0·04	48·1	41·0	(185)	2·6	
626	Hot pot	2·8	1·3	3·2	35	(164)	132	6·2	7·1	0·66	—	42·2	33·2	(253)	0·5	⟨0·1
627	Irish stew	1·1	3·1	2·2	42	(101)	63	2·9	3·4	0·26	—	16·2	14·2	(159)		
628	Kedgeree	3·4	2·0	2·8	43	(312)	46	6·0	6·8	0·29	—	47·8	44·8	(459)	3·3	
629	Sausage roll, flaky pastry	2·1	10·2	10·1	142	(115)	32	(4)	3·8	(0·37)	0·02	22·6	20·3	(173)	1·3	
630	Sausage roll, short pastry	2·3	8·8	11·4	134	(128)	36	(4)	4·3	(0·41)	0·02	25·4	22·5	(189)	1·3	
631	Shepherd's pie	2·8	1·2	2·7	32	(100)	55	3·2	4·6	0·49	—	24·5	31·5	(158)	1·5	
632	Steak and kidney pie	4·4	5·4	4·8	86	(134)	69	(3)	5·9	(1·58)	—	60·5	44·4	(201)	4·0	
633	Toad-in-the-hole	2·2	5·8	5·3	82	(199)	46	(19)	4·5	(0·40)	0·02	35·5	22·8	(297)	0·9	

mg. per oz. — Acid-base balance, m-equiv. per oz.

Egg and Cheese Dishes

No.	Food	g. per oz.			Calories per oz.	mg. per oz.									Acid-base balance, m-equiv. per oz.	
		Protein	Fat	Available carbohydrate (as monosaccharides)		Na	K	Ca	Mg	Fe	Cu	P	S	Cl	Acid	Base
634	Buck rarebit	3·9	5·1	4·8	81	(192)	35	(78)	7·9	(0·42)	0·02	75·5	38·4	(450)	6·1	
635	Cheese omelette	5·0	8·8	Tr.	102	(402)	42	89·9	7·3	0·63	0·02	101·0	60·7	(620)	4·0	
636	Cheese straws	4·7	13·5	7·3	172	(234)	32	(116)	8·9	(0·27)	0·02	93·0	44·9	(376)	2·0	
637	Cheese pudding	3·2	3·2	3·5	54	(129)	47	69·3	7·2	0·28	0·02	59·4	—	(210)	—	
638	Macaroni cheese	2·2	3·6	4·3	59	(110)	39	56·6	7·3	0·10	0·01	45·9	19·7	(195)	—	<0·1
639	Omelette	2·9	4·8	Tr.	57	(280)	34	14·2	5·0	0·62	0·01	53·7	42·0	(423)	3·8	
640	Scotch egg	3·1	5·5	2·9	75	(153)	47	10·1	4·0	0·77	0·02	47·2	35·8	(210)	2·5	
641	Scrambled egg	2·9	7·1	0·2	79	(246)	38	17·4	3·4	0·59	0·01	54·0	41·0	(370)	3·6	
642	Welsh rarebit	4·1	6·1	7·5	102	(281)	35	(113)	10·5	(0·29)	0·02	79·5	35·5	(456)	0·6	

Sauces and Soups

No.	Food	Protein (g. per oz.)	Fat (g. per oz.)	Available carbohydrate (as monosaccharides) (g. per oz.)	Calories per oz.	Na (mg./oz.)	K	Ca	Mg	Fe	Cu	P	S	Cl	Acid (m-equiv./oz.)	Base
643	Bone and vegetable broth..	1·1	1·3	0·3	18	(21)	18	4·8	0·9	0·08	0·01	2·8	—	(21)	—	—
644	Bone and vegetable broth (Bickiepegs)	1·3	—	0·1	—	14	12	2·9	1·1	0·08	0·01	2·0	—	76	—	0·6
645	Bread sauce	1·1	1·4	3·6	32	(92)	44	(30)	4·4	(0·06)	0·01	26·1	9·5	(145)	—	—
646	Brown sauce, bottled	0·3	Tr.	7·2	28	(278)	112	12·3	8·3	0·88	0·09	10·2	—	(438)	—	—
647	Brown sauce	0·8	2·2	2·5	33	(167)	39	5·7	13·8	0·26	0·04	6·3	—	(258)	—	—
648	Cheese sauce	1·9	3·7	2·5	52	(155)	45	57·6	5·5	0·06	0·01	42·5	17·2	(248)	0·1	—
649	Chicken Noodle Soup Mix (Batchelor's)	3·7	1·7	16·7	95	(1599)	45	9·9	11·5	0·81	0·05	46·9	—	(2249)	—	—
650	Egg sauce	1·4	2·9	2·4	42	(133)	45	29·9	4·1	0·14	0·01	32·3	15·6	(209)	—	0·4
651	Lentil soup	1·5	1·4	2·6	29	(116)	68	11·1	3·7	0·03	0·03	18·2	—	(188)	—	—
652	Onion sauce	0·7	1·6	2·0	25	(86)	36	21·7	3·1	0·06	0·02	17·9	7·9	(137)	—	0·6
653	Potato soup	0·6	1·2	3·1	26	(94)	27	13·1	4·5	0·11	0·02	14·8	8·4	(155)	<0·1	—
654	Salad Cream (Heinz)	0·9	10·2	2·9	111	(238)	22	9·7	5·9	0·23	0·02	25·6	—	(369)	—	—
655	Soup, mixed	0·6	0·4	1·2	11	(62)	38	9·6	2·0	0·40	Tr.	11·4	—	(110)	—	—
656	Spaghetti, canned in tomato sauce (Heinz)	0·5	0·2	3·5	17	(142)	36	6·1	3·2	0·21	0·04	8·4	—	(227)	—	—
657	Thick Pea Soup Mix (Batchelor's)	5·1	2·0	17·3	106	(678)	173	21·5	17·1	1·31	0·16	97·1	—	(930)	—	—
658	Tomato Ketchup	0·6	Tr.	6·8	28	(316)	168	7·2	5·3	0·30	0·11	12·2	—	(514)	—	—
659	Tomato sauce	0·7	1·1	2·1	21	(109)	131	10·7	3·5	0·02	0·02	12·2	—	(180)	—	—
660	Tomato soup, canned (Heinz)	0·2	0·9	2·6	19	(137)	59	5·2	1·6	0·09	0·03	6·5	—	(225)	—	—
661	Vegetable soup, canned (Heinz)	0·5	0·1	2·3	12	(142)	54	5·8	3·4	0·12	0·04	11·7	—	(220)	—	—
662	White sauce, savoury	1·1	2·8	2·8	41	(148)	46	32·2	4·2	0·04	0·01	27·3	10·1	(236)	—	0·6
663	White sauce, sweet	1·0	2·5	5·2	47	18	42	29·5	3·8	0·04	0·01	25·0	9·3	34	—	0·5

M

Phytic Acid Phosphorus in Foods

	Phytic acid phosphorus as per cent. of total phosphorus
Cereals and cereal foods—	
All-Bran, Kellogg's ..	76
Barley, pearl	66
Biscuits, digestive ..	61
Bread, brown (92%) ..	55
„ "National wheat-meal" (85%)	30
„ white	15
„ Hovis	38
Cornflakes	25
Flour, English or Manitoba, 100% extraction	70
„ 85% „	55
„ 80% „	47
„ white ..	30
Oatmeal, raw	70
Rice, polished	61
Rye, 100% extraction	72
„ 85% „	54
„ 75% „	44
„ 60% „	31
Ryvita	54
Sago	Tr.
Shredded Wheat ..	80
Soya. Full fat or low fat flour or grits ..	31
Tapioca	0
Vita-Weat	59
Fruit—	
Apples	0
Bananas	0
Blackberries	16
Figs, dried	13
Prunes, dried	0

	Phytic acid phosphorus as per cent. of total phosphorus
Nuts—	
Almonds	82
Barcelona nuts ..	83
Brazil nuts	86
Chestnuts	18
Cob nuts	74
Coconuts	81
Peanuts	57
Walnuts.	42
Vegetables—	
Artichokes, Jerusalem, boiled	25
Beans, broad, boiled ..	5
„ butter, raw ..	84
„ haricot, raw ..	73
Carrots, raw	16
Cauliflower, boiled ..	0
Celery, raw	0
Lentils, raw	51
Mushrooms, raw ..	0
Onions, raw	0
Parsnips, raw	31
Peas, fresh, raw ..	11
„ dried, raw ..	80
„ split, raw ..	57
„ canned	17
Potatoes, old, boiled ..	19
„ new, boiled	23
Spinach, boiled ..	0
Swedes, raw	0
Turnips, raw	0
Cocoa and chocolate—	
Chocolate, milk ..	18
Cocoa	15

Note on the Calculation of the Calorific Value of Foods and of Diets

E. M. WIDDOWSON

The energy value of a food is measured in Calories, which are physical units of heat. The number of Calories the body can derive from a food is, however, less than the number of Calories produced when the food is burned in a calorimeter because the calorie-producing nutrients, which are mainly protein, fat and carbohydrate, are not completely digested; the products of digestion, moreover, are not completely absorbed in the human gut, and the portion of the protein which is digested and absorbed is not completely oxidized to yield energy in the body.

The calorific value of a food is usually calculated from the amounts of protein, fat and carbohydrate it contains: these amounts are determined by chemical methods and the values are then multiplied by factors representing the number of Calories thought to be produced in the body by 1 gram of protein, fat or carbohydrate. The sum of these products gives the calorific value of the food. These "calorie conversion factors" do not represent the number of Calories which 1 gram of protein, fat, or carbohydrate would produce in a calorimeter. They are arrived at by applying to the values found by physical calorimetry various corrections allowing for losses occurring in digestion and absorption, and through incomplete oxidation. Since no two foods and no two people are ever exactly alike, and since these physiological corrections are based on averages the calorie conversion factors do not have the same accuracy as the values for Calories arrived at by physical calorimetry, or the values for protein, fat and carbohydrate found by chemical determination. Furthermore, different corrections are applied in different countries; and even within one country the method used may vary from one set of tables to another, and individual workers may use different methods from time to time. The problem is a complicated one, and there is no clear-cut answer to it.

The difference between the number of Calories which a diet would provide were the protein, fat and carbohydrate in it completely digested, and the number of Calories which it does in fact provide, is mainly due to the so-called "unavailable carbohydrates" which are contained in plant foods. These are made up of hemicelluloses and fibre, and the digestive tract of man secretes no enzymes capable of digesting them, though micro-organisms in the gut may break down some of them and convert them to lower fatty acids, part of which may be absorbed and become a minor source of energy (McCance and Lawrence, 1929). In sheep and cattle, however, the large rumen provides space in which bacteria and protozoa can break down the hemicelluloses present in grasses and these contribute considerably to the nutrition of the animal. Although complex carbohydrates may, therefore, contribute a few Calories to man, their chief importance to the calorific value of a diet is a negative one. Fibre reduces the calorific value of a food or diet by hastening transport through the gut, and increasing the weight of the stools and the amount of nitrogen and fat in them. The more fibre a food or diet contains, the more nitrogen and fat will be excreted in the faeces and the less energy will therefore be derived from the protein and fat of the food or diet (McCance and Widdowson, 1947; McCance and Walsham 1948; McCance and Glaser, 1948).

HISTORY OF CALORIE CONVERSION FACTORS

Most of the fundamental work on the calorific value of foods was carried out by Rubner and by Atwater and his colleagues more than 50 years ago. Rubner worked in Germany and Atwater in America during the last 20–25 years of the 19th century and the first part of the present one. In his early days, Atwater spent some time in Germany as Rubner's pupil, and it was undoubtedly this experience that inspired his later work. Rubner's most important papers for the present purpose were published in 1885 and 1901. He measured the heats of combustion of a number of different proteins, fats and carbohydrates in a bomb calorimeter, and also studied the heat of combuston of urine passed by a dog, a man, a boy and a baby. He realised that the heat of combustion of protein in the bomb calorimeter was greater than its calorific value to the body because the body oxidises protein only to urea, creatinine, uric acid and other nitrogenous end-products which are themselves capable of further oxidation. Rubner also analysed the faeces of the man who acted as his experimental subject and he found that the loss of energy in the nitrogenous substances in the urine and faeces were $16 \cdot 3$ and $6 \cdot 9$ per cent. of the intake respectively, making a total loss of about 23 per cent. He deducted 23 per cent. from the heats of combustion of animal and vegetable protein and arrived at a figure of $4 \cdot 1$ Calories per gram of mixed protein. Rubner made no allowances for losses in digestion and absorption of fat and carbohydrate, and his factors ($9 \cdot 3$ Calories per gram of fat and $4 \cdot 1$ Calories per gram of carbohydrate) represent the average heats of combustion of a variety of fats and carbohydrates.

Atwater, working over 50 years ago, contributed more to our knowledge about the energy value of foods than any one else before or since his time. The heats of combustion of different proteins, fats and carbohydrates were measured in a bomb calorimeter (Atwater and Bryant, 1900). These authors also analysed the urine from forty-six persons and measured its heat of combustion. They found that for every gram of nitrogen in the urine there was unoxidized material sufficient to yield an average of $7 \cdot 9$ Calories. This is equivalent to $1 \cdot 25$ Calories per gram of protein in the food, if the person is in nitrogen equilibrium.

Atwater (1902) also made extensive studies of the "availability" of nutrients, and he was careful to distinguish between what he called "available" and "digestible". He regarded the faeces as being made up of two parts, the undigested and therefore unabsorbed food residues, and the "metabolic products" of digestion, consisting of desquamated cells, bacteria and nitrogenous substances in the digestive juices. By "digestible" nitrogen he meant the nitrogen in the food minus the nitrogen in the undigested, unabsorbed food residues, and this he could not measure. By "available" nitrogen he meant the nitrogen in the food minus the nitrogen in the food residues together with the metabolic products of digestion, that is, the nitrogen in the food minus the nitrogen in the faeces.

Three men, aged 32, 29 and 22 years, served as subjects for Atwater's studies on "availability". Atwater made a total of fifty experiments on these men, each lasting for 3–8 days. The subjects ate what were described as mixed diets, which varied in the amount of fat and carbohydrate they contained, but none of the diets contained much roughage, i.e. unavailable carbohydrate. The foods were analysed for nitrogen and fat, and the faeces were analysed also.

Atwater and Bryant (1900) collected what they could find in the literature, including the results of their own work (Atwater and Benedict, 1897), on the "availability" to man of single foods. From these data they prepared tentative coefficients for the "availability" of the protein, fat and carbohydrate in the common classes of food, and they applied these coefficients to the mixed diets that their own subjects had eaten. They then compared the calculated "availability" of the protein, fat and carbohydrate of the mixed diets with the "availability" of these nutrients in the diets as found by experiment. They did the same with the results of sixty-one other experiments in which, apparently, ten men served as subjects, though no detailed description of these experiments was published. They found the "coefficients of availability" of the protein, fat and carbohydrate in the mixed diets as determined by experiment to agree very well with the values as calculated by the proposed factors for availability of the protein, fat and carbohydrate in separate classes of foods.

For the calculation of the 'available energy" from mixed diets Atwater and Bryant (1900) suggested the use of the average factors 4·0, 8·9 and 4·0 for protein, fat and carbohydrate respectively. The figure 8·9 was later rounded off to 9·0 (Atwater 1910). These factors, which Atwater had intended should be used only for calculating the Calories to be obtained from the protein, fat and carbohydrate in mixed diets, came to be widely used for calculating the available energy value of individual foods (Sherman 1911, 1952; Chatfield and Adams 1940; Platt 1945).

In 1936, Morey published a paper in which she reviewed the work done by Rubner and Atwater at the turn of the century, and showed how the calorie conversion factors suggested by these two pioneers had been derived. It was Maynard (1944), however, who really opened up the whole subject again, and he was the first to draw attention to Atwater's original intention that the calorie conversion factors for protein, fat and carbohydrate should not be the same for all foods. Osmond (1948) was the first to adopt Maynard's suggestions as to the correct use of Atwater's factors in his tables of composition of Australian foods. Shortly after Maynard's paper was published, the Nutrition Division of the Food and Agriculture Organization of the United Nations appointed a Committee to discuss the question of calorie conversion factors, and the conclusions of the Committee were set out in a Report (1947), in which a table was given showing Atwater's suggested factors for calculating the physiological energy values of different classes of foods.

In 1955, the United States Department of Agriculture issued a handbook entitled "Energy Value of Foods" (Merrill and Watt, 1955) in which the fundamental work of Atwater was described in some detail, and the steps followed in his procedure for determining the energy value of foods were set out. The authors examined the results of work done since Atwater's time on the availability of the protein, fat and carbohydrate in individual foods, and prepared a more detailed table of factors for different classes of food. This table had formed the basis of the calculation of calorific values of foods in the current U.S. Department of Agriculture's publication "Composition of Foods" (Watt and Merrill, 1950). At about the time that Merrill and Watt's (1955) handbook was published the British Nutrition Society held a symposium on the "Assessment of the energy value of human and animal foods", when the differences and difficulties of the problem were discussed from a more general point of view (Blaxter and Graham, 1955; Widdowson, 1955; Hollingsworth, 1955).

CHOICE OF CALORIE CONVERSION FACTORS FOR THE 1ST AND 2ND EDITIONS OF THE PRESENT REPORT

In the first edition of these tables an important departure from traditional practice was the method used for the determination of carbohydrate. In Atwater's own work, and in the work of those who followed him, the percentage of carbohydrate in foods was generally not determined directly but was calculated "by difference", i.e. as the difference between 100 and the sum of the percentage of water, protein, fat and ash in the food. Thus it included not only sugars, dextrins and starch which are known to be available to man, but also all the complex carbohydrates, most of which are not available as carbohydrate at all. When the first edition of this report was being prepared it was decided that the values found by direct determination of the available carbohydrates were likely to approximate more closely to the physiological values, and the method of calculating carbohydrate "by difference" was abandoned. The glucose, fructose, sucrose, dextrins and starch were separately determined and their sum, expressed in terms of "monosaccharides" was given as "available carbohydrate". Glucose and other monosaccharides have a heat of combustion of 3·75 Calories per gram, and this was the value assigned to the available carbohydrate fraction in the second edition of the present publication. The unavailable carbohydrate was considered to contribute no Calories to the diet:

The figure chosen for protein in the first and second editions was 4·1 Calories per gram, which was Rubner's factor for mixed meat and vegetable protein; this makes an allowance of about 7 per cent. for nitrogen lost in the faeces, and the correction for unoxidized nitrogenous material in the urine is the same as Atwater's. Rubner's factor of 9·3 was chosen for fat; this is the average heat of combustion of animal and vegetable fats, and it makes little or no allowance for losses of fat in the faeces. The heat of combustion of ethyl alcohol is 7·07 Calories per gram, and a factor of 7·0 was used in the first and second edition of these tables.

FACTORS USED IN "NUTRITIVE VALUES OF WARTIME FOODS"

The second World War brought a need for tables giving the composition of the foods which were being produced and imported at that time, and the Council's Accessory Food Factors Committee undertook to compile such tables. These were published under the title "Nutritive Values of Wartime Foods" (Medical Research Council: Accessory Food Factors Committee, 1945). The figures for the protein, fat and carbohydrate in many of the foods were taken from the first edition of the present tables, the values for carbohydrate being based on direct chemical estimations of "available carbohydrate", but expressed in terms of starch. To calculate the calorific value of the protein, fat and carbohydrate the factors 4, 9 and 4 Calories per gram respectively were used. In that publication the calorific value of the carbohydrate fraction of foods was definitely under-estimated since only the available fraction was considered, and a figure even lower than the physical, and probably also physiological, calorific value of starch (4·2 Calories per gram) was applied to it.

CHOICE OF CALORIE CONVERSION FACTORS FOR THE PRESENT EDITION

Much thought has been given to the calorie conversion factors that should be used in the present edition of these tables. All the methods in current use are open to criticism. The use of different factors for protein and fat from various sources as worked out by Atwater and recommended by Maynard (1944), the F.A.O. Committee (1947) and Merrill and Watt (1955) is undoubtedly a more correct approach than the use of the same factors for all foods, whether 4 and 9 or 4·1 and 9·3. On the other hand, the determination of the available carbohydrate fractions directly is acknowledged to be the better method, though there are few published tables in which this method has been used. The F.A.O. Committee (1947) concluded that "the correct chemical approach is by the extension of analytical work to include all substances covered by 'carbohydrates by difference'. Further studies of the digestibility of these substances are also required. Only when all the constituents of food have been determined and their physiological effects defined, can their role in metabolism and their fuel value be accurately described".

Work is in progress along both lines suggested by the F.A.O. Committee at the present time and, after much consideration, and with the advice of the Council's Diet and Energy Committee, the authors have decided that in order to avoid confusion the method of calculating the calorific values of foods shall remain unchanged in the present edition of these tables. The factors used, therefore, are 4·1 Calories per gram of protein, 9·3 Calories per gram of fat, 3·75 Calories per gram of available carbohydrate expressed as monosaccharides and 7·0 Calories per gram of alcohol. It is hoped that, when further evidence is available, a uniform method will be agreed upon, and used internationally.

Table 1 gives the calorific values of various foods as calculated by four different methods. It shows that in fact the agreement between the values arrived at by the different methods is in most instances quite close. The use of the factor 9·3 instead of 9 gives a slightly higher value for butter and other fats, but only in the case of fruit and vegetables where much of the carbohydrate is present in an "unavailable" form do the figures really differ. Since these foods contribute a relatively small proportion of the calorific value of a whole diet it will not make much difference which factors are used to calculate the calorific value of mixed diets. In this respect it is of interest to note that calculations of the calorific value of National Food Supplies for the years 1947, 1955, 1956 and 1957 have been made by the various methods, and the results compared. The difference between the highest and lowest value was of the order of 2 per cent.

TABLE 1

Comparison of the calorific values of foods calculated by three methods
Calories per 100 grams

	Present tables Protein × 4·1 Fat × 9·3 Available carbohydrate (as monosaccharides) × 3·75	M.R.C. War Memorandum No. 14 (1945) Protein × 4·0 Fat × 9·0 Available carbohydrate (as starch) × 4·2*	F.A.O. (1947) Merrill and Watt (1955) Specific factors for different foods
Cereals			
Bread, brown	242	245	251
Bread, white..	243	242	242
Flour, Manitoba, wholemeal	339	336	327
Flour, Manitoba, white ..	352	350	353
Oatmeal	404	400	399
Rice, polished	361	359	368
Dairy-products			
Butter	793	768	748
Cheese, Cheddar	425	412	414
Cheese, Gorgonzola ..	393	380	382
Eggs	163	158	169
Milk, fresh, whole	66	65	68
Meat			
Beef, corned	231	224	231
Beef, frozen, raw	151	147	153
Beef, steak, raw	177	172	177
Liver, raw	143	139	144
Fruit			
Apples, English, eating ..	45	45	55
Apricots, dried	183	182	297
Bananas	77	76	103
Currants, black, raw ..	29	28	79
Currants, red, raw	21	21	60
Gooseberries, green, raw ..	17	17	35
Grapefruit	22	22	32
Oranges	35	35	49
Vegetables			
Beans, butter, raw	266	264	350
Beans, runner, raw	15	15	31
Cabbage, Savoy, raw ..	26	26	30
Carrots, old, raw	23	23	32
Peas, fresh, raw	64	63	81
Potatoes, old, raw	87	86	92
Nuts			
Peanuts	603	586	576
Walnuts	549	535	519

* *See* p. 175.

References to Part 1

Association of Official Agricultural Chemists (1930). *Official and tentative methods of analysis.* Washington, D.C.

Atwater, W. O. (1902). On the digestibility and availability of food materials. *Conn. (Storrs) Agric. Exp. Sta. 14th Annu. Rep.,* 1901.

Atwater, W. O. (1910). Principles of nutrition and nutritive value of food. *Fmrs' Bull. U.S. Dep. Agric.* No. 142 (2nd rev.).

Atwater, W. O. and Benedict, F. G. (1897). Experiments on the digestion of food by man. *Conn. (Storrs) Agric. Exp. Sta. Bull.,* No. 18.

Atwater, W. O. and Bryant, A. P. (1900). The availability and fuel value of food materials. *Conn. (Storrs) Agric. Exp. Sta., 12th Annu. Rep.,* 1899.

Blaxter, K. L. and Graham, N. McC. (1955). Methods of assessing the energy values of foods for ruminant animals. *Proc. Nutr. Soc.,* 14, 131.

Chatfield, C. and Adams, G. (1940). Proximate composition of American food materials. *Circ. U.S. Dep. Agric.,* No. 549.

Coppock, J. B. M., Knight, R. A. and Vaughan, M. C. (1958). The moisture content of white bread. *Nutrition, Lond.,* 12, 63.

Food and Agriculture Organization of the United Nations. Committee on Calorie Conversion Factors and Food Composition Tables (1947). *Energy yielding components of food and computation of calorie values.* United Nations, Food and Agriculture Organization, Washington, U.S.A.

Hollingsworth, D. F. (1955). Some difficulties in estimating the energy values of human diets. *Proc. Nutr. Soc.,* 14, 154.

Leach, A. E. and Winton, A. L. (1920). *Food inspection and analysis.* J. Wiley & Son, New York.

McCance, R. A. and Glaser, E. M. (1948). The energy value of oatmeal and the digestibility and absorption of its proteins, fats and calcium.. *Brit. J. Nutr.,* 2, 221.

McCance, R. A. and Lawrence, R. D. (1929). The carbohydrate content of foods. *Spec. Rep. Ser. med. Res. Coun., Lond.,* No. 135. H.M. Stationery Office.

McCance, R. A., Sheldon, W. and Widdowson, E. M. (1934). Bone and vegetable broth. *Arch. Dis. Childh.,* 9, 251.

McCance, R. A. and Shipp, H. L. (1933). The chemistry of flesh foods and their losses on cooking. *Spec. Rep. Ser. med. Res. Coun., Lond.,* No. 187. H.M. Stationery Office.

McCance, R. A. and Walsham, C. M. (1948). The digestibility and absorption of the calories, proteins, purines, fat and calcium in wholemeal wheaten bread. *Brit. J. Nutr.,* 2, 26.

McCance, R. A. and Widdowson, E. M. (1935). Phytin in human nutrition. *Biochem. J.,* 29, 2694.

McCance, R. A. and Widdowson, E. M. (1942). Mineral metabolism of healthy adults on white and brown bread dietaries. *J. Physiol.,* 101, 44.

McCance, R. A. and Widdowson, E. M. (1947). The digestibility of English and Canadian wheats, with special reference to the digestibility of wheat protein by man. *J. Hyg., Camb.,* 45, 59.

178

McCance, R. A., Widdowson, E. M., Moran, T., Pringle, W. J. S. and Macrae, T. F. (1945). The chemical composition of wheat and rye and of the flours derived therefrom. *Biochem. J.*, **39**, 213.

McCance, R. A., Widdowson, E. M. and Shackleton, L. R. B. (1936). The nutritive value of fruits, vegetables and nuts, *Spec. Rep. Ser. med. Res. Coun., Lond.*, No. 213. H.M. Stationery Office.

Masters, M. and McCance R., A. (1939). The sulphur content of foods, *Biochem. J.*, **33**, 1304.

Maynard, L. A. (1944). The Atwater system of calculating the caloric value of diets. *J. Nutr.*, **28**, 443.

Medical Research Council: Accessory Food Factors Committee (1945). Nutritive values of wartime foods. *M.R.C. (War) Memor.* No. 14. H.M. Stationery Office.

Merrill, A. L. and Watt, B. K. (1955). Energy value of foods—basis and derivation. *U.S. Dep. Agric.*, Handbook No. 74.

Monier-Williams, G. W. (1927). The determination of SO_2 in foods. *Rep. publ. Hlth. med. Subj., Lond.*, No. 43. H.M. Stationery Office.

Morey, N. B. (1936). An analysis and comparison of different methods of calculating the energy value of diets. *Nutr. Abstr. Rev.*, **6**, 1.

Osmond, A. (1948). Tables of composition of Australian foods. *Spec. Rep. Ser. nat. Hlth. med. Res. Coun., Canberra*, No. 2.

Platt, B. S. (1945). Tables of representative value of foods commonly used in tropical count-ries. *Spec. Rep. Ser. med. Res. Coun., Lond.*, No. 253. H.M. Stationery Office.

Rubner, M. (1885). Calorimetrische Untersuchungen. *Z. Biol.*, **21**, 250.

Rubner, M. (1901). Der Energiewert der Kost des Menschen. *Z. Biol.*, **42**, 261.

Sherman, H. C. (1911). *The chemistry of food and nutrition.* The Macmillan Co., New York.

Sherman, H. C. (1952). *The chemistry of food and nutrition*, 8th ed. The Macmillan Co., New York.

von Lieberman, L. and Szekely, S. (1898). Eine neue Methode der Fettbestimmung in Futtermitteln, Fleisch, Koth u.s.w. *Pflüg. Arch. ges. Physiol.*, **72**, 360.

Watt, B. K. and Merrill, A. L. (1950). Composition of foods—raw, processed, prepared. *U.S. Dep. Agric.* Handbook No. 8.

Widdowson, E. M. (1955). Assessment of the energy value of human foods. *Proc. Nutr. Soc.*, **14**, 142.

Widdowson, E. M. and McCance, R. A. (1935). The available carbohydrate of fruits. Deter-mination of glucose, fructose, sucrose and starch. *Biochem. J.*, **29**, 151.

Part II. Vitamins

I. M. BARRETT AND E. M. WIDDOWSON

Introduction

This part of the report is concerned with the vitamins in raw and cooked foods. The tables are divided into two main sections. The first gives figures for the vitamin A potency, carotene, vitamin D, thiamine, riboflavine, nicotinic acid and ascorbic acid. The second, a shorter section, has been included in response to many requests. It gives figures for pantothenic acid, vitamin B_6, biotin, folic acid, and vitamin B_{12}, and for the tocopherols. The published figures for the amounts of these vitamins present in foods are sometimes conflicting; many are based on only one analysis; and in several cases the methods of estimation have not yet been fully investigated for all foods. The figures may therefore require revision later, and should be used only as an approximate guide.

Within the two sections the foods have been classified into groups to correspond as nearly as possible to the grouping of the foods in Part I—cereals and cereal foods; milk products and eggs; meat and poultry; fish; fruit; nuts; vegetables; sugar, preserves and sweetmeats; beverages; alcoholic beverages.

Throughout these tables the signs (—) and Tr. have the same significance as they have in Part I (p. 4).

SELECTION OF THE VALUES

These tables have been prepared from a compilation consisting almost entirely of published results. The scientific literature was surveyed from the beginning of 1939 to the end of 1956, and the following twenty-five journals were individually perused:—*Analyst*, 1939–1953; *Analytical Chemistry*, 1939–1953; *Archives of Biochemistry and Biophysics*, 1942–1953; *Biochemical Journal*, 1940–1953; *Biochemische Zeitschrift*, 1939–1940, 1948–1953; *British Journal of Nutrition*, 1947–1953; *Cereal Chemistry*, 1939–1953; *Chemistry and Industry (Review)*, 1939–1953; *Food Research*, 1939–1953; *Journal of Agricultural Science*, 1939–1953; *Journal of the American Dietetic Association*, 1939–1944; 1946–1948, 1951–1953; *Journal of the Association of Official Agricultural Chemists*, 1939–1953; *Journal of Biological Chemistry*, 1938–1953; *Journal of Dairy Research*, 1938–1953; *Journal of Dairy Science*, 1939–1953; *Journal of Nutrition*, 1939–1953; *Journal of Pharmacy and Pharmacology*, 1949–1952; *Journal of the Science of Food and Agriculture*, 1950–1953; *Journal of the Society of Chemical Industry*, 1939–1949; *Report of the Agricultural and Horticultural Research Station, University of Bristol, Long Ashton*, 1940–1952; *Nutrition Abstracts and Reviews*, 1939–1958; *Poultry Science*, 1939–1953; *Proceedings of the Nutrition Society*, 1944–1947, 1953; *Proceedings of the Society for Experimental Biology and*

Medicine, 1940–1953; *Quarterly Journal of Pharmacy and Pharmacology*, 1939–1948.

Reports, bulletins and circulars from various organizations, books, and papers in other journals have also been consulted.   In all, about 1,000 publications have been read in the original and abstracted, and the information catalogued and classified.   The figures given are those considered most nearly to represent the amount of the vitamin in the food, and all the figures given are based on at least one published experimental result.   The references on which the selected figures are based are listed on pp. 207–246.

For some foods and some vitamins there was much more information than for others.   It is well known that the published values for vitamins in a foodstuff are more variable than those for other constituents, and for many foods the range of published values was very wide.   This variability is partly caused by real differences; for example, in the case of fruit and vegetables the vitamins are affected by soil and climate, degree of maturity, and methods of storage and processing; in the case of meat they are affected by the food given to the animal and by the proportion of fat in the sample.   Part of the variability, however, is due to differences in the techniques used to determine the vitamins. In assessing the representative figure for a foodstuff special consideration was given to the results of analyses of British food materials and to the results of analyses of large numbers of samples.   Preference was given to the more recently published values, particularly when these were based on modified and more accurate methods of analysis.   When a representative value had been decided upon from the published results of original analytical work it was compared with the figures given by other compilers.   The chosen values were generally close to one or other of these, but where they were not and there was no clue as to the source of the compiler's figures, the values selected from the results of analytical work were retained.   Most of the figures have been submitted to experts in various fields and much helpful advice has been received.

Although in most instances one rounded figure is given, for some foods that are a very rich source of a particular vitamin, and for foods that are a very variable source, the range of the published values is given in a footnote.   A few foods have been shown to contain none, or only traces of any of the vitamins, and have therefore been omitted.   Notes to this effect have been inserted where appropriate in the tables.

The figures indicate the total vitamin in the foods and take no account of digestibility.   They should not be confidently applied to an individual food which, if grown in a particular way may contain quite an unusual amount of a vitamin.   The figures are most suitable for application to a mixed diet over a considerable period.

In these tables the values for meat are intended to apply to meat of average fatness.

Few figures were available for the vitamins in fish, and among white fish there seemed to be as much variation between different samples of the same fish as between fish of different species; only one set of figures, therefore, is given for white fish.   It is probably safe to assume that the vitamin content of a white fish not specified in the tables is approximately the same as the general figure for this group.

DEFINITIONS AND ANALYTICAL METHODS

Vitamin A potency

Figures based on biological or chemical determinations were used in assessing vitamin A potency. The most common biological method depends upon a measurement of the rate of growth of rats. Figures obtained by U.V. spectrophotometric methods, after extraction and purification, have also been considered.

The figures for carotene were based on chemical determinations involving extraction of the lipid fraction, column separation of carotenoids and comparison of the colour with pure β-carotene.

In expressing vitamin A potency the vitamin itself has been differentiated from carotene in most foods. Values for the preformed vitamin are given in international units, one i.u. having by definition the potency of 0·300 μg. vitamin A. The biological activity of carotene is, in general, less than that of preformed vitamin A, and values for carotene are given in mg. carotene which for most foods represents the β-carotene equivalent of all the active carotenoids (Fraps, 1947). When no information was available as to the proportion of different carotenoids in the food the figure given represents total carotene. In such instances the vitamin A potency will be slightly over-estimated, but the error introduced in this way can only be small.

To obtain an approximate figure for the total vitamin A potency of a mixed diet the total carotene in mg. should be converted to international units (1,000 i.u. carotene $\equiv$ 0·6 mg. β-carotene), divided by 3, and added to the total preformed vitamin A.

In some foods, notably dairy products and liver, which contain preformed vitamin A and some carotene, the digestibility of the provitamin may be considered to be the same as that of the preformed vitamin and for all these foods one figure only for the vitamin A potency is given.

Thiamine

The figures preferred in assessing the representative values for thiamine were those based on chemical determinations. The method most frequently applied has been the thiochrome method, modified with various extraction procedures to suit different foods. Figures obtained by microbiological methods using the organism *Lactobacillus fermenti*, which has been found to give good results under certain conditions, have also been considered.

Thiamine values are expressed as mg. per 100 grams. 1,000 international units have been taken as equivalent to 3 mg. thiamine, and early results reported in the literature in this way have been converted accordingly.

Riboflavine

Values given for riboflavine have been based on microbiological determinations using the organism *Lactobacillus casei*, and also on chemical determinations depending on fluorescence in pyridine-butanol. Preliminary acid or enzyme extraction, often using papain and takadiastase, is required to release riboflavine from the bound forms riboflavine mononucleotide and flavine adenine dinucleotide which occur in natural products. Riboflavine values are expressed in mg. per 100 grams.

Nicotinic Acid

The figures for nicotinic acid include free nicotinic acid, nicotinamide, coenzymes I and II, and bound forms in cereals.

Results obtained both microbiologically, with *Lactobacillus arabinosus*, and chemically by the addition of cyanogen bromide and an aromatic amine to yield a coloured compound which may be determined photometrically, have been considered in assessing the representative figures. Both methods of estimation require a preliminary acid or enzyme extraction to release free nicotinic acid from its bound forms. Values are expressed as mg. per 100 grams.

Ascorbic Acid

Nearly all the figures for ascorbic acid considered in this compilation have been obtained by the well-established chemical methods using either the dye 2, 6-dichlorophenolindophenol or 2, 4-dinitrophenylhydrazine.

Values for ascorbic acid are expressed as mg. per 100 grams and, for fresh foods, represent reduced ascorbic acid, the form in which it generally occurs in raw foods. Since the reversibly oxidised form of ascorbic acid, or dehydroascorbic acid, is often increased after cooking or processing, whenever possible the figures given for these foods represent total ascorbic acid. Any other physiologically inactive reducing substances present have been disregarded. Sufficient information was generally available to ensure little error being introduced by this procedure.

Vitamin D

Only results determined by rat biological tests have been considered. Figures for vitamin D are expressed in international units, one i.u. being equivalent to $0 \cdot 025$ µg. crystalline D_3.

Pantothenic Acid

Pantothenic acid is usually present in animal tissues in coenzyme A, from which it must be freed before estimation. This has usually been carried out by enzyme hydrolysis using papain and takadiastase, or chick liver enzyme plus intestinal phosphatase, the pantothenic acid then being determined microbiologically using either the organism *Lactobacillus arabinosus* or *Saccharomyces carlsbergensis*. Results determined by other methods or before 1948 have generally been disregarded.

Figures for pantothenic acid are expressed as mg. per 100 grams.

Vitamin B_6

Vitamin B_6 occurs naturally as pyridoxine, pyridoxal and pyridoxamine, and also as their respective phosphates, and in some other conjugated forms. Extraction has usually been carried out by autoclaving in the presence of sulphuric acid. The vitamin B_6 activity was then determined using generally the organisms, *Neurospora sitophila* and *Saccharomyces carlsbergensis*. Other organisms, specific for the particular form required, have been used. Results after about 1945 were preferred.

Figures for vitamin B_6 are expressed as mg. per 100 grams.

Biotin

Biotin occurs naturally in strongly bound forms which often make extraction difficult. It also occurs in some foods together with chemical compounds having unspecific biotin activity. This has sometimes led to confusion. Extraction has generally been carried out by autoclaving in sulphuric acid after which the biotin was determined microbiologically using the organism *Lactobacillus arabinosus* or a yeast. The more recent results published after about 1945 were preferred.

Figures for biotin are expressed as µg. per 100 grams.

Folic Acid

Folic acid also occurs naturally in foods in bound forms, and preliminary extraction from the tissue is necessary. This has usually been carried out by enzyme extraction using takadiastase, hog kidney conjugase, or chicken pancreas conjugase. This has been followed by microbiological estimation with the organisms *Streptococcus faecalis* and *Lactobacillus casei*. Results reported after about 1950 have been preferred.

Figures for folic acid are expressed as µg. per 100 grams.

Vitamin B_{12}

Information about vitamin B_{12} has accumulated during the last few years and some values are included in the tables.

Before estimation of vitamin B_{12} from foods preliminary extraction of the vitamin is necessary. This has been carried out by various methods, often including an enzymic hydrolysis. Values obtained since about 1950 by a microbiological estimation using the organism *Lactobacillus leichmannii* 313(7830) have been preferred.

Figures for vitamin B_{12} are expressed as µg. per 100 grams.

Tocopherols

The tocopherols are present in several forms, the most important being α-, β-, γ-, and δ-tocopherols, which are all fat soluble, and are biological antioxidants. In foods α-tocopherol is the most common form, γ- and δ-tocopherols are present in some products but β-tocopherol has not yet been found. Results of early biological tests with rats have been considered, as well as those obtained by the more recent chemical methods. The most important of these is oxidation by ferric chloride in the presence of $αα'$-dipyridyl, the resulting ferrous chloride being measured by the red colour produced. Separation of the various forms was achieved by molecular distillation and also by paper chromatography.

Figures for tocopherols are expressed as mg. per 100 grams.

EFFECTS OF COOKING

More information was available concerning the vitamins in raw foods than in cooked or processed foods. Cooking introduces another variable in addition to those already mentioned, and the published figures for cooked foods differ even more widely than those for raw. Many workers who have analysed cooked foods have also analysed the same foods before cooking, and they have studied the losses of vitamins when foods are cooked in various ways. The methods of

N

cooking which have been considered are described below under headings for the different groups of foods. For foods cooked by methods very different from those described, some adjustment of the figures for ascorbic acid, thiamine, and probably riboflavine will be necessary. Nicotinic acid and vitamins A and D are more stable to heat, and little error will probably be introduced if no adjustment is made for these vitamins, provided that allowance is made for leaching into the cooking water or fat, or, in the case of meat, for loss in dripping. Since little information was available about the effect of cooking on pantothenic acid, vitamin B$_6$, biotin, folic acid, vitamin B$_{12}$, and tocopherols, few figures for cooked or processed foods have been included in the tables of values for these vitamins, and no general assessment of the effect of cooking has been attempted for them.

Meat and Poultry

Figures for the vitamins in cooked meats can only be rough approximations depending upon the vitamin content of the raw meat which in turn depends upon the amount of fat that was in it, and also upon the method of cooking. The figures are not intended to illustrate more than trends in vitamin composition after cooking, and in practice there may be considerable variation from the values given.

In whatever way meat is cooked it loses about one-quarter to one-third of its original weight, and cooked meat is more concentrated than raw meat in that it contains more protein and less water. There may be more or less of a vitamin in 100 grams of the cooked meat than in 100 grams of the raw, depending upon the method of cooking and the stability of the vitamin to heat. Allowance has been made for these variables by calculating an average retention factor which is defined as the amount of a vitamin in 100 grams of the cooked meat expressed as a percentage of the amount in 100 grams of the raw meat. Average retention factors were calculated from previous workers' results, and the values for cooked meats in these tables were arrived at by the application of the appropriate retention factors to the selected value for the raw meat.

The following table shows the percentage retention factors which have been used to calculate the amounts of thiamine, riboflavine and nicotinic acid in cooked meats.

Method of cooking	Beef and Veal			Mutton and Lamb			Pork			Bacon and Ham			Poultry		
	Thiamine	Riboflavine	Nicotinic acid	Thiamine	Riboflavine	Nicotinic acid	Thiamine	Riboflavine	Nicotinic acid	Thiamine	Riboflavine	Nicotinic acid	Thiamine	Riboflavine	Nicotinic acid
Roast ..	70	110	100	70	100	90	80	100	100	—	—	—	50	80	80
Fried and grilled	120	120	110	70	100	90	80	100	100	100	100	100	—	80	70
Stewed ..	70	110	100	70	100	90	—	—	—	—	—	—	—	—	—

Cooking leads to a destruction of 20–50 per cent. of the pantothenic acid, vitamin B_6, biotin and vitamin B_{12} in beef, mutton and lamb.   In pork the losses are probably lower.   There may be 50–90 per cent. destruction of folic acid during cooking.   There tends to be a greater loss of these B vitamins after roasting, frying or grilling, than after stewing.

Fish

No information has been found concerning the effect of cooking on the vitamins in fish.   The effect of canning has been described by Lunde (1937). Vitamins A and D, riboflavine and nicotinic acid are stable to canning, but there may be a slight loss of thiamine.   Cooked fish, except roe, probably contains no ascorbic acid; cooked roe may contain up to 10 mg. of ascorbic acid per 100 grams.

Fruit

The carotene, thiamine, riboflavine, nicotinic acid and ascorbic acid in fruits after stewing have been calculated from the value in the raw fruit and the ratio of cooked weight to raw weight (see p. 7).   It has been assumed that there is a 10 per cent. loss due to destruction of ascorbic acid, thiamine and riboflavine; carotene and nicotinic acid are not affected.

There may be a loss of up to 30 per cent. of the pantothenic acid and biotin, and 70 per cent., or even all of the folic acid may be destroyed.

Vegetables

The carotene, thiamine, riboflavine, nicotinic acid and ascorbic acid in boiled and drained vegetables have been arrived at by subtracting the average losses due to cooking from the value for the raw vegetables; figures given in the literature for boiled vegetables have also been taken into account.

Boiling has been taken to mean cooking the prepared vegetable in a covered saucepan containing sufficient water just to cover the contents.   Prolonged boiling or standing before serving will rapidly lower the ascorbic acid content of cooked vegetables.

Losses of carotene due to boiling vegetables should generally be insignificant and no allowance has been made for them.   It has been assumed that after boiling the loss of thiamine, riboflavine and nicotinic acid is about 40 per cent. and of ascorbic acid about 70 per cent.   In the vegetables generally classed as "seeds and fruits" the percentage loss of thiamine, riboflavine and nicotinic acid was assumed to be 30 and of ascorbic acid 50.   In root vegetables the percentage losses after boiling have been assumed to be as follows:—thiamine 25, riboflavine and nicotinic acid 30, ascorbic acid 40.

In boiled vegetables there may be a loss of up to 30 per cent. of the pantothenic acid and biotin, and 70–100 per cent. of the folic acid.

There will probably be considerable divergence from these average values according to the cooking procedure adopted, and the nature of the raw vegetables.

Tables to Part II

VITAMIN A POTENCY, CAROTENE, VITAMIN D,
THIAMINE, RIBOFLAVINE, NICOTINIC ACID, ASCORBIC ACID
PER 100 GRAMS (PAGES 190–201)

PANTOTHENIC ACID, VITAMIN B_6, BIOTIN,
FOLIC ACID, VITAMIN B_{12}, TOCOPHEROLS
PER 100 GRAMS (PAGES 201–206)

VITAMIN A POTENCY, CAROTENE, VITAMIN D, THIAMINE, RIBOFLAVINE, NICOTINIC ACID, ASCORBIC ACID
per 100 grams

Cereals and Cereal Foods

Food	Carotene (mg.)	Vitamin D (i.u.)	Thiamine (mg.)	Ribo-flavine (mg.)	Nicotinic acid (mg.)	Ascorbic acid (mg.)
Barley, pearl, raw	0	0	0·12	—	2·5	0
Bread, wholemeal	0	0	0·20[3]	0·10	3·5	0
Bread, brown	0	0	0·21[3]	—	2·5	0
Bread, Hovis	0	0	0·29[3]	—	2·0	0
Bread, white	0	0	0·18[1,3]	—	1·7[1]	0
Flour, wholewheat, 100% extraction	0	0	0·40[5]	0·16	5·0	0
Flour, white, mixed grist, basic grade	0	0	0·28[1,2]	0·04	2·3[1,2]	0
Flour, white, mixed grist, patent	0	0	0·28[1,2,4]	0·04	1·8[1,2]	0
Macaroni, raw	0	0	0·14	—	2·0	0
Oatmeal, raw	0	0	0·50	0·10	1·0	0
Oatmeal, porridge	0	0	0·05	0·01	0·10	0
Rice, polished, raw	0	0	0·08	0·03	1·5	0
Rice, polished, boiled	0	0	0·01	0·01	0·30	0
Rye, 100% extraction	0	0	0·40	0·25	1·0	0
Semolina	0	0	0·12	—	2·0	0
Soya. Full fat flour	Tr.	0	0·75	—	2·0	0
Soya. Low fat flour	Tr.	0	0·90	—	2·4	0

[1] Contains added constituent.

[2] The statutory requirement for thiamine is 0·24 mg. per 100 g., and for nicotinic acid is 1·6 mg. per 100 g.

[3] There is a 15–30 per cent. loss after toasting bread of 5–12 mm. thickness.

[4] Losses of 20–30 per cent. have been found as a result of cake and biscuit making.

[5] About 15 per cent. is lost on baking bread.

Arrowroot, cornflour, custard powder, sago and tapioca contain no more than traces of any of these vitamins.

Milk Products and Eggs

Food	Vitamin A potency (i.u.)	Vitamin D (i.u.)	Thiamine (mg.)	Ribo-flavine (mg.)	Nicotinic acid (mg.)	Ascorbic acid (mg.)
Milk and milk products						
Butter, slightly salted ..	3,500[1]	40	Tr.	Tr.	Tr.	Tr.
Cheese, Camembert (23% fat)	800[2]	8[2]	0·05[3]	0·80	1·2	0
Cheese, Cheddar (34·5% fat)	1,400[2]	14[2]	0·04	0·50	0·1	0
Cheese, Cheshire (31% fat)	1,200[2]	12[2]	0·04	0·50	—	0
Cheese, cream (86% fat)..	3,500[2]	35[2]	Tr.	0·20	Tr.	0
Cheese, Danish Blue (29% fat)	1,100[2]	11[2]	Tr.	—	—	0
Cheese, Edam (23% fat)..	900[2]	9[2]	0·02	0·40	—	0
Cheese, Gorgonzola (31% fat)	1,200[2]	12[2]	0·01	—	—	0
Cheese, Gruyère (33% fat)	1,300[2]	13[2]	0·01	0·40	0·10	0
Cheese, Norwegian Mysost (29% fat)	1,100[2]	11[3]	—	—	—	0
Cheese, Parmesan (30% fat)	1,200[2]	12[2]	Tr.	—	—	0
Cheese, processed (30% fat)	1,200[2]	12[2]	0·01	0·40	0·05	0
Cheese Spread (23% fat)	900[2]	9[2]	Tr.	—	—	0
Cheese, Stilton (40% fat)	1,600[2]	16[2]	0·07	0·30	—	0
Cheese, Wensleydale (31% fat)	1,200[2]	12[2]	0·02	—	—	0
Cream, double (48% fat)	Summer 1,900[2] Winter 1,300[2]	Summer 20[2] Winter 7[2]	0·02[4]	0·08[4]	0·04[4]	0·8[4]
Cream, single (18–48% fat)	Summer 700[2] Winter 500[2]	Summer 7[2] Winter 3[2]	0·03[4]	0·12[4]	0·07[4]	1·2[4]
Milk, whole, raw.. ..	Summer 150 Winter 100	Summer 1·5 Winter 0·5	0·04	0·15[5]	0·08[6]	2·0
Milk, whole, pasteurised..	Summer 150 Winter 100	Summer 1·5 Winter 0·5	0·04	0·15[5]	0·08[6]	1·5[7]
Milk, whole, sterilized ..	Summer 150 Winter 100	Summer 1·5 Winter 0·5	0·03	0·15[5]	0·08[6]	1·0
Milk, skimmed	Tr.	Tr.	0·04	0·16	0·08[6]	1·5[7]
Milk, condensed, whole, sweetened	350	3·5	0·10	0·40	0·20	3·0
Milk, condensed, whole, unsweetened	350	3·5	0·06	0·37	0·20	1·5
Milk, dried, skimmed ..	Tr.	Tr.	0·36	1·6	0·80	10
Milk, dried, whole ..	1,200	12	0·28	1·2	0·70	10
Human milk	170	1·0	0·02	0·03	0·17	3·5

Milk Products and Eggs—*continued*

Food	Vitamin A potency (i.u.)	Vitamin D (i.u.)	Thiamine (mg.)	Ribo-flavine (mg.)	Nicotinic acid (mg.)	Ascorbic acid (mg.)
Eggs						
Eggs, whole, raw ..	1,000	70[8]	0·10[9]	0·35[9]	0·07	0
Egg white, raw	0	0	0	0·33	0·09	0
Egg yolk, raw	3,000	200[8]	0·30	0·40	0·02	0
Eggs, dried	5,000[10]	240	0·35[11]	1·2	0·20	0

[1] This is an average figure. European winter butter may contain about half this amount, but New Zealand and European summer butter may contain as much as 4,500 i.u.

[2] Calculated from vitamins A and D in whole milk, and the percentage of fat in milk and cream or cheese.

[3] May contain up to 0·5 mg. in the rind.

[4] Calculated from the values for whole milk and the percentage of non-fat material in milk and cream.

[5] Value for milk that has not been exposed to sunshine. When bottled milk is left in bright light about 10 per cent. of the riboflavine is lost per hour. When milk is heated in an open pan there may be a further loss of about 7 per cent. after 5 minutes.

[6] This is an average figure. The value will be slightly higher in the summer and lower in the winter.

[7] Value immediately after pasteurising. After about 12 hours storage it will be 1·0 mg. and after 24 hours storage 0·5 mg. Boiling leads to a loss of 12–22 per cent.

[8] If poultry have been fed a supplement of vitamin D the values may be considerably higher.

[9] There is a 5–15 per cent. loss after boiling, frying and poaching.

[10] There is a loss on storage, particularly at high temperatures. Storage for 9 months at 15° C. may lead to a loss of about 60 per cent.

[11] When stored in air for 9 months at 20–37° C. there may be a loss of 50–100 per cent. of the thiamine originally present.

Fats and Oils

Food	Vitamin A potency (i.u.)	Vitamin D (i.u.)	Thiamine (mg.)	Ribo-flavine (mg.)	Nicotinic acid (mg.)	Ascorbic acid (mg.)
Cod liver oil	75,800	8,700	—	0	0	—
Margarine	3,000	300	Tr.	Tr.	Tr.	0

Dripping, lard, suet and olive oil contain no more than traces of any of these vitamins.

Meat and Poultry

(Figures for cooked meats were calculated as described on p. 186)

Food	Vitamin A potency (i.u.)	Vitamin D (i.u.)	Thiamine (mg.)	Ribo-flavine (mg.)	Nicotinic acid (mg.)	Ascorbic acid (mg.)
Bacon, raw	Tr.	Tr.	0·40	0·15	1·5	0
Bacon, fried	Tr.	Tr.	0·40	0·15	1·5	0
Beef, raw	Tr.	Tr.	0·07	0·20	5	0
Beef, corned	Tr.	Tr.	Tr.	0·20	3·5	0
Beef, fried or grilled ..	Tr.	Tr.	0·08	0·25	5·5	0
Beef, roast	Tr.	Tr.	0·05	0·22	5	0
Beef, stewed	Tr.	Tr.	0·05	0·22	5	0
Brain, ox or pig, raw ..	Tr.	Tr.	0·10	0·25	4	Tr.
Chicken, raw	Tr.	Tr.	0·10	Breast 0·07 Leg 0·25	Breast 10 Leg 5	0
Chicken, canned	Tr.	Tr.	0·02	Breast 0·06 Leg 0·20	Breast 8 Leg 4	0
Chicken, roast	Tr.	Tr.	0·05	Breast 0·06 Leg 0·20	Breast 8 Leg 4	0
Ham, raw	Tr.	Tr.	0·80	0·20	4	0
Ham, boiled or canned ..	Tr.	Tr.	0·50	0·20	3·5	0
Heart, ox, raw	200	—	0·60	0·90	7	0
Heart, ox, braised or stewed	200	—	0·40	1·0	7	0
Heart, pig or sheep, raw	—	—	0·30	0·80	5	0
Kidney, ox, raw	1,000	—	0·30	2·0	6	12

Meat and Poultry—*continued*

(Figures for cooked meats were calculated as described on p. 186)

Food	Vitamin A potency (i.u.)	Vitamin D (i.u.)	Thiamine (mg.)	Ribo-flavine (mg.)	Nicotinic acid (mg.)	Ascorbic acid (mg.)
Kidney, ox, braised ..	1,000	—	—	2·0	5	—
Kidney, pig or sheep, raw	1,000	—	0·30	2·0	8	12
Liver, calf, raw	5,000([1])	10	0·30	3·0	13	30
Liver, ox, raw	20,000([2])	45	0·30	3·0	13	30
Liver, pig, raw	10,000([3])	45	0·30	3·0	13	30
Liver, sheep, raw.. ..	45,000([4])	20	0·30	3·0	13	30
Liver, fried	([5])	([5])	0·30	3·5	15	20
Luncheon meat	Tr.	Tr.	0·40	0·20	3·5	0
Mutton and lamb, raw ..	Tr.	Tr.	0·15	0·25	5	0
Mutton and lamb, roast, fried, grilled or stewed	Tr.	Tr.	0·10	0·25	4·5	0
Pork, raw	Tr.	Tr.	1·0	0·20	5	0
Pork, roast, fried or grilled	Tr.	Tr.	0·80	0·20	5	0
Rabbit, raw	Tr.	—	0·03	—	12	—
Tongue, ox, raw	Tr.	Tr.	0·10	0·30	6	0
Tongue, ox, cooked or canned	Tr.	Tr.	0·04	0·35	—	0
Turkey, raw	Tr.	Tr.	0·06	Breast 0·08 Leg 0·22	Breast 11 Leg 5	0
Turkey, roast	Tr.	Tr.	0·04	Breast 0·06 Leg 0·18	Breast 8 Leg 4	0
Veal, raw	Tr.	Tr.	0·10	0·25	7	0
Veal, roast	Tr.	Tr.	0·06	0·27	7	0

[1] May vary from 3,500 to 25,000 i.u.
[2] May vary from 10,000 to 40,000 i.u.
[3] May vary from 5,000 to 25,000 i.u.
[4] May vary from 10,000 to 100,000 i.u.
[5] Take figures for raw liver.

Fish

Food	Vitamin A potency (i.u.)	Vitamin D (i.u.)	Thiamine (mg.)	Ribo-flavine (mg.)	Nicotinic acid (mg.)	Ascorbic acid (mg.)
White fish, raw						
Cod						
Haddock						
Hake	Tr.	0	0·06	0·10	3	Tr.
Plaice						
Sole						
Whiting						
Haddock, smoked ..	Tr.	0	0·05	0·10	2·5	Tr.
Halibut	400[1]	40[1]	0·08	0·10	5	Tr.
Trout	Tr.	0	0·08	0·06	3	Tr.
Turbot	Tr.	0	0·02	0·15	3	Tr.
Fatty fish						
Eel, raw	4,000[2]	[3]	0·20	0·35[4]	1·5	Tr.
Herring, raw	150	900	0·03	0·30	3·5	Tr.
Bloater, raw ..	150	900	Tr.	0·30	3·5	Tr.
Kippers, raw ..						
Mackerel (Atlantic), raw	150	700	0·09	0·50	8	Tr.
Salmon, raw	300[1]	500[1]	0·10	0·10	7	Tr.
Salmon, canned	300[1]	500[1]	0·03	0·10	7	Tr.
Sardines, canned in oil ..	100[5]	300[5]	Tr.	0·20	5	Tr.
Fish roe and milt, raw						
Cod roe (hard)	—	80	1·5	1·0	1·5	30
Herring roe (soft) ..	—	—	0·20	0·50	2·0	—
Shell fish						
Crab, boiled	Tr.	0	0·10	0·15	2·5	Tr.
Lobster, boiled	Tr.	0	—	0·05	1·5	Tr.
Oyster, raw	250	Tr.	0·10	0·20	1·5	Tr.[6]
Shrimps, boiled	Tr.	Tr.	0·03	0·03	3	Tr.

[1] This is the value for Pacific fish. The value for the Atlantic variety may be considerably lower, and may even be 0.

[2] This is an average figure. The value may vary from 870 i.u. in very young eels of 0·37 Kg. weight to 8,330 i.u. in more mature eels of 3·0 Kg. weight (Edisbury, 1937).

[3] Whole body oil is a rich source of vitamin D. Values of about 5,000 and 20,000 i.u. per 100 g. have been reported.

[4] There may be a considerable range of values from 0·05 to 0·50 mg. according to species.

[5] Canned brislings contain 1,000 i.u. vitamin A; 1,000–2,000 i.u. vitamin D per 100 g.

[6] The flesh of some oysters is high in ascorbic acid; Pacific oysters (*Ostrea gigas*) have been shown to contain 22 mg., and Olympia oysters (*Ostrea lurida*) 38 mg. per 100 g.

Fruit

(Figures for cooked fruit were calculated as described on p. 187)

Food	Carotene (mg.)	Vitamin D (i.u.)	Thiamine (mg.)	Riboflavine (mg.)	Nicotinic acid (mg.)	Ascorbic acid (mg.)
Apples, eating, raw	0·03	0	0·04	0·02	0·1	5
Apples, stewed	0·02	0	0·03	0·01	0·1	3
Apricots, raw	1·5	0	0·04	0·05	—	7
Apricots, fresh, stewed	1·12	0	0·02	0·03	—	5
Apricots, canned	1·0	0	0·02	0·01	0·3	5
Apricots, dried, raw	3·6	0	Tr.	0·2	3·0	Tr.
Apricots, dried, stewed	1·2	0	Tr.	0·06	1·0	Tr.
Avocado pears, raw	0·10	0	0·10	0·10	1·0	20
Bananas, raw	0·20	0	0·04	0·07	0·6	10
Blackberries, raw	0·10	0	0·03	0·04	0·4	20
Blackberries, stewed	0·08	0	0·02	0·03	0·3	13
Blackberries, canned	0·10	0	0·01	0·02	0·2	15
Cherries, eating, raw	0·12	0	0·05	—	0·3	5
Cherries, stewed	0·09	0	0·03	—	0·2	3
Cherries, red sour, canned	0·50	0	0·02	0·02	0·2	4
Cranberries, raw	0·02	0	—	Tr.	0·1	12
Currants, black, raw	0·20	0	0·03	0·06	0·25	200
Currants, black, stewed	0·15	0	0·02	0·04	0·2	140
Currants, red, raw	—	0	0·04	—	0·1	40
Currants, red, stewed	—	0	0·03	—	0·1	28
Currants, dried, raw	—	0	0·03	—	—	0
Damsons, raw	—	0	0·10	0·03	0·25	—
Damsons, stewed	—	0	0·07	0·02	0·2	—
Dates, dried, raw	0·05	0	0·07	0·04	2·0	0
Figs, green, raw	—	0	0·06	—	0·4	2
Figs, dried, raw	0·05	0	0·10	—	1·7	0
Figs, dried, stewed	0·03	0	0·05	—	0·9	0
Fruit salad, canned in syrup	0·30(¹)	0	0·02(¹)	0·01(¹)	0·3(¹)	3(¹)
Gooseberries, raw	0·18	0	—	0·03	0·3	40
Gooseberries, stewed	0·14	0	—	0·02	0·2	28
Grapes, white, raw	Tr.	0	0·04	0·02	0·3	4
Grapefruit or grapefruit juice, raw	Tr.	0	0·05	0·02	0·2	40
Grapefruit or grapefruit juice, canned	Tr.	0	0·04	0·01	0·2	Flesh 25 Juice 35
Lemons or lemon juice, raw	0	0	0·02	Tr.	0·1	50
Limes, raw	0	0	Tr.	Tr.	0·2	25
Loganberries, raw	—	0	—	0·03	—	35
Loganberries, stewed or canned	—	0	0·03	0·02	—	25
Melons, raw	White Tr. Yellow 2·0	0	0·05	—	0·5	25
Olives, processed, green, canned	0·15	0	Tr.	Tr.	—	0
Oranges, raw	0·05	0	0·10	0·03	0·2	50
Orange juice, raw	0·05	0	0·08	0·02	0·2	50

Fruit—*continued*

(Figures for cooked fruit were calculated as described on p. 187)

Food	Carotene (mg.)	Vitamin D (i.u.)	Thiamine (mg.)	Ribo-flavine (mg.)	Nicotinic acid (mg.)	Ascorbic acid (mg.)
Orange juice, canned ..	0·05	0	0·07	0·02	0·2	40
Peaches, raw	0·50	0	0·02	0·05	1·0	8
Peaches, canned	0·25	0	0·01	0·02	0·6	4
Peaches, dried, raw	2·0	0	Tr.	—	—	Tr.
Peaches, dried, stewed ..	0·70	0	Tr.	—	—	Tr.
Pears, eating, raw ..	0·01	0	0·03	0·03	0·2	3
Pears, stewed	0·01	0	0·02	0·02	0·15	2
Pears, canned	0·01	0	0·01	0·01	0·2	1
Pineapple, raw	0·06	0	0·08	—	—	25
Pineapple or pineapple juice, canned	0·04	0	0·05	0·02	0·2	8
Plums, raw	0·22	0	0·05	0·03	0·5	3
Plums, stewed	0·17	0	0·04	0·02	0·4	2
Prunes, dried, raw ..	1·0	0	0·10	0·2	1·5	Tr.
Prunes, stewed	0·50	0	0·04	0·09	0·75	Tr.
Prunes, canned	0·60	0	0·02	—	0·5	Tr.
Raisins, dried, raw ..	Tr.	0	0·10	—	0·5	0
Raspberries, raw ..	0·08	0	0·02	0·03	0·4	25(²)
Raspberries, stewed ..	0·08	0	0·02	0·03	0·38	21
Raspberries, canned ..	—	0	0·01	—	—	10
Rhubarb, raw	0·06	0	0·01	—	—	10
Rhubarb, stewed ..	0·05	0	Tr.	—	—	7
Strawberries, raw ..	0·03	0	0·02	0·03	0·4	60(²)
Sultanas, dried, raw ..	Tr.	0	0·10	—	—	0
Tangerines, raw	0·10	0	0·07	0·02	0·2	30

(¹) Calculated assuming that canned fruit salad contains canned fruit in the following proportion: –35 per cent. apricots or peaches; 35 per cent. pears; 10 per cent. cherries; 10 per cent. grapes and 10 per cent. pineapple.
(²) There is a 20 per cent. loss on freezing.

Nuts

Raw Food	Carotene (mg.)	Vitamin D (i.u.)	Thiamine (mg.)	Ribo-flavine (mg.)	Nicotinic acid (mg.)	Ascorbic acid (mg.)
Almonds	0	0	—	—	2·0(¹)	Tr.
Barcelona nuts	0	0	0·11	—	—	Tr.
Brazil nuts	0	0	1·00	—	—	Tr.
Chestnuts	0	0	0·20	—	0·20(¹)	Tr.
Cob nuts	0	0	0·40	—	—	Tr.
Coconut	0	0	0·03	0·02	0·30	Tr.
Peanuts (without skins) ..	0	0	0·90(²)	0·10	16	Tr.
Walnuts, mature	0	0	0·30	0·13	1·0(¹)	Tr.
Walnuts, unripe	0	0	—	—	—	1,300–3,000

(¹) Value for peeled kernel.
(²) 75 per cent. of thiamine may be lost during roasting.

Vegetables

(Figures for cooked vegetables were calculated as described on p. 187)

Food	Carotene (mg.)	Vitamin D (i.u.)	Thiamine (mg.)	Ribo-flavine (mg.)	Nicotinic acid (mg.)	Ascorbic acid (mg.)
Artichokes, globe, raw ..	—	0	0·20	0·01	—	8
Artichokes, Jerusalem, raw	—	0	0·20	Tr.	—	5
Asparagus, raw	0·5	0	0·18	0·15	1·2	40
Asparagus, boiled ..	0·5	0	0·10	0·08	0·8	20
Asparagus, canned ..	0·4	0	0·08	0·08	0·8	17
Beans, broad, raw ..	—	0	—	0·05	4·0	30
Beans, broad, boiled ..	—	0	—	0·04	3·0	15
Beans, butter or haricot, raw	0	0	0·45	0·13	2·5	0
Beans, French, raw ..	0·5	0	0·05	0·10	0·6	10
Beans, French, boiled ..	0·5	0	0·04	0·07	0·3	5
Beans, runner, raw ..	0·3	0	0·05	0·10	0·9	20
Beans, runner, boiled ..	0·3	0	0·03	0·07	0·5	5
Beet greens, raw	5·0	0	0·10	0·20	0·6	50
Beet greens, boiled ..	5·0	0	0·06	0·12	0·4	15
Beetroot, raw	Tr.	0	0·03	0·05	0·1	6
Beetroot, boiled	Tr.	0	0·02	0·04	0·06	5
Broccoli tops, raw ..	2·5	0	0·10	0·30	1·0	120
Broccoli tops, boiled ..	2·5	0	0·06	0·20	0·6	40
Brussels sprouts, raw ..	0·4	0	0·10	—	0·7	100
Brussels sprouts, boiled ..	0·4	0	0·06	—	0·4	35
Cabbage, raw	0·3[1]	0	0·06	0·05	0·25	60[2]
Cabbage, boiled	0·3	0	0·03	0·03	0·15	20
Carrots, young or mature, raw	Young 6·0 Mature 12·0	0	0·06	0·05	0·6	6
Carrots, young or mature, boiled	Young 6·0 Mature 12·0	0	0·05	0·04	0·4	4
Carrots, canned	7·0	0	0·04	0·02	0·3	3
Cauliflower, raw	0·03	0	0·10	0·10	0·6	70
Cauliflower, boiled ..	0·03	0	0·06	0·06	0·4	20
Celery, raw	0	0	0·03	0·03	0·3	7
Celery, boiled	0	0	0·02	0·02	0·2	5
Cucumber, raw	0	0	0·04	0·04	0·2	8
Endive, raw	2·0	0	0·06	0·10	—	12
Horseradish, raw.. ..	—	0	0·06	—	—	120
Kale, raw	5·0	0	0·10	—	1·0	120
Kale, boiled	5·0	0	0·06	—	0·6	30
Leeks, raw	0·04[3]	0	0·10	—	0·6	18
Leeks, boiled	0·04[3]	0	0·07	—	0·4	15
Lentils, raw	Tr.	0	0·50	0·25	2·5	0
Lettuce, raw	1·0[1]	0	0·07	0·08	0·3	15
Marrow, raw	—	0	Tr.	—	0·3	5
Marrow, boiled	—	0	Tr.	—	0·2	2
Mint, raw	11·0	0	—	—	—	30
Mushrooms, raw ..	0	0	0·10	0·40	4·0	3
Mushrooms, fried ..	0	0	—	0·35	3·5	1

Vegetables—*continued*

(Figures for cooked vegetables were calculated as described on p. 187)

Food	Carotene (mg)	Vitamin D (i.u.)	Thiamine (mg.)	Ribo-flavine (mg.)	Nicotinic acid (mg.)	Ascorbic acid (mg.)
Mushrooms, canned ..	0	0	0·02	0·30	3·0	2
Mustard and cress, raw ..	5·0	0	—	—	—	80
Onions, raw	0	0	0·03	0·05	0·2	10
Onions, boiled	0	0	0·02	0·04	0·1	6
Onions, spring, raw ..	Tr.	0	—	—	—	25
Parsley, raw	8·0	0	0·15	0·30	1·0	150
Parsnips, raw	Tr.	0	0·10	—	1·0	15
Parsnips, boiled	Tr.	0	0·07	—	0·7	10
Peas, raw	0·30	0	0·32	0·15	2·5	25
Peas, boiled	0·30	0	0·25	0·11	1·5	15
Peas, canned	0·30	0	0·12	0·07	1·2	10(⁴)
Peas, dried, raw	0·25	0	0·60	0·30	3·0	Tr.
Peas, dried, boiled ..	0·08	0	0·11	0·07	1·0	Tr.
Peas, split, dried, raw ..	—	0	0·70	0·20	3·2	Tr.
Potatoes, raw	Tr.	0	0·11	0·04	1·2	(⁵)
Potatoes, boiled	Tr.	0	0·08	0·03	0·8	(⁶)
Potatoes, steamed, baked or fried (chips)	Tr.	0	0·10	0·04	1·2	(⁶)
Pumpkin, raw	1·5	0	0·04	0·04	0·4	—
Radishes, raw	Tr.	0	0·04	0·02	0·2	25
Seakale, raw	—	0	0·08	—	—	35
Shallots, raw	—	0	0·05	—	—	5
Spinach, raw	6·0	0	0·12	0·20	0·6	60
Spinach, boiled	6·0	0	0·07	0·15	0·4	25
Swedes, raw	Tr.	0	0·06	0·04	1·2	25
Swedes, boiled	Tr.	0	0·04	0·03	0·8	17
Sweet potatoes, raw ..	4·0(⁷)	0	0·10	0·06	0·8	25
Tomatoes, fruit or juice, raw	0·7	0	0·06	0·04	0·6	20
Tomatoes, flesh or juice, canned	0·5	0	0·05	0·03	0·6	16
Turnips, raw	0	0	0·04	0·05	0·6	25
Turnips, boiled	0	0	0·03	0·04	0·4	17
Turnip tops, raw ..	6·0	0	0·10	0·30	0·8	120
Turnip tops, boiled ..	6·0	0	0·06	0·20	0·5	40
Watercress, raw	3·0	0	0·10	—	0·6	60

(¹) This is an average figure. The amount of carotene in leafy vegetables depends upon the amount of chlorophyll, and outer green leaves may contain 50 times as much as inner white ones.

(²) Raw shredded cabbage may contain 20 per cent. less.

(³) Bulb only. Leaves contain about 2 mg.

(⁴) Canned processed peas may contain no ascorbic acid.

(⁵)	Raw Potatoes	Ascorbic acid mg. per 100 g.
	Early	30
	Maincrop, freshly dug	30
	,, stored for 1–3 months ..	20
	,, stored for 4–5 months ..	15
	,, stored for 6–7 months ..	10
	,, stored for 8–9 months ..	8

Vegetables—continued

(⁶)

Method of cooking	Ascorbic acid as percentage of value in raw potato
Boiled, peeled	50–70
Boiled, unpeeled	60–80
Baked	
Roast	
Steamed	
Fried in deep fat (chips)	65–75

(⁷) There is considerable variation according to variety; some yellow sweet potatoes contain 12 mg. but the white variety only a trace.

Sugar, Preserves and Sweetmeats

Food	Carotene (mg.)	Vitamin D (i.u.)	Thiamine (mg.)	Ribo-flavine (mg.)	Nicotinic acid (mg.)	Ascorbic acid (mg.)
Blackcurrant purée ..	Tr.	0	—	—	—	55
Chocolate	0·04	—	0·03	0·35	1·0	0
Honey	0	0	Tr.	0·05	0·20	Tr.
Jam, blackcurrant ..	Tr.	0	Tr.	Tr.	Tr.	50
Jam, gooseberry, raspberry, redcurrant, strawberry	Tr.	0	Tr.	Tr.	Tr.	10
Jelly, blackcurrant ..	Tr.	0	Tr.	Tr.	Tr.	25
Jelly, redcurrant	Tr.	0	Tr.	Tr.	Tr.	5
Marmalade	0·05	0	Tr.	Tr.	Tr.	10

The following contain no more than a trace of any of these vitamins:—sugar, syrup, boiled sweets, toffee, jam made with stone fruits, apple and blackberry jelly, and packet jelly.

Beverages

Food	Carotene (mg.)	Vitamin D (i.u.)	Thiamine (mg.)	Ribo-flavine (mg.)	Nicotinic acid (mg.)	Ascorbic acid (mg.)
Cocoa powder	0·04	0	0·08	0·30	1·7	0
Coffee, ground, roasted ..	—	0	—	0·20(¹)	10(¹,²)	0
Orange juice, concentrated M.A.F.F.	Tr.	0	—	—	—	150
Ribena	Tr.	0	—	—	—	55
Rose hip syrup	0	0	—	—	—	150
Tea, Indian	0	0	—	0·90(¹)	6·0(¹)	0

(¹) 90–100 per cent. is extracted into an infusion.

(²) Increases during roasting of coffee beans; a dark roasted variety may contain 3 or 4 times as much.

Fruit squashes may or may not contain any natural ascorbic acid and some have the synthetic vitamin added to them; undiluted dairy "orange drink" contains only a trace of ascorbic acid.

Alcoholic Beverages

Food	Carotene (mg.)	Vitamin D (i.u.)	Thiamine (mg.)	Ribo-flavine (mg.)	Nicotinic acid (mg.)	Ascorbic acid (mg.)
Beers, ales and stout ..	Tr.	0	0·004	0·05	0·7	0
Strong ale	Tr.	0	0·01	0·10	1·5	0
Ciders	Tr.	0	Tr.	0·02	0·07	Tr.
Table wine, red. Port ..	Tr.	0	0·005	0·02	0·15	0
Table wine, white. Champagne, sherry	Tr.	0	0·003	0·01	0·08	0

Spirits contain none of any of these vitamins.

PANTOTHENIC ACID, VITAMIN B_6, BIOTIN, FOLIC ACID, VITAMIN B_{12}, TOCOPHEROLS

per 100 grams

Cereals and Cereal Foods

Food	Panto-thenic acid (mg.)	Vitamin B (mg.)	Biotin (μg.)	Folic acid (μg.)	Vitamin B_{12} (μg.)	Toco-pherols (total) (mg.)
Bread, wholemeal ..	0·7	0·30	2·0	20	0	1·9
Flour, whole wheat, 100% extraction	1·5	0·40	5·0	35	0	2·6
Flour, white, mixed grist, basic grade	0·8	0·10	0·8	14	0	1·7
Flour, white, mixed grist, patent	—	0·10	0·5	7	0	—
Oatmeal, raw	1·0	0·12	20·0	30	0	2·0[1]
Oatmeal, porridge ..	0·1	0·01	—	—	0	—
Rice, polished, raw ..	0·6	0·30	3·0	10	0	0·4[2]
Rye, 100% extraction ..	1·0	0·35	6·0	30	0	3·0

[1] About 90 per cent. is α-tocopherol.

[2] About 60 per cent. is α-tocopherol.

Milk Products and Eggs

Food	Pantothenic acid (mg.)	Vitamin B_6 (mg.)	Biotin (μg.)	Folic acid (μg.)	Vitamin B_{12} (μg.)	Tocopherols (total) (mg.)
Milk and milk products						
Butter	Tr.	Tr.	—	—	—	Summer 2·3([2],[3]) Winter 1·6([2],[3])
Cheese, Cheddar (34·5% fat)	0·30	0·05	2·0	—	2·0	1·0([2],[3])
Cream, double (48% fat)	0·19([1])	0·03([1])	—	—	—	Summer 1·3([2],[3]) Winter 0·91([2],[3])
Cream, single (18–48% fat)	0·30([1])	0·05([1])	—	—	—	Summer 0·49([2],[3]) Winter 0·34([2],[3])
Milk, whole, raw.. ..	0·35	0·04	2·0	0·3	0·3	Summer 0·10([3]) Winter 0·07([3])
Milk, whole, pasteurised	0·35	0·04	2·0	0·3	0·3	—
Milk, whole, sterilized ..	0·35	0·04([4])	2·0	—	Tr.	—
Milk, skimmed	0·36	0·04	2·0	0·3	0·3	Tr.([3])
Milk, condensed, whole, sweetened	0·85	0·06	3·0	—	0·5	—
Milk, condensed, whole, unsweetened	0·85	0·03([4])	3·0([4])	0·7	Tr.	0·20([3])
Milk, dried, skimmed ..	3·5	0·40	16	2·4	2·0	—
Milk, dried, whole ..	2·7	0·30	13	—	2·0	—
Human milk	0·20	0·01	Tr.	0·2	0·1	0·30
Eggs						
Eggs, whole, raw ..	1·3	0·25	25([5])	8([6])	0·7([7],[8])	2·0([9])
Egg white, raw	0·3	0·01	([5])	1·5([6])	0·08([7],[8])	—
Egg yolk, raw	3·5	0·75	60([5])	22([6])	1·8([7],[8])	—

([1]) Calculated from the values for whole milk and the percentage of non-fat material in milk and cream.

([2]) Calculated from the total tocopherols in whole milk and the percentage of fat in milk and cream or butter.

([3]) In both cow's and human milk the total tocopherols are mainly α-tocopherol.

([4]) There may be an appreciable loss of biological availability during manufacture.

([5]) Nearly all present in egg yolk. Raw egg white contains the natural antibiotin, avidin, and when this is mixed with the yolk, the avidin in the white binds with the biotin in the yolk to form a complex unavailable to man. Avidin in cooked egg white is inactive.

([6]) About half the folic acid may be lost on cooking.

([7]) Assuming the hens have been fed a normal English commercial breeders' ration containing animal protein and about 1·2 μg. vitamin B_{12} per 100 g. ration.

([8]) Value for fresh eggs; there is likely to be a loss on storage.

([9]) About 60 per cent. is α-tocopherol.

Meat and Poultry

(For the effect of cooking on these vitamins in meat and poultry, see p. 186)

Raw Food	Panto-thenic acid (mg.)	Vitamin B_6 (mg.)	Biotin (μg.)	Folic acid (μg.)	Vitamin B_{12} (μg.)	Toco-pherols (total) (mg.)
Bacon	0·3	0·30	7·0	—	—	0·5[1]
Beef	0·4	0·30	3·0	10	2	0·6[2]
Brain, ox or pig	2·5		—	—	4	—
Chicken	Breast 0·7 Leg 1·0	Breast 1·0 Leg —	10·0	3	—	0·2[1]
Ham	0·5	0·50	5·0	8	1	—
Heart	2·0	0·20	8·0	3	10	—
Kidney, ox	4	0·70	80	60	25	—
Kidney, pig	3	—	150	—	7	—
Liver, ox	8	0·70	100	300	50	1·4[3]
Liver, pig	7	0·50	80	220	30	—
Liver, sheep	7	0·30	100	280	30	—
Mutton and lamb ..	0·5	0·35	3·0	3	2	0·8[1]
Pork	0·6	0·50	4·0	3	2	0·7[4]
Veal	0·6	0·30	5·0	5	—	—

[1] About 80–84 per cent. is α-tocopherol.
[2] About 75 per cent. is α-tocopherol.
[3] About 100 per cent. is α-tocopherol.
[4] About 90 per cent. is α-tocopherol.

Fish

Food	Panto-thenic acid (mg.)	Vitamin B_6 (mg.)	Biotin (μg.)	Folic acid (μg.)	Vitamin B_{12} (μg.)	Toco-pherols (total) (mg.)
White fish, raw						
Cod .. .. ⎫ Haddock .. .. ⎬ Halibut .. .. ⎭	0·20	0·20	10	50	1	—
Fatty fish						
Herring, raw	1·0	0·45	—	—	10	—
Mackerel, raw	—	0·70	—	—	5	—
Salmon, canned	0·50	0·30	10	5	2	—
Sardines, canned in oil ..	0·50	0·16	5	2	10	—
Shell fish						
Crab, boiled or canned ..	0·60	0·35	—	Tr.	0·5	—
Oyster, raw	0·50	0·03	10	240	15	—
Shrimps, boiled or canned	0·30	0·10	—	2	—	—

Fruit

(For the effect of cooking on these vitamins in fruit, see p. 187)

Food	Panto- thenic acid (mg.)	Vitamin B_6 (mg.)	Biotin (µg.)	Folic acid (µg.)	Vitamin B_{12} (µg.)	Toco- pherols (total) (mg.)
Apples, raw	0·07	0·03	0·3	1	0	0·7[1]
Apricots, raw	0·30	—	—	3	0	—
Apricots, canned	0·10	0·05	—	Tr.	0	—
Apricots, dried, raw	0·70	—	—	5	0	—
Bananas, raw	0·20	0·30	—	10	0	0·4[2]
Blackberries, raw	0·25	0·05	0·4	12	0	—
Cherries, eating, raw	0·08	0·05	0·4	6	0	—
Currants, black, raw	0·40	0·08	2·4	—	0	—
Currants, red, raw	0·06	0·05	2·6	—	0	—
Damsons, raw	0·27	—	0·1	—	0	—
Dates, dried	0·80	0·10	—	25	0	—
Figs, green, raw	0·40	0·13	—	10	0	—
Figs, dried, raw	0·50	0·32	—	30	0	—
Gooseberries, green, raw	0·15	0·02	0·5	—	0	—
Gooseberries, ripe, raw	0·30	—	0·1	—	0	—
Grapes, raw	0·05	0·10	—	6	0	—
Grapefruit, raw	0·25	0·02	—	3	0	0·3[1]
Grapefruit or grapefruit juice, canned	0·13	0·02	1·0	Tr.	0	—
Lemons, raw	0·20	0·06	—	7	0	—
Melon, raw	0·23	0·04	—	6	0	—
Olives, canned	0·02	0·02	—	1	0	—
Oranges or orange juice, raw	0·25	0·03	1·0	5	0	0·2[1]
Orange juice, canned	0·15	0·03	0·8	Tr.	0	—
Peaches, raw	0·15	0·02	—	2	0	—
Peaches, canned	0·05	0·02	0·2	Tr.	0	—
Pears, eating, raw	0·05	0·02	0·1	2	0	—
Pears, canned	0·02	Tr.	—	Tr.	0	—
Pineapple, raw	0·17	—	—	4	0	—
Pineapple or pineapple juice, canned	0·10	0·20	—	Tr.	0	—
Plums, raw	0·15	0·05	Tr.	2	0	—
Prunes, dried, raw	0·35	0·50	—	5	0	—
Prunes, canned	0·10	—	—	Tr.	0	—
Raspberries, raw	0·20	0·09	1·9	5	0	—
Rhubarb, raw	0·08	0·04	—	3	0	—
Strawberries, raw	0·10	0·04	1·1	5	0	—

[1] About 96–97 per cent. is α-tocopherol.
[2] About 92 per cent. is α-tocopherol.

Nuts

Raw Food	Panto-thenic acid (mg.)	Vitamin B_6 (mg.)	Biotin (μg.)	Folic acid (μg.)	Vitamin B_{12} (μg.)	Toco-pherols (total) (mg.)
Almonds	0·08[1]	0·06	0·4[1]	45	0	—
Brazil nuts	—	1·0	—	4	0	—
Chestnuts	0·30[1]	—	1·3[1]	—	0	—
Coconuts	—	0·06	—	28	0	—
Peanuts	2·7	—	—	55	0	—
Walnuts, mature	0·70[1]	1·0	2·0[1]	77	0	—

[1] Value for peeled kernel.

Vegetables

(For the effect of cooking on these vitamins in vegetables, see p. 187)

Food	Panto-thenic acid (mg.)	Vitamin B_6 (mg.)	Biotin (μg.)	Folic acid (μg.)	Vitamin B_{12} (μg.)	Toco-pherols (total) (mg.)
Asparagus, raw	0·18	0·06	0·5	100	0	—
Asparagus, canned ..	0·15	0·03	1·7	6	—	—
Beans, broad, raw ..	5·4	—	3·2	—	0	—
Beans, French, raw ..	0·10	0·10	1·2	—	0	—
Beans, runner, raw ..	0·05	—	0·7	—	0	—
Beet greens, raw	0·20	—	—	50	0	—
Beetroot, raw ..	0·12	0·05	Tr.	20	0	—
Broccoli tops, raw ..	1·0	—	—	50	0	—
Brussels sprouts, raw ..	0·40	0·28	0·4	30	0	—
Cabbage, raw	0·18	0·12	0·1	20	0	0·1[1]
Carrots, raw	0·25	0·10	0·6	10	0	0·5[2]
Carrots, canned	0·10	0·02	1·5	2	—	—
Cauliflower, raw	0·60	0·20	1·5	30	0	—
Celery, raw	0·40	0·10	0·1	7	0	0·5[3]
Cucumber, raw	0·30	0·04	—	6	0	—
Kale, raw	0·30	0·35	0·5	50	0	—
Leeks, raw	0·12	0·25	1·4	—	0	—
Lettuce, raw	0·10	0·07	0·7	20	0	0·5[1]
Marrow, raw	0·10	0·05	0·4	—	0	—
Mushrooms, raw ..	2·0	0·10	—	20	0	—
Onions, raw	0·10	0·10	0·9	10	0	0·3[4]
Parsley, raw	0·03	0·20	0·4	40	0	—
Parsnips, raw	0·50	0·10	0·1	20	0	—
Peas, raw	1·5	0·16	0·5	20	0	2·1[5]
Peas, canned	0·15	0·05	2·0	2	—	—
Peas, split, dried, raw ..	2·0	0·30	—	20	0	—
Potatoes, raw	0·30	0·20	0·1	6	0	0·1

Vegetables—continued

(For the effect of cooking on these vitamins in vegetables, see p. 187)

Food	Panto-thenic acid (mg.)	Vitamin B_6 (mg.)	Biotin (µg.)	Folic acid (µg.)	Vitamin B_{12} (µg.)	Toco-pherols (total) (mg.)
Radishes, raw	0·18	0·10	—	10	0	—
Spinach, raw	0·30	0·10	0·1	80	0	—
Swedes, raw	0·11	0·20	0·1	5	0	—
Sweet potatoes, raw ..	0·94	—	—	10	0	4·0(^{2})
Tomatoes, raw	0·05	0·10	1·2	5	0	0·4(^{4})
Tomatoes, canned ..	0·2	0·07	1·8	3	—	—
Turnips, raw	0·02	0·11	0·1	4	0	—
Watercress, raw	0·10	—	0·4	50	0	—

(^{1}) About 55–60 per cent. is α-tocopherol.
(^{2}) 100 per cent. is α-tocopherol.
(^{3}) About 96 per cent. is α-tocopherol.
(^{4}) About 75–80 per cent. is α-tocopherol.
(^{5}) About 5 per cent. is α-tocopherol and 95 per cent. γ and δ-tocopherol.

Alcoholic Beverages

Food	Panto-thenic acid (mg.)	Vitamin B_6 (mg.)	Biotin (µg.)	Folic acid (µg.)	Vitamin B_{12} (µg.)	Toco-pherols (total) (mg.)
Beers, ales and stout ..	0·10	0·06	0·5	—	—	—
Ciders	0·10	0·005	0·4	—	—	—
Table wine, red	0·04	0·05	—	2	—	—
Table wine, white ..	0·03	0·02	—	1	—	—

Spirits contain none of any of these vitamins.

References to Part II *

1. Abderhalden, R. (1948). Der Vitamin E—Gehalt der Frauen—und Kuhmilch. *Biochem. Z.*, **318**, 47.
2. Adam, W. B., Horner, G., and Stanworth, J. (1942). Changes occurring during the blanching of vegetables. *J. Soc. chem. Ind., Lond.*, **61**, 96.
3. Adrian, J. (1952). Teneurs de l'oeuf de poule en riboflavine, niacine et acide panto-thénique. Variabilité et corrélations. *Ann. Inst. nat. Rech. agron., Paris.* Series D Ann-Zootech., **1**, (3), 17.
4. Adrian, J. (1958). Variabilité et déterminisme des teneurs de l'oeuf de poule en certaines vitamines du groupe B. *Arch. Sci.physiol.*, **12**, 1.
5. Alexander, O. R. and Feaster, J. F. (1947). Thiamin and ascorbic acid values of raw and canned peas. *Food Res.*, **12**, 468.
6. Allen, D. I. (1943). The assay of vitamin B_1 in New Zealand materials by the thiochrome method. *J. Nutr.*, **25**, 521.
7. Allen, M. A. and Burgess, S. G. (1950). The losses of ascorbic acid during the large-scale cooking of green vegetables by different methods. *Brit. J. Nutr.*, **4**, 95.
8. Allen, R. J. L., Barker, J. and Mapson, L. W. (1943). The drying of vegetables. 1. Cabbage. *J. Soc. chem. Ind. Lond.*, **62**, 145.
9. Allen, R. J. L. and Mapson, L. W. (1944). The drying of vegetables. 2. The loss of ascorbic acid during cooking of fresh and dried cabbage. *J. Soc. chem. Ind. Lond.*, **63**, 78
10. Allinson, R. M. and Driver, C. M. (1953). The effect of variety, storage and locality on the ascorbic acid content of the potato tuber. *J. Sci. Food Agric.*, **4**, 386.
11. Alston, J. M. (1942). Vitamin C in fruit preparations. *Brit. med. J.*, i, 559.
12. Anderson, E. E., Fagerson, I. S., Hayes, K. M. and Fellers, C. R. (1954). Ascorbic acid and sodium chloride content of commercially canned tomato juice. *J. Amer. diet. Ass.*, **30**, 1250.
13. Anderson, E. E. and Fellers, C. R. (1942). The food value of mushrooms (*Agaricus campestris*). *Proc. Amer. Soc. hort. Sci.*, **41**, 301.
14. Andrews, J. S., Boyd, H. M. and Gortner, W. A. (1942). Nicotinic acid content of cereals and cereal products. Microbiological method of assay. *Industr. Engng. Chem. (Anal.)*, **14**, 663.
15. Andrews, J. S., Boyd, H. M. and Terry, D. E. (1942a). The riboflavine content of cereal grains and bread and its distribution in products of wheat milling. *Cereal Chem.*, **19**, 55.
16. Andrews, J. S., Boyd, H. M. and Terry, D. E. (1942b). Riboflavine analysis of cereals. Application of the microbiological method. *Industr. Engng. Chem. (Anal.)*, **14**, 271.
17. Andrews, M. M. and Schweigert, B. S. (1953). Studies on the measurement of the folic acid and citrovorum factor potencies of certain natural products. *Arch. Biochem.*, **44**, 165.
18. Andross, M. (1941). Vitamin C content of wild fruit products. *Analyst*, **66**, 358.
19. Andross, M. (1946). Losses of nutrients in the preparation of foodstuffs. Some aspects of the waste problem: cooking and plate waste. *Proc. Nutr. Soc.*, **4**, 155.
20. Andross, M. (1949). Effect of cooking on meat. *Brit. J. Nutr.*, **3**, 396.

*When an abstract number in Nutrition Abstracts and Reviews is given, or when it is stated "quoted by Fixsen and Roscoe 1939–40," the reviewers did not have access to the original paper.

21. Aschehoug, V., Kringstad, H. and Lunde, G. (1939). The vitamin-D potency of different fish and fish products. *J. Soc. chem. Ind., Lond.,* **58,** 220.

22. Asenjo, C. F. and Muñiz, A. I. (1955). Pantothenic acid content of tropical foods. *Food Res.,* **20,** 47.

23. Askew, H. O. and Kidson, E. B. (1947). Changes in vitamin C content and acidity of apples during cool storage. *N.Z.J. Sci. Tech.* (A), **28,** 344.

24. Asp, E., Noble, I. and Gomez, L. (1953). Thiamine and riboflavin retention in veal. *J. Amer. diet. Ass.,* **29,** 251.

25. Atkin, L., Schultz, A. S., Williams, W. L. and Frey, C. N. (1943). Yeast microbiological methods for determination of vitamins. Pyridoxine. *Industr. Engng. Chem. (Anal.),* **15,** 141.

26. Aughey, E. and Daniel, E. P. (1940). Effect of cooking upon the thiamin content of foods. *J. Nutr.,* **19,** 285.

27. Ayres, A. and Fallows, P. (1951). The chemical composition of some English market apples and their juices. *J. Sci. Food Agric.,* **2,** 488.

28. Bacharach, A. L. (1941). The distribution of nicotinic acid in human and animal foods. *Nutr. Abstr. Rev.,* **10,** 459.

29. Bacharach, A. L. (1942). The nation's food. V. Meat as food. 4. The mineral and vitamin content of meat. *Chem. & Ind. (Rev.),* **61,** 404.

30. Bacharach, A. L. and Coates, M. E. (1945). A note on day to day variations in the vitamin-C content of bought and culled vegetables. *Chem. & Ind. (Rev.),* No. 2, 10.

31. Bacharach, A. L., Cruickshank, E. M., Henry, K. M., Kon, S. K., Lovern, J. A., Moore, T. and Morton, R. A. (1942). The herring as a source of vitamins A and D: a collaborative investigation. *Brit. med. J.,* ii, 691.

32. Bailey, B. E. (1942). Chart of the nutritive values of British Columbia fishery products. *Fish. Res. Bd. Canada, Progr. Rep. Pac. coast Stat.,* No. 53, 9.

33. Bailey, B. E. (Ed.), Carter, N. M. and Swain, L. A. (1952). Marine oils with particular reference to those of Canada. *Fish. Res. Bd. Can. Bull.* No. 89, 66.

34. Bailey, E. A. (Jr.), Dann, W. J., Satterfield, G. H. and Grinnells, C. D. (1941). A method for the estimation of nicotinic acid in milk. *J. Dairy Sci.,* **24,** 1047.

35. Bailey, M. I. and Thomas, A. W. (1942). The thiamine and riboflavin contents of citrus fruits. *J. Nutr.,* **24,** 85.

36. Baird, E. A. and Howatt, J. L. (1948). Ascorbic acid in potatoes grown in New Brunswick. *Canad. J. Res.* (C), **26,** 433.

37. Baker, A. Z. and Wright, M. D. (1935). The vitamin B_1 content of foods. *Biochem. J.,* **29,** 1802.

38. Baker, A. Z. and Wright, M. D. (1938). The vitamin B_1 content of foods. II. Additional values. *Biochem. J.,* **32,** 2156.

39. Baker, L. C. (1947). Nutritional aspects of the chemical preservation, colouring and flavouring of fruit and vegetables. *Brit. J. Nutr.,* **1,** 258.

40. Baker, L. C., Lampitt, L. H., Money, R. W. and Parkinson, T. L. (1950). The composition and cooking quality of potatoes from fertilizer trials in the East Riding of Yorkshire. *J. Sci. Food Agric.,* **1,** 109.

41. Baker, L. C. and Parkinson, T. L. (1947). Vitamin C content of vegetables. 6. Tomatoes. *J. Soc. chem. Ind., Lond.,* **66,** 1.

42. Baker, L. C., Parkinson, T. L. and Knight, P. M. (1948). The vitamin C content of potatoes grown on reclaimed land. 2. Potatoes grown in 1946. *J. Soc. chem. Ind., Lond.,* **67,** 118.

43. Baker, L. C., Parkinson, T. L. and Lampitt, L. H. (1946). The vitamin C content of potatoes grown on reclaimed land. *J. Soc. chem. Ind., Lond.,* **65,** 428.

44. Bamford, E. and Fenton, F. (1953). Home-freezing vs. home-canning of peas. Palatability, ascorbic acid, total solids, and color. *J. Amer. diet. Ass.,* **29,** 1221.

45. Bandier, E. (1939). Quantitative estimation of nicotinic acid in biological material. *Biochem. J.,* **33,** 1130.

46. Barnes, B., Tressler, D. K. and Fenton, F. (1943). Thiamin content of fresh and frozen peas and corn before and after cooking. *Food Res.*, **8**, 420.

47. Barnicoat, C. R. (1947). Variations in the carotene and vitamin A contents of certain New Zealand butterfats. *J. Dairy Res.*, **15**, 80.

48. Barton-Wright, E. C. (1944). The microbiological assay of nicotinic acid in cereals and other products. *Biochem. J.*, **38**, 314.

49. Barton-Wright, E. C., Moran, T. and Sarson, H. S. (1943). Riboflavin and vitamin B₁ in nineteenth century buns and ale. *Nature, Lond.*, **152**, 273.

50. Bedford, C. L. and McGregor, M. A. (1948). Effect of canning on the ascorbic acid and thiamine in vegetables. *J. Amer. diet. Ass.*, **24**, 866.

51. Bell, T. A., Yarbrough, M., Clegg, R. E. and Satterfield, G. H. (1942). Ascorbic acid content of seven varieties of muscadine grapes. *Food Res.*, **7**, 144.

52. Benne, E. J. (1942). Report on chlorophyll and carotene in plant tissue. *J. Ass. off. agric. Chem., Wash.*, **25**, 573.

53. Berl, S. and Peterson, W. H. (1943). Determination and content of carotene and vitamin A in Wisconsin butter. *J. Nutr.*, **26**, 527.

54. Berl, S. and Peterson, W. H. (1945). Distribution of carotene and vitamin A in butter-making. *J. Dairy Sci.*, **28**, 103.

55. Bessey, O. A. (1938). A method for the determination of small quantities of ascorbic acid and dehydroascorbic acid in turbid and coloured solutions in the presence of other reducing substances. *J. biol. Chem.*, **126**, 771.

56. Biswas, H. G. and Das, K. L. (1939). Vitamin-C content of the chillies, onion and garlic, both in the raw state and when boiled with water. *Indian J. med. Res.*, **27**, 135. (*Nutr. Abstr. Rev.*, 1939, **9**, *Abstr.* 3062).

57. Blaxter, K. L., Kon, S. K. and Thompson, S. Y. (1946). The effect of feeding shark-liver oil to cows on the yield and composition, and on the vitamin A and carotene content of the milk. *J. Dairy Res.*, **14**, 225.

58. Bohren, B. B. and Hauge, S. M. (1946). Vitamin A retention in dried eggs as affected by compression and packaging in tin cans. *Food Res.*, **11**, 39.

59. Boisselot, J. and Causeret, J. (1946). Recherches experimentales sur le lait de vache actinisé. II. Influence de l'actinisation sur la teneur du lait en vitamine B₁ et en vitamine B₂. *Bull. Soc. sci. Hyg. aliment., Paris*, **34**, 176.

60. Bondi, A. and Meyer, H. (1946a). Carotene in Palestinian crops. *J. agric. Sci.*, **36**, 1.

61. Bondi, A. and Meyer, H. (1946b). The riboflavin content of poultry feeding stuffs. *J. agric. Sci.*, **36**, 6.

62. Booher, L. E. and Hartzler, E. R. (1939). The vitamin B₁ content of foods in terms of crystalline thiamin. *Tech. Bull. U.S. Dep. Agric.*, No. 707.

63. Booher, L. E., Hartzler, E. R. and Hewston, E. M. (1942). A compilation of the vitamin values of foods in relation to processing and other variants. *Circ. U.S. Dep. Agric.*, No. 638.

64. Booher, L. E. and Marsh, R. L. (1941). The vitamin A values of 128 foods as determined by the rat-growth method. *Tech. Bull. U.S. Dep. Agric.*, No. 802.

65. Booth, R. G. and Barton-Wright, E. C. (1944). Nicotinic acid and riboflavin in beef extracts and corned beef. *Lancet*, **246**, 565.

66. Booth, R. G., James, G. V., Marrack, J. R., Payne, W. W. and Wokes, F. (1942). Ascorbic Acid in Meals in British Restaurants and School Canteens. *Lancet*, **243**, 569.

67. Booth, V. (1942). Carotene as provitamin A. *Food Manuf.*, **17**, 60.

68. Booth, V. H. (1945). Simplified procedure for estimation of total carotenoids in carrots. *J. Soc. chem. Ind., Lond.*, **64**, 194.

69. Booth, V. H. (1947). The relationship between carotene concentration and vitamin A activity of carrots for rats. *Brit. J. Nutr.*, **1**, 113.

70. Booth, V. H. (1951a). Distribution of carotenoids in different parts of the carrot. *J. Sci. Food Agric.*, **2**, 350.

71. Booth, V. H. (1951b). Chromogenesis in stored carrots. *J. Sci. Food Agric.*, **2**, 353.

72. Booth, V. H. (1957). *Carotene, its determination in biological materials.* W. Heffer and Sons Ltd., Cambridge.

73. Booth, V. H. and Dark, S. O. S. (1949). The influence of environment and maturity on total carotenoids in carrots. *J. agric. Sci.*, **39**, 226.

74. Bradford, E. A. M. and Hughes, E. B. (1945a). The riboflavin content of tea and some results for the pantothenic acid content. *Analyst*, **70**, 2.

75. Bradford, E. A. M. and Hughes, E. B. (1945b). The riboflavin content of tea. *Analyst*, **70**, 86.

76. Brady, D. E., Peterson, W. J. and Shaw, A. O. (1944a). Riboflavin and thiamin contents of pork loin muscles and their retention during cooking. *Food Res.*, **9**, 400.

77. Brady, D. E., Peterson, W. J. and Shaw, A. O. (1944b). Riboflavin content of beef. *Food Res.*, **9**, 406.

78. Braekkan, O. R. (1956). Function of the red muscle in fish. *Nature, Lond.*, **178**, 747.

79. Braekkan, O. R. and Probst, A. (1953). Vitaminer i norsk fisk. 1. Nikotinsyre—, riboflavin—, pantotensyre—, vitamin B₁₂—og vitamin A—innholdet i hel fisk og forskjellige orgaaner fra fersk sild (*Clupea harengus*) og makrell (*Scomber scombrus*). *Fiskeridir. Skr. Ser. Teknol Under-Søkelser.* **11**, No. 13.

80. Branion, H. D. (1934). Vitamin D content of egg yolk. *U.S. Egg Poultry Mag.*, **40**, Jul. 20.

81. Branion, H. D. and Cameron, C. R. (1947). The retention of ascorbic acid in canned fruit juices and tomatoes during storage after opening. *Canad. J. publ. Hlth.*, **38**, 283.

82. Branion, H. D., Roberts, J. S., Allman, R. T., Billingsley, L. W. and Woodward, H. E. (1947). The ascorbic acid content of some foods commonly used in Canada. *Canad. J. publ. Hlth.*, **38**, 330.

83. Branion, H. D., Roberts, J. S. and Cameron, C. R. (1947). The loss of ascorbic acid in potatoes during storage. *J. Amer diet. Ass.*, **23**, 420.

84. Branion, H. D., Roberts, J. S., Cameron, C. R. and McCready, A. M. (1947). The loss of ascorbic acid in the preparation of old and freshly harvested potatoes. *J. Amer. diet. Ass.*, **23**, 414.

85. Branion, H. D., Roberts, J. S., Cameron, C. R. and McCready, A. M. (1948). The ascorbic acid content of cabbage. *J. Amer. diet. Ass.*, **24**, 101.

86. Bray, H. G. and Thorpe, W. V. (1944). Sampling of cooked cabbage in nutrition surveys. The sampling of cooked cabbage for estimation of ascorbic acid in nutrition surveys. *Nature, Lond.*, **154**, 638. *Biochem. J.*, **38**, xxiii.

87. Brence, J. L. and Nelson, J. A. (1949). The vitamin A potency of Montana butter. *Bull. Mont. agric. Exp. Sta.*, No. 465.

88. Brence, J. L. and Nelson, J. A. (1951a). The vitamin A potency of fresh and of stored butter made from sweet and from neutralized sour cream. *J. Dairy Sci.*, **34**, 949.

89. Brence, J. L. and Nelson, J. A. (1951b). A comparison of the vitamin A potency of milk fat from cows fed on dry feed and on green pasture. *J. Dairy Sci.*, **34**, 960.

90. Briant, A. M., MacKenzie, V. E. and Fenton, F. (1946a). Vitamin retention in frozen peas and frozen green beans in quantity food service. *J. Amer. diet. Ass.*, **22**, 507.

91. Briant, A. M., MacKenzie, V. E. and Fenton, F. (1946b). Vitamin content of frozen peas, green beans and lima beans, and market-fresh yams prepared in a Navy mess hall. *J. Amer. diet. Ass.*, **22**, 605.

92. Briggs, G. M. and Daft, F. S. (1954). In *The vitamins: chemistry, physiology, pathology*, edited by W. H. Sebrell (Jr). and R. S. Harris, Vol. II, p. 634. Academic Press Inc. New York.

93. Bro-Rasmussen, F. (1956). Statens Vitamin-Laboratoriums undersøgelser over danske mejeriprodukters indhold af A-vitamin og caroten. *Statens Husholdningsrads Faglige Medd.*, No. **10**, 37.

94. Brown, A. P. and Moser, F. (1941). Vitamin C content of tomatoes. *Food Res.*, **6**, 45.

95. Brown, E. J. and Fenton, F. (1942). Losses of vitamin C during cooking of parsnips. *Food Res.*, **7**, 218.

96. Brown, E. J., Schuele, H. and Fenton, F. (1941). Loss of vitamin C during cooking of rhubarb. *Food Res.*, **6**, 217.

97. Brown, F. (1952a). The estimation of vitamin E. 1. Separation of tocopherol mixtures occurring in natural products by paper chromotography. *Biochem. J.*, **51**, 237.

98. Brown, F. (1952b). The estimation of vitamin E. 2. Quantitative analysis of tocopherol mixtures by paper chromotography. *Biochem. J.*, **52**, 523.

99. Brown, F. (1953). The tocopherol content of farm feeding stuffs. *J. Sci. Food Agric.*, **4**, 161.

100. Brush, M. K., Hinman, W. F. and Halliday, E. G. (1944). The nutritive value of canned foods. 5. Distribution of water soluble vitamins between solid and liquid portions of canned vegetables and fruits. *J. Nutr.*, **28**, 131.

101. Bryan, J. D. and Pollard, A. (1947). The effect of manurial treatment on the composition of blackcurrants. *Rep. agric. hort. Rer. Sta., Bristol*, p. 216.

102. *Bull. Minist. Fd.*, No. 742. H.M. Stationery Office, London.

103. Burger, M., Hein, L. W., Teply, L. J., Derse, P. H. and Krieger, C. H. (1956). Vitamin, mineral and proximate composition of frozen fruits, juices and vegetables. *J. agric. Food Chem.*, **4**, 418.

104. Burkhart, L. and Lineberry, R. A. (1942). Determination of vitamin C and its sampling variation in strawberries. *Food Res.*, **7**, 332.

105. Burkholder, P. R., Collier, J. and Moyer, D. (1943). Synthesis of vitamins by micro-organisms in relation to vitamin content of fancy cheeses. *Food Res.*, **8**, 314.

106. Burrell, R. C., Brown, H. D. and Ebright, V. R. (1940). Ascorbic acid content of cabbage as influenced by variety, season, and soil fertility. *Food Res.*, **5**, 247.

107. Burrell, R. C. and Ebright, V. R. (1940). The vitamin C content of fruits and vegetables. *J. chem. Educ.*, **17**, 180.

108. Cailleau, R., Adrian, J. and Lévy, J. (1949). Teneur de différénts types de fromage en riboflavine, niacine et acide pantothénique. *Ann. agron., Paris*, **19**, 443.

109. Cailleau, R. and Chevillard, L. (1949). Teneur de quelques vins francais en aneurine, riboflavine, acide nicotinique et acide pantothénique. *Ann. agron., Paris*, **19**, 277.

110. Cailleau, R., Kidder, L. E. and Morgan, A. F. (1945). The thiamine content of raw and parboiled rices. *Cereal Chem.*, **22**, 50.

111. Callison, E. C., Bear, J. E. and Orent-Keiles, E. (1948). The effect of cooking on some nutrients in soy grits. *J. Amer. diet. Ass.*, **24**, 966.

112. Callison, E. C. and Orent-Keiles, E. (1947). Availability of carotene from carrots and further observations on human requirements for vitamin A and carotene. *J. Nutr.*, **34**, 153.

113. Callison, E. C., Orent-Keiles, E., Frenchman, R. and Zook, E. G. (1949). Comparison of chemical analysis and bioassay as measures of vitamin A value of some vegetables and the effect of comminution upon the bioassay value. *J. Nutr.*, **37**, 139.

114. Campbell, R., Hiltz, M. C. and Robinson, A. D. (1946). The thiamin content of meat. *Canad. J. Res. (F)*, **24**, 140.

115. Carroll, J. C. and Lee Peng, C. (1951). A comparison of the niacin and pantothenic acid content of certain cereal grains grown under the same environmental conditions. *Science*, **113**, 211.

116. Causey, K., Andreassen, E. G., Hausrath, M. E., Along, C., Ranstad, P. E. and Fenton, F. (1950). Effect of thawing and cooking methods on palatability and nutritive value of frozen ground meat. 1. Pork. *Food Res.*, **15**, 237.

117. Causey, K. and Fenton, F. (1950). Effects of four cooking pressures on commercially frozen broccoli. *J. Home Econ.*, **42**, 649.

118. Causey, K. and Fenton, F. (1951). Effect of reheating on palatability, nutritive value, and bacterial count of frozen cooked foods. 1. Vegetables. *J. Amer. diet. Ass.*, **27**, 390.

119. Causey, K., Hausrath, M. E., Ramstad, P. E. and Fenton, F. (1950a). Effect of thawing and cooking methods on palatability and nutritive value of frozen ground meat. 2. Beef. *Food Res.*, **15**, 249.

120. Causey, K., Hausrath, M. E., Ramstad, P. E. and Fenton, F. (1950b). Effect of thawing and cooking methods on palatability and nutritive value of frozen ground meat 3. Lamb. *Food Res.*, **15**, 256.

121. Chanda, R. (1953a). The effect of mastitis on the carotenoids, vitamin A and phosphorus compounds of milk. *Biochem. J.*, **54**, 68.

122. Chanda, R. (1953b). The partition of carotenoids and vitamin A in the colostrum and milk of the cow and the goat. *J. agric. Sci.*, **43**, 54.

123. Chanda, R. and Owen, E. C. (1952). The partition of phosphorus and aneurin in relation to phosphatase in the colostrum and milk of the cow. *J. agric. Sci.*, **42**, 403.

124. Chanda, R., Owen, E. C. and Cramond, B. (1951). The composition of human milk with special reference to the relation between phosphorus partition and phosphatase and to the partition of certain vitamins. *Brit. J. Nutr.*, **5**, 228.

125. Chapman, H. R., Ford, J. E., Kon, S. K., Thompson, S. Y., Rowland, S. J., Crossley, E. L. and Rothwell, J. (1957). Further studies of the effect of processing on some vitamins of the B complex in milk. *J. Dairy Res.*, **24**, 191.

126. Chappell, G. M. (1940). The distribution of vitamin C in foods sold on the open market. *J. Hyg., Camb.*, **40**, 699.

127. Chappell, G. M. and Hamilton, A. M. (1949). Effect of pressure cooking on vitamin C content of vegetables. *Brit. med. J.*, **i**, 574.

128. Charkey, L. W., Dyar, E. and Wilgus, H. S. (Jr.) (1947). The nutrient content of high and low quality fresh eggs. 2. Vitamins. *Poult. Sci.*, **26**, 632.

129. Charles, V. R. and Van Duyne, F. O. (1952). Comparison of fresh, frozen concentrated, canned concentrated, and canned orange juice. *J. Amer. diet. Ass.*, **28**, 534.

130. Chatfield, C. (1949). Food composition tables for international use. *F.A.O. Nutritional Studies*, No. 3, United Nations Food and Agricultural Organization, Rome.

131. Chatfield, C. (1954). Food composition tables—minerals and vitamins—for international use. *F.A.O. Nutritional Studies*, No. 11, United Nations Food and Agricultural Organization, Rome.

132. Cheldelin, V. H. and Williams, R. R. (1942). Extraction and assay of nicotinic acid from animal and plant tissues. Comparison of methods. *Industr. Engng. Chem. (Anal.)*, **14**, 671.

133. Cheldelin, V. H. and Williams, R. J. (1942). The B vitamin content of foods. *Univ. Texas Publi.*, No. 4237, 103.

134. Cheldelin, V. H. ,Woods, A. M. and Williams, R. J. (1943). Losses of B vitamins due to cooking of foods. *J. Nutr.*, **26**, 477.

135. Chen, S. D., Elliott, K. J. and Schuck, C. (1948). Total, dehydro, and reduced ascorbic acid in cantaloupes. *J. Amer. diet. Ass.*, **24**, 863.

136. Chen, S. D. and Schuck, C. (1951). Diketogulonic acid, dehydroascorbic acid, and ascorbic acid content of four fruits. *Food Res.*, **16**, 507.

137. Chipault, J. R., Lundberg, W. O. and Burr, G. O. (1945). The chemical determination of tocopherols in animal fats: the stability of hog fats in relation to fatty acid composition and tocopherol contents. *Arch. Biochem.*, **8**, 321.

138. Clark, R. K. and Van Duyne, F. O. (1949). Cooking losses, tenderness, palatability, and thiamine and riboflavin content of beef as affected by roasting, pressure saucepan cooking, and broiling. *Food Res.*, **14**, 221.

139. Clark, V. and Ohlson, M. A. (1942). The ascorbic acid content of certain "dairy beverages". *J. Amer. diet. Ass.*, **18**, 460.

140. Clayton, M. M., Pressey, E. F. and Lees, K. H. (1948). Vitamin C content of home-canned tomatoes as determined by variety and method of processing. *Food Res.*, **13**, 36.

141. Clayton, M. M., Wells, B. O., Goos, C. and Murphy, E. F. (1944). Ascorbic acid content of vegetables as determined by variety and method of processing. *Bull. Me. agric. Exp. Sta.*, No. 426.

142. Clegg, K. M. (1958a). The microbiological determination of pantothenic acid in wheaten flour. *J. Sci. Food Agric.*, **9**, 366.

143. Clegg, K. M. (1958b). The microbiological determination of vitamin B₆ in wheaten flour, and in fractions of the wheat grain. *J. Sci. Food Agric.*, **9**, 717.

144. Clegg, K. M., Kodicek, E. and Mistry, S. P. (1952). A modified medium for *Lactobacillus casei* for the assay of B vitamins. *Biochem. J.*, **50**, 326.

145. Clemow, N. J. (1951). Riboflavin content of New Zealand Milks. *N.Z. J. Sci. Tech.* (*A*), **32**, 14.

146. Clifcorn, L. E. (1944). The nutritive value of canned foods. 1. Introduction and sampling procedure. *J. Nutr.*, **28**, 101.

147. Clifcorn, L. E. and Heberlein, D. G. (1944). Thiamine content of vegetables. Effect of commercial canning. *Industr. Engng. Chem.* (*Industr.*), **36**, 168.

148. Clouse, R. C. (1942). Compilation of recent data on mineral and vitamin values of foods· *J. Amer. diet. Ass.*, **18**, 553.

149. Clouse, R. C. (1943a). Compilation of recent data on mineral and vitamin values of foods. *J. Amer. diet. Ass.*, **19**, 496.

150. Clouse, R. C. (1943b). Compilation of recent data on mineral and vitamin values of foods. *J. Amer. diet. Ass.*, **19**, 746.

151. Coates, M. E., Ford, J. E., Harrison, G. F., Kon, S. K., Shepheard, E. E. and Wilby, F. W. (1952). The use of chicks for the biological assay of members of the vitamin B complex. 2. Tests on natural materials and comparison with microbiological and other assays. *Brit. J. Nutr.*, **6**, 75.

152. Collins, R. A., Boldt, R. E., Elvehjem, C. A. and Hart, E. B. (with Bomstein, R. A) (1953). Further studies on the folic acid and vitamin B₁₂ content of cow's milk. *J. Dairy Sci.*, **36**, 24.

153. Collins, R. A., Harper, A. E., Schreiber, M. and Elvehjem, C. A. (1951). The folic acid and vitamin B₁₂ content of the milk of various species. *J. Nutr.*, **43**, 313.

154. Committee on Milk and Dairy Products—American Health Association (1947). Food values of dairy products as affected by methods of handling in production, distribution and use. *Amer. J. publ. Hlth.*, **37**, 1113.

155. Conner, R. T. and Straub, G. J. (1941a). The thiamin and riboflavin contents of wheat and corn. *Cereal Chem.*, **18**, 671.

156. Conner, R. T. and Straub, G. J. (1941b). Combined determination of riboflavin and thiamin in food products. *Industr. Engng. Chem.* (*Anal.*), **13**, 385.

157. Cook, B. B., Morgan, A. F. and Smith, M. B. (1949). Thiamine, riboflavin, and niacin content of turkey tissues as affected by storage and cooking. *Food Res.*, **14**, 449.

158. Cooperman, J. M. and Elvehjem, C. A. (1944). The B vitamin content of groats and rolled oats. *J. Nutr.*, **27**, 329.

159. Cooperman, J. M. and Elvehjem, C. A. (1945). Retention of B vitamins in oatmeal during cooking. *J. Amer. diet. Ass.*, **21**, 155.

160. Copping, A. M. (1943). Riboflavin, vitamin B₆ and filtrate factors in wheaten flours and offals. *Biochem. J.*, **37**, 12.

161. Copping, A. M. (1946). Factors affecting the nutritive value of bread as human food. Vitamin values of different types of flour. *Proc. Nutr. Soc.*, **4**, 9.

162. Coryell, M. N., Harris, M. E., Miller, S., Williams, H. H. and Macy, I. G. (1945). Human milk studies. 22. Nicotinic acid, pantothenic acid and biotin contents of colostrum and mature human milk. *Amer. J. Dis. Child.*, **70**, 150.

163. Council for Scientific and Industrial Research, Australia (1947). The ascorbic acid and carotene content of some Australian fruits and vegetables. *J. Coun. sci. industr. Res., Aust.*, **20**, 1.

164. Cover, S. and Dilsaver, E. M. (1947a). Retention of the B vitamins in beef and lamb after stewing. 2. Thiamine. *J. Amer. diet. Ass.*, **23**, 613.

165. Cover, S. and Dilsaver, E. M. (1947b). Retention of the B vitamins in beef and lamb after stewing. 5. Riboflavin. *J. Amer. diet. Ass.*, **23**, 865.

166. Cover, S., Dilsaver, E. M. and Hays, R. M. (1947a). Retention of the B vitamins in beef and lamb after stewing. 1. Experimental design and standardized cooking procedure. *J. Amer. diet. Ass.*, **23**, 501.

167. Cover, S., Dilsaver, E. M. and Hays, R. M. (1947b). Retention of the B vitamins in beef and lamb after stewing. 3. Pantothenic acid. *J. Amer. diet. Ass.*, **23**, 693.

168. Cover, S., Dilsaver, E. M. and Hays, R. M. (1947c). Retention of the B vitamins in beef and lamb after stewing. 4. Niacin. *J. Amer. diet. Ass.*, **23**, 769.

169. Cover, S., Dilsaver, E. M. and Hays, R. M. (1947d). Retention of the B vitamins in beef and lamb after stewing. 6. Similarities and differences among the four vitamins. *J. Amer. diet. Ass.*, **23**, 962.

170. Cover, S., Dilsaver, E. M. and Hays, R. M. (1947e). Variation among lamb carcasses in the B vitamin content of meat. *Science*, **105**. 364.

171. Cover, S., Dilsaver, E. M. and Hays, R. M. (1948). Retention of B vitamins after large-scale cooking of meat. 1. Suitability of left and right muscles for retention studies. *Food Res.*, **13**, 472.

172. Cover, S., Dilsaver, E. M. and Hays, R. M. (1949). Retention of B vitamins in beef and veal after home canning and storage. *Food Res.*, **14**, 104.

173. Cover, S., Dilsaver, E. M., Hays, R. M. and Smith, W. H. (1949). Retention of B vitamins after large-scale cooking of meat. 2. Roasting by two methods. *J. Amer. diet. Ass.*, **25**, 949.

174. Cover, S., McLaren, B. A. and Pearson, P. B. (1944). Retention of the B vitamins in rare and well-done beef. *J. Nutr.*, **27**, 363.

175. Cover, S. and Smith, W. H. (1948). Effect on thiamin retention of adding a carbohydrate vegetable to beef stew. *Food Res.*, **13**, 475.

176. Cover, S. and Smith, W. H. (Jr.) (1952). Retention of thiamine and pantothenic acid in pork after stewing. *Food Res.*, **17**, 148.

177. Cover, S. and Smith, W. H. (Jr.) (1956a). Effect of moist and dry heat cooking on vitamin retention in meat from beef animals of different levels of fleshing. *Food Res.*, **21**, 209.

178. Cover, S. and Smith, W. H. (Jr.) (1956b). Variation in thiamine content of raw beef muscle. *J. Anim. Sci.*, **15**, 902.

179. Coward, K. H. and Morgan, B. G. E. (1935). Quantitative estimation of vitamins A and D in various food substances cooked and fresh. *Brit. med. J.*, ii, 1041.

180. Cowgill, G. R. (1934). *The vitamin-B requirements of man.* Oxford University Press.

181. Crang, A., James, D. and Sturdy, M. (1946). The retention of ascorbic acid and riboflavin in preserved vegetables. *Rep. agric. hort. Res. Sta., Bristol*, p. 145.

182. Crang, A., James, D. P. and Sturdy, M. (1947). A comparison of the preserving qualities of certain varieties of rhubarb. *Rep. agric. hort. Res. Sta., Bristol*, p. 225.

183. Crang, A. and Sturdy, M. (1946). A comparison of five methods of making tomato juice. *Rep. agric. hort. Res. Sta., Bristol*, p. 156.

184. Crang, A. and Sturdy, M. (1950). The retention of ascorbic acid in preserved fruits. 2. *J. Sci. Food Agric.*, **1**, 252.

185. Crosby, M. W., Fickle, B. E., Andreassen, E. G., Fenton, F., Harris, K. W. and Burgoin, A. M. (1953). Vitamin retention and palatability of certain fresh and frozen vegetables in large-scale food service. *Bull. Cornell agric. Exp. Sta.*, No. 891.

186. Crowe, H. W. and Bradford, E. A. M. (1943). Winter sources of vitamin C. *Nature, Lond.*, **151**, 505.

187. Cruickshank, E. M. (1941). The effect of diet on the chemical composition, nutritive value and hatchability of the egg. *Nutr. Abstr. Rev.*, **10**, 645.

188. Cruickshank, E. M., Kodicek, E. and Wang, Y. L. (1945). Vitamins in spray-dried eggs. *J. Soc. chem. Ind., Lond.*, **64**, 15.

189. Cunningham, M. M. (1935). The vitamin D content of some New Zealand fish oils. With a note on the prophylactic method of biological assay. *N.Z. J. Sci. Tech.*, **17**, 563.

190. Cutlar, K. L., Jones, J. B., Harris, K. W. and Fenton, F. (1944). Ascorbic acid, thiamin, and riboflavin retention in fresh spinach in institution food service. *J. Amer. diet. Ass.*, **20**, 757.

191. Daglish, C. (1951a). The spectrophotometric determination of ascorbic acid in tissue extracts, particularly those of the walnut (*Juglans regia*). *Biochem. J.*, **49**, 635.

192. Daglish, C. (1951b). The occurrence of ascorbic acid in the walnut (*Juglans regia*). *Biochem J.*, **49**, 639.

193. Daniel, E. P. and Munsell, H. E. (1937). Vitamin content of foods. *Misc. Publ. U.S. Dep. Agric.*, No. 275.

194. Daniel, L. and Norris, L. C. (1944). Riboflavin content of milk and milk products. *Food Res.*, **9**, 312.

195. Daniel, L. and Norris, L. C. (1945). The riboflavin, niacin and thiamine content of dried leguminous seeds. *J. Nutr.*, **30**, 31.

196. Dann, W. J. and Handler, P. (1941). The quantitative estimation of nicotinic acid in animal tissues. *J. biol. Chem.*, **140**, 201.

197. Dann, W. J. and Handler, P. (1942). The nicotinic acid content of meat. *J. Nutr.*, **24**, 153.

198. Dark, S. O. S. and Booth, V. H. (1946). Total carotenoids in carrots. *J. agric. Sci.*, **36**, 192.

199. Daum, K., Aimone, M. and Hollister, S. (1943). Ascorbic acid in institutional food. *J. Amer. diet. Ass.*, **19**, 693.

200. Daum, M. G. (1955). La Niacina en el café y su importancia nutricional en Venezuela. *Arch. venez. Nutr.*, **6**, 61.

201. Davies, A. W. and Moore, T. (1939). The vitamin A content of cheese. *Biochem. J.*, **33**, 1645.

202. Deaker, E. M. (1952). Comparison of the ascorbic acid content of Meyer and Standard types of lemons. *N.Z. J. Sci. Tech.* (*B*), **34**, 146.

203. Dearden, D. V., Henry, K. M., Houston, J., Kon, S. K. and Thompson, S. Y. (1945). A study of the balance of certain milk nutrients in the making of Cheddar, Cheshire and Stilton cheeses, and of their fate during the ripening of the cheeses. *J. Dairy Res.*, **14**, 100.

204. Debrit, F. P. (1952). Étude de la vitamine B_6 dans le lait et les produits laitiers. *Int. Z. Vitaminforsch.*, **24**, 331.

205. Defelice, D. (1942). Effect of processing on carotenoid (provitamin A) content of peaches. *Food Res.*, **7**, 16.

206. De Heus, J. G. and De Man, T. J. (1951). Het gehalte aan vitamine B_{12} van enige voedermiddelen. *Voeding*, **12**, 361.

207. Denton, C. A., Cabell, C. A., Bastron, H. and Davies, R. (1944). The effect of spray-drying and the subsequent storage of the dried product on the vitamin A, D, and riboflavin content of eggs. *J. Nutr.*, **28**, 421.

208. Denton, C. A. and Kellogg, W. L. (1953). The vitamin B_{12} activity of eggs and some materials as affected by extraction in the presence of sodium cyanide or sodium-bisulphite. *Arch. Biochem.*, **46**, 105.

209. Denton, C. A., Kellogg, W. L. and Bird, H. R. (1947). The effect of diet, age. and sex on the nicotinic acid content of the tissues of chickens. *Poult. Sci.*, **26**, 299.

210. Devaney, G. M. and Munsell, H. E. (1935). Vitamin D content of calf, beef, lamb and hog liver. *J. Home Econ.*, **27**, 240.

211. Devaney, G. M. and Putney, L. K. (1935). The vitamin A and D content of canned salmon. *J. Home Econ.*, **27**, 658.

212. Devaney, G. M., Titus, H. W. and Nestler, R. B. (1935). Vitamin A content of eggs produced by chickens fed viosterol and various percentages of cod-liver oil. *J. agric. Res.*, **50**, 853.

213. Diemair, W., Timmling, E. and Fox, H. (1939). Über den Vitamin-C-gehalt on Gemüse-und Obstkonserven. *Vorratspfl. u. Lebensmittelforsch.*, **2**, 152.

214. Doan, F. J. and Josephson, D. V. (1943). Observations on the ascorbic acid content of evaporated milk. *J. Dairy Sci.*, **26**, 1031.

215. Doesburg, J. J. (1955). The vitamin C content of sliced végetables. *Voeding*, **16**, 503.

216. Donelson, E. G. and Grambow, D. (1947). The effect of soda on ascorbic acid in tomato juice. *J. Amer. diet. Ass.*, **23**, 1057.

217. Downs, D. E. and Meckel, R. B. (1943). Thiamin losses in toasting bread. *Cereal Chem.*, **20**, 352.

218. Drummond, J. C., Gray, C. H. and Richardson, N. E. G. (1939). The antirachitic value of human milk. *Brit. med. J.*, **ii**, 757.

219. Drummond, J. C. and Moran, T. (1944). Unconsidered trifles in our diet. Vitamin content of beverages. *Nature, Lond.*, **153**, 99.

220. Dryden, L. P., Riedel, G. H. and Hartman, A. M. (1956). Comparative assay for vitamin B_{12} in certain milk products by various rat growth methods. *J. Nutr.*, **59**, 89.

221. Dunker, C. F., Fellers, C. R. and Esselen, W. B. (Jr.) (1942). A comparison of four methods for determining vitamin C with a 25-day, weight-response bioassay. *Food Res.*, **7**, 260.

222. Dunn, K. R. and Goddard, V. R. (1948). Effect of heat upon the nutritive values of peanuts. 2. Riboflavin and pantothenic acid content. *Food Res.*, **13**, 512.

223. Edisbury, J. R., Lovern, J. A. and Morton, R. A. (1937). Distribution of vitamin A in the tissues of the eels *Anguilla vulgaris* and *A. aucklandi* Rich. *Biochem. J.*, **31**, 416.

224. Edisbury, J. R., Morton, R. A., Simpkins, G. W. and Lovern, J. A. (1938). The distribution of vitamin A and factor A_2. 1. *Biochem. J.*, **32**, 118.

225. Eggitt, P. W. R. and Ward, L. D. (1953a). The estimation of vitamin-E activity by paper chromatography. *J. Sci. Food Agric.*, **4**, 176.

226. Eggitt, P. W. R. and Ward, L. D. (1953b). The chemical estimation of vitamin-E activity in cereal products. 1. The tocopherol pattern of wheat-germ oil. *J. Sci. Food Agric.*, **4**, 569.

227. Eheart, J. F., Young, R. W., Massey, P. H. (Jr.) and Havis, J. R. (1955). Crop, light intensity, soil pH, and minor element effects on the yield and vitamin content of turnip greens. *Food Res.*, **20**, 575.

228. Eheart. M. S. (1941). Factors which affect the vitamin C content of apples. *Tech. Bull. Va. agric. Exp. Sta.*, **69**, 16.

229. Eheart, M. S. and Sholes, M. L. (1946). Effects of method of sulphuring, dehydration, and temperature of storage on ascorbic acid and carotene content of dehydrated peaches. *Food Res.*, **11**, 332.

230. Ellenberger, H. A., Guerrant, N. B. and Fardig, O. B. (1947). Seasonal variations in the vitamin A and the carotene content of retail butters. *J. Nutr.*, **33**, 39.

231. Ellis, G. H. and Hamner, K. C. (1943). The carotene content of tomatoes as influenced by various factors. *J. Nutr.*, **25**, 539.

232. Elvehjem, C. A. (1942). Meat and human health. *J. Amer. diet. Ass.*, **18**, 145.

233. Embden, C. and Jaffé, W. G. (1955). Nota preliminar sobre la presencia de vitamina B_{12} en alimentos criollos. *Arch. venez. Nutr.*, **6**, 121.

234. *Emergency Laws* (1954). No. 613, Foods Standards (Margarine) Order, 1954. H.M. Stationery Office, London.

235. Emmerie, A. and Engel, C. (1943). The tocopherol (vitamin E) content of foods and its chemical determination. *Z. Vitaminforsch.*, **13**, 259.

236. Engel, C. (1942). The tocopherol (vitamin E) content of milling products from wheat, rye and barley and the influence of bleaching. *Z. Vitaminforsch.*, **12**, 220.

237. Engel, C. (1955). Vitamin D in milk. *Ned. melk-en Zuiveltijdschr.*, **9**, 139.

238. Erdsiek, A. V., Kanapaux, M. S., Richmond, G. V., Weis, A. E. and Bisbey, B. (1951). The vitamin content of chicken tissue as affected by the method of preparation and of storage after canning. *Bull. Mo. agric. Exp. Sta.*, No. 482.

239. Erikson, S. E. and Boyden, R. E. (1947a). Effect of different methods of cooking on the thiamine, riboflavin, and niacin content of pork. *Bull. Ky. ag-ic. Exp. Sta.*, No. 503

240. Erikson, S. E. and Boyden, R. E. (1947b). Thiamine and riboflavin content of turkey cooked by institution methods. *Bull. Ky. agric. Exp. Sta.*, No. 504.

241. Erikson, S. E. and Boyden, R. E. (1947c). Effect of calcium chloride on firmness of some canned products and on their content of ascorbic acid. *Bull. Ky. agric. Exp. Sta.*, No. 511. (*Nutr. Abstr. Rev.*, 1949, **19**, *Abstr.* 587.)

242. Escudero, A., Herraiz, M. L. and De Alvarez Herrero, H. G. (1943). Influencia de la coccion de la leche sobre su contenido de flavina, acido nicotinico y tiamina. *Rev. Asoc. argent. Diet.*, **1**, 119.

243. Escudero, A., Herraiz, M. L. and De Alvarez Herrero, H. G. (1944). Influencia de la coccion sobre el valor nutritivo de la leche de vaca. *Rev. Asoc. argent. Diet.*, **2**, 165.

244. Esselen, W. B. (Jr.), Lyons, M. E. and Fellers, C. R. (1942). The composition and nutritive value of potatoes with special emphasis on vitamin C. *Bull. Mass. agric. Exp. Sta.*, No. 390.

245. Evans, E. V., Irvine, O. R. and Bryant, L. R. (1946). The retention of nutrients in cheese making. 4. Thiamine in cheddar cheese made from raw and pasteurized milk. *J. Nutr.*, **32**, 227.

246. Evans, R. J., Bandemer, S. L., Bauer, D. H. and Davidson, J. A. (1955). The vitamin B_{12} content of fresh and stored shell eggs. *Poult. Sci.*, **34**, 922.

247. Evans, R. J., Butts, H. A. and Davidson, J. A. (1951a). The niacin content of fresh and stored shell eggs. *Poult. Sci.*, **30**, 132.

248. Evans, R. J., Butts, H. A. and Davidson, J. A. (1951b). The vitamin B_6 content of fresh and stored shell eggs. *Poult. Sci.*, **30**, 515.

249. Evans, R. J., Butts, H. A. and Davidson, J. A. (1952). The riboflavin content of fresh and stored shell eggs. *Poult. Sci.*, **31**, 269.

250. Evans, R. J., Davidson, J. A., Bauer, D. and Butts, H. A. (1952). Changes in content of nutrients in shell eggs during storage. IV. Biotin, folic acid and vitamin B_{12}. *Poult. Sci.*, **31**, 915.

251. Evans, R. J., Davidson, J. A., Bauer, D. and Butts, H. A. (1953a). Folic acid in fresh and stored shell eggs. *J. agric. Food Chem.*, **1**, 170.

252. Evans, R. J., Davidson, J. A., Bauer, D. and Butts, H. A. (1953b). The biotin content of fresh and stored shell eggs. *Poult. Sci.*, **32**, 680.

253. Evans, R. J., Davidson, J. A. and Butts, H. A. (1952). The pantothenic acid content of fresh and stored shell eggs. *Poult. Sci.*, **31**, 777.

254. Ezell, B. D., Darrow, G. M., Wilcox, M. S. and Scott, D. H. (1947). Ascorbic acid content of strawberries. *Food Res.*, **12**, 510.

255. Fager, E. E. C., Olson, O. E., Burris, R. H. and Elvehjem, C. A. (1949). Folic acid in vegetables and certain other plant materials. *Food Res.*, **14**, 1.

256. Fardig, O. B., Guerrant, N. B. and Dutcher, R. A. (1951). A study of the discrepancy in the thiamine content of meat as measured by the thiochrome and rat growth methods. *J. Nutr.*, **44**, 29.

257. Farrer, K. T. H. (1949). The influence of mineral content on the loss of vitamin B_1 in baking bread. *Aust. J. exp. Biol. med. Sci.*, **27**, 157.

258. Farrer, K. T. H. (1950). The thermal loss of vitamin B_1 on storage of foodstuffs. *Aust. J. exp. Biol. med. Sci.*, **28**, 245.

259. Farrer, K. T. H. (1955). The thermal destruction of vitamin B_1 in foods. *Advanc. Food Res.*, **6**, 257.

260. Fawns, H. T. and Martin, E. J. (1938). The chemical composition of fresh apple juice. *J. Soc. chem. Ind., Lond.*, **57**, 60.

261. Feaster, J. F. (1944). Nutritive values of canned fruits and vegetables. *Amer. J. publ Hlth.*, **34**, 593.

262. Fellers, C. R. and Buck, R. E. (1941). Retention of vitamins C and A in glass-packed foods. *Food Res.*, **6**, 135.

263. Fellers, C. R., Esselen, W. B. (Jr.) and Fitzgerald, G. A. (1940). Vitamin B_1 and vitamin B_2 (G) content of vegetables as influenced by quick-freezing and canning. *Food Res.*. **5**, 495.

264. Fenton, F. (1940). Vitamin C retention as a criterion of quality and nutritive value in vegetables. *J. Amer. diet. Ass.*, **16**, 524.

265. Fenton, F., Gleim, E., Albury, M., Visnyei, K. and McCartney, J. R. (1945). Effect of quantity preparation procedures on vitamin retention: canned peas. *J. Amer. diet. Ass.*, **21**, 700.

266. Fenton, F., Gleim, E. and Chappell, V. M. (1947). Vitamin retention and palatability of evaporated apricots. *J. Amer. diet. Ass.*, **23**, 423.

267. Fenton, F. and Tressler, D. K. (1938). Losses of vitamin C during the cooking of certain vegetables. *J. Home Econ.*, **30**, 717.

268. Filios, A. M. and Esselen, W. B. (Jr.) (1946). The vitamin content of canned and cooked fresh mushrooms. *J. Amer. diet. Ass.*, **22**, 772.

269. Fincke, M. L., Little, R., Redelings, E. and Perkins, J. (1943). Further studies on the thiamin values of frozen peas. *Food Res.*, **8**, 123.

270. Fincke, M. L., McGregor, M. A., Storvick, C. A. and Woods, E. (1948). Ascorbic acid content of foods as served. *J. Amer. diet. Ass.*, **24**, 957.

271. Fischer, N. A., Benson, E. M. and Swendseid, M. E. (1958). The distribution of vitamin B_{12} in the developing chick egg. *Arch. Biochem.*, **74**, 458.

272. Fisher, K. H. and Dodds, M. L. (1952). Ascorbic acid and ash in vegetables cooked in stainless steel utensils. Variation with cooking at three levels of water. *J. Amer. diet. Ass.*, **28**, 726.

273. Fisher, K. H. and Dodds, M. L. (1955). Reduced and total ascorbic acid values of thirty-four foods. *Food Res.*, **20**, 247.

274. Fisher, L. R., Kon, S. K. and Thompson, S. Y. (1954). Vitamin A and carotenoids in certain invertebrates. 2. Studies of seasonal variations in some marine crustacea. *J. Mar. biol. Ass. U.K.*, **33**, 589.

275. Fitzgerald, G. A. and Feliers, C. R. (1938). Carotene and ascorbic acid content of fresh market and commercially frozen fruits and vegetables. *Food Res.*, **3**, 109.

276. Fixsen, M. A. B. and Roscoe, M. H. (1938). Tables of the vitamin content of human and animal foods. *Nutr. Abstr. Rev.*, **7**, 823.

277. Fixsen, M. A. B. and Roscoe, M. H. (1940). Tables of the vitamin content of human and animal foods. *Nutr. Abstr. Rev.*, **9**, 795.

278. Flavier, H. and Genevois, L. (1939). Dosage des vitamines B_1 et B_2 dans les tissus vegetaux. *C. R. Soc. Biol., Paris*, **130**, 497.

279. Floyd, W. W. and Fraps, G. S. (1939). Vitamin C content of some Texas fruits and vegetables. *Food Res.*, **4**, 87.

280. Floyd, W. W. and Fraps, G. S. (1940). Changes in vitamin C content during boiling of turnip greens in various waters in covered and uncovered containers. *Food Res.*, **5**, 33.

281. Floyd, W. W. and Fraps, G. S. (1942). Ascorbic acid content of some canned grapefruit juices prepared under various processing conditions. *Food Res.*, **7**, 382.

282. Flynn, L. M., Williams, V. B. and Hogan, A. G. (1949). Cracked ice and preservation of stored fruits and vegetables. *Food Res.*, **14**, 231.

283. Ford, J. E. (1953). The microbiological assay of "vitamin B_{12}". The specificity of the requirement of *Ochromonas malhamensis* for cyanocobalamin. *Brit. J. Nutr.*, **7**, 299.

284. Ford, J. E. (1957). Factors influencing the destruction of vitamin B_{12} in milk. *J. Dairy Res.*, **24**, 360.

285. Fournier, S. A., Beuk, J. F., Chornock, F. W., Brown, L. C. and Rice, E. E. (1949). Determination of effect of heat on peanuts and the stability of thiamine in enriched peanut butter. *Food Res.*, **14**, 413.

286. Fraps, G. S. (1947). Vitamin A and carotene in human foods. *Bull. Tex. agric. Exp. Sta.*, No. 690.

287. Fraps, G. S. and Kemmerer, A. R. (1943). Carotene and vitamin A in commercial butter. *J. Ass. off. agric. Chem., Wash.*, **26**, 158.

288. Fraps, G. S., Kemmerer, A. R. and Meinke, W. W. (1941). Relation of chemical analysis of butter to its vitamin A potency. *J. Ass. off. agric. Chem., Wash.*, **24**, 31.

289. Fraps, G. S., Kemmerer, A. R. and Treichler, R. (1942). Relation of chemical analyses of liver to its vitamin A potency. *J. Ass. off. agric. Chem., Wash.*, **25**, 529.

290. Fraps, G. S. and Meinke, W. W. (1943). Biological value of spectro vitamin A in liver. *J. Ass. off. agric. Chem., Wash.*, **26**, 399.

291. Fraps, G. S. and Meinke, W. W. (1945). Relative values of carotenes in foods as measured by storage of vitamin A in livers of rats. *Food Res.*, **10**, 187.

292. Fraps, G. S., Meinke, W. W. and Kemmerer, A. R. (1941). Determination of pure carotene in green vegetables and green foods. *J. Ass. off. agric. Chem., Wash.*, **24**, 739.

293. Fraser, J. R. (1951). National flour survey 1946–1950. *J. Sci. Food Agric.*, **2**, 193.

294. Fraser, J. R. (1958). Flour survey 1950–1956. *J. Sci. Food Agric.*, **9**, 125.

295. Fratoni, A. and Spadoni, M. A. (1950). Contenuto in acido ascorbico di diverse varietà di arance italiane in due annate successive. *Quad. Nutr.*, **11**, 463. (*Nutr. Abstr. Rev.*, 1952, **22**, *Abstr.* 2158.)

296. Frazier, E. I. (1950). Niacin content of cereals and legumes as determined by two methods of assay. *J. Amer. diet. Ass.*, **26**, 264.

297. Freeman, J. A. and Harris, G. H. (1951). The effect of nitrogen, phosphorus, potassium and chlorine on the carotene content of the carrot. *Sci. Agric.*, **31**, 207.

298. French, R. B. and Abbott, O. D. (1940). Investigation of the vitamin C content of Florida fruits and vegetables. 1. Effects of maturation and of cold storage on the vitamin C potency of oranges and grapefruit. *J. Nutr.*, **19**, 223.

299. French, R. B. and Abbott, O. D. (1948). Carotene and ascorbic acid in Florida-grown foods. *Tech. Bull. Fla. agric. Exp. Sta.*, No. 444.

300. French, R. B., Abbott, O. D. and Townsend, R. O. (1951). Levels of thiamine, riboflavin and niacin in Florida-produced foods. *Bull. Fla. agric. Exp. Sta.*, No. 482.

301. Frey, K. J. (1953). Effects of variety and location on thiamine, pantothenic acid, riboflavin and niacin contents in oats. *Quart. Bull. Mich. agric. Exp. Sta.*, **36**, 13.

302. Frey, K. J. and Watson, G. I. (1950). Chemical studies on oats. 1. Thiamine, niacin, riboflavin, and pantothenic acid. *Agron. J.*, **42**, 434.

303. Fukui, S. (1953). Differential determination of vitamin B_6 group. *Analyt. Chem.*, **25**, 1884.

304. Gillam, A. E., Henry, K. M., Kon, S. K. and White, P. (1938). The effect of commercial sterilization on the nutritive value of milk. 3. Effect on the vitamin A and carotene content of milk. *J. Dairy Res.*, **9**, 17.

305. Gleim, E., Albury, M., McCartney, J. R., Visnyei, K. and Fenton, F. (1946). Ascorbic acid, thiamin, riboflavin, and niacin content of potatoes in large-scale food service. *Food Res.*, **11**, 461.

306. Gleim, E., Albury, M., Visnyei, K., McCartney, J. R. and Fenton, F. (1946). Effect of quantity preparation procedures on vitamin retention: canned tomatoes. *J. Amer. diet. Ass.*, **22**, 29.

307. Gleim, E. G., Tressler, D. K. and Fenton, F. (1944). Ascorbic acid, thiamin, riboflavin, and carotene contents of asparagus and spinach in the fresh, stored, and frozen states both before and after cooking. *Food Res.*, **9**, 471.

308. Goldbeck, C. G. (1947). Some studies on the content of thiamine and anti-thiamine factor in fishery products. *Comm. Fish. Rev.*, **9**, (8), 13.

309. Goldberg, L., Kropman, M. and Thorp, J. M. (1947). A survey of vitamins in African foodstuffs. 7. The riboflavin and nicotinic acid content of beans and other legumes. *S. Afr. J. med. Sci.*, **12**, 171.

310. Goldberg, L. and Thorp, J. M. (1946). Loss of thiamin during the baking of bread. *Nature, Lond.*, **158**, 22.

311. Goldberg, L., Thorp, J. M. and Sussman, S. (1945). A survey of vitamins in African foodstuffs. 4. The thiamin content of beans and other legumes. *S. Afr. J. med. Sci.*, **10**, 87.

312. Goldberg, L., Thorp, J. M. and Sussman, S. (1946). A survey of vitamins in African foodstuffs. 5. The thiamin content of processed cereals and legumes. *S. Afr. J. med. Sci.*, **11**, 121.

313. Goldblith, S. A. and Harris, R. S. (1948).   Estimation of ascorbic acid in food preparations.   *Analyt. Chem.*, **20**, 649.

314. Gorham, P. R. (1948).   Canadian Wiltshire bacon.   29.   Changes in the thiamine, riboflavin, and niacin contents produced by curing, storage, and cooking.   *Canad. J. Res.*, (*F*), **26**, 8.

315. Grant, E. P. (1947).   Apples as a source of vitamin C.   *Sci. Agric.*, **27**, 162.

316. Graves, H. C. H. (1942).   The vitamin-A value of carotene in vegetables.   *Chem. & Ind. (Rev.)*, No. 1, 8.

317. Green, M. E. (1954).   Factors affecting vitamin values and palatability.   2. Review of literature on cabbage.   *Bull. Ohio agric. Exp. Sta.*, No. 742, p. 52.

318. Greenwood, D. A., Kraybill, H. R., Feaster, J. F. and Jackson, J. M. (1944).   Vitamin retention in processed meat.   Effect of thermal processing.   *Industr. Engng. Chem. (Industr.)*, **36**, 922.

319. Greer, E. N., Ridyard, H. N. and Kent, N. L. (1952).   The composition of British-grown winter wheat.   1. Vitamin-B_1 content.   *J. Sci. Food Agric.*, **3**, 12.

320. Gregory, M. E., Ford, J. E. and Kon, S. K. (1952).   A vitamin B_{12}—binding factor in sow's milk.   *Biochem. J.*, **51**, 29.

321. Gregory, M. E., Ford, J. E. and Kon, S. K. (1958).   The B-Vitamin content of milk in relation to breed of cow and stage of lactation.   *J. Dairy Res.*, **25**, 447.

322. Grimbleby, F. H. and Black, D. J. G. (1950).   Variations in the pigment and vitamin A contents of egg yolk.   *Brit. J. Nutr.*, **4**, 323.

323. Grimbleby, F. H. and Black, D. J. G. (1952).   Variations in the composition of egg-yolk pigment.   *Brit. J. Nutr.*, **6**, 393.

324. Griswold, R. M., Jans, L. M. and Halliday, E. G. (1949).   Retention of thiamine, riboflavin, and niacin in pork hearts and beef kidneys.   *J. Amer. diet. Ass.*, **25**, 866.

325. Guerrant, N. B. (1957).   Changes in light reflectance and ascorbic acid content of foods during frozen storage.   *J. agric. Food Chem.*, **5**, 207.

326. Guerrant, N. B., Vavich, M. G. and Fardig, O. B. (1945).   Nutritive value of canned foods.   Comparison of vitamin values obtained by different methods of assay.   *Industr. Engng. Chem. (Anal).*, **17**, 710.

327. Guerrant, N. B., Vavich, M. G., Fardig, O. B., Dutcher, R. A. and Stern, R. M. (1946).   The nutritive value of canned foods.   Changes in the vitamin content of foods during canning.   *J. Nutr.*, **32**, 435.

328. Guggenheim, K. (1944).   The biological value of carotene from various sources and the effect of vitamin E on the utilisation of carotene and of vitamin A.   *Biochem. J.*, **38**, 260.

329. Gunsalus, I. C. and Hand, D. B. (1941).   The use of bacteria in the chemical determination of total vitamin C.   *J. biol. Chem.*, **141**, 853.

330. Gunther, M. and Stanier, J. E. (1951).   Studies of undernutrition, Wuppertal 1946-9.   xxix.   The volume and composition of human milk.   *Spec. Rep. Ser. med. Res. Coun., Lond.*, No. 275.   H.M. Stationery Office.

331. György, P. (1954).   In *The vitamins: chemistry, physiology, pathology*, edited by W. H. Sebrell, (Jr.) and R. S. Harris, Vol. I, p. 595.   Academic Press Inc., New York.

332. Haagen-Smit, A. J., Strickland, A. G. R., Jefferys, C. E. P. and Kirchner, J. G. (1946).   Studies on vitamin content of canned pineapple.   *Food Res.*, **11**, 142.

333. Hale, E. B., Davis, G. K. and Baldwin, H. R. (1942a).   The chemical determination of nicotinic acid in plant materials.   *J. biol. Chem.*, **146**, 553.

334. Hale, E. B., Davis, G. K. and Baldwin, H. R. (1942b).   The distribution of nicotinic acid in feeds.   *J. biol. Chem.*, **146**, 565.

335. Halick, J. V., Reid, B. L., Brown, C. L. and Couch, J. R. (1953).   The vitamin B_{12} content of egg yolks as influenced by oral and parental administration of the vitamin.   *J. Nutr.*, **50**, 331.

336. Hall, A. P., Brinner, L., Amerine, M. A. and Morgan, A. F. (1956).   The B vitamin content of grapes, wines and musts.   *Food Res.*, **21**, 362.

337. Hall, A. P., Moore, J. G. and Morgan, A. F. (1955). B vitamin content of California-grown avocados. *J. agric. Food Chem.*, **3**, 250.

338. Hall, A. P., Morgan, A. F. and Wheeler, P. (1953). The amounts of six B-vitamins in fresh and dried figs. *Food Res.*, **18**, 206.

339. Hall, A. P., Wheeler, P., Thielen, A. and Morgan, A. F. (1953). A new B vitamin study of walnuts. *Food Res.*, **18**, 574.

340. Halliday, N. and Deuel, H. J. (Jr.) (1941). The presence of free and combined thiamine in milk. *J biol. Chem.*, **140**, 555.

341. Hallsworth, E. G. and Lewis, V. M. (1947). Some factors affecting the ascorbic-acid content of tomatoes in New South Wales. *Emp. J. exp. Agric.*, **15**, 132.

342. Hallsworth, E. G. and Lewis, V. M. (1949). Ascorbic acid in cabbages. *Emp. J. exp. Agric.*, **17**, 28.

343. Hamner, K. C., Bernstein, L. and Maynard, L. A. (1945). Effects of light intensity, day length, temperature, and other environmental factors on the ascorbic acid content of tomatoes. *J. Nutr.*, **29**, 85.

344. Hamner, K. C. and Maynard, L. A. (1942). Factors influencing the nutritive value of the tomato. A review of the literature. *Misc. Publ. U.S. Dep. Agric.*, No. 502.

345. Hamner, K. C. and Nightingale, G. T. (1946). Ascorbic acid content of pineapples as correlated with environmental factors and plant composition. *Food Res.*, **11**, 535.

346. Hand, D. B. (1943). Reduced and total vitamin C in milk. *J. Dairy Sci.*, **26**, 7.

347. Hand, D. B. and Sharp, P. F. (1939). The riboflavin content of cow's milk. *J. Dairy Sci.*, **22**, 779.

348. Hanning, F. and Mitts, M. L. (1949). Effect of cooking on the folic acid content of eggs. *J. Amer. diet. Ass.*, **25**, 226.

349. Hansen, E. and Waldo, G. F. (1944). Ascorbic acid content of small fruits in relation to genetic and environmental factors. *Food Res.*, **9**, 453.

350. Harding, P. L. and Thomas, E. E. (1942). Relation of ascorbic acid concentration in juice of Florida grapefruit to variety, rootstock, and position of fruit on the tree. *J. agric. Res.*, **64**, 57.

351. Hargrave, P. D. and Hogg, N. J. (1946). Precanning treatment on processed plums as it affects quality and vitamin C content. *Sci. Agric.*, **26**, 95.

352. Harper, R. H. and Zscheile, F. P. (1945). Carotenoid content of carrot varieties and strains. *Food Res.*, **10**, 84.

353. Harris, L. J. and Mapson, L. W. (1947). Determination of ascorbic acid in presence of interfering substances by the "continuous-flow" method. *Brit. J. Nutr.*, **1**, 7.

354. Harris, L. J., Mapson, L. W. and Wang, Y. L. (1942). Vitamin methods. 4. A simple potentiometric method for determining ascorbic acid, suitable for use with coloured extracts. *Biochem. J.*, **36**, 183.

355. Harris, L. J. and Olliver, M. (1942). Vitamin methods. 3. The reliability of the method for estimating vitamin C by titration against 2:6-dichlorophenolindophenol. 1. Control tests with plant tissues. *Biochem. J.*, **36**, 155.

356. Harris, L. J. and Wang, Y. L. (1941). Vitamin methods. 1. An improved procedure for estimating vitamin B_1 in foodstuffs and biological materials by the thiochrome test including comparisons with biological assays. *Biochem. J.*, **35**, 1050.

357. Harris, P. L. and Poland, G. L. (1937). Vitamin studies on bananas. 1. The vitamin A, B_1, and C contents of ripe bananas. *Food Res.*, **2**, 311.

358. Harris, P. L. and Poland, G. L. (1939). Variations in ascorbic acid content of bananas. *Food Res.*, **4**, 317.

359. Harris, P. L., Quaife, M. L. and O'Grady, P. (1952). Tocopherol content of human milk and of cow's milk products used for infant feeding. *J. Nutr.*, **46**, 459.

360. Harris, P. L., Quaife, M. L. and Swanson, W. J. (1950). Vitamin E content of foods. *J. Nutr.*, **40**, 367.

361. Harris, R. S., Procter, B. E., Goldblith, S. and Brody, J. (1940). Effect of processing on the vitamin B_1 content of foods. *Proc. 1st Food Conf. Inst. Food Tech.*, **1**, 109.

362. Harris, S. C. (1945). Carotene and ascorbic acid in fresh and salted vegetables. *J. Amer. diet. Ass.*, **21**, 360.

363. Hartman, A. M., Dryden, L. P. and Hargrove, R. E. (1956). Vitamin B_{12} potency of Cheddar, Swiss and cottage cheese. *Food Res.*, **21**, 540.

364. Hartman, A. M., Dryden, L. P. and Riedel, G. H. (1956). Vitamin B_{12} content of milk and milk products as determined by rat assay. *J. Nutr.*, **59**, 77.

365. Hartzler, E., Ross, W. and Willett, E. L. (1949). Thiamin, riboflavin and niacin content of raw and cooked pork from grain-fed and garbage-fed pigs. *Food Res.*, **14**, 15.

·366. Hassan, H. H. and McCollum, J. P. (1954). Factors affecting the content of ascorbic acid in tomatoes. *Bull. Ill. Exp. agric. Sta.*, No. 573.

367. Hassinen, J. B., Durbin, G. T. and Bernhart, F. W. (1954). The vitamin B_6 content of milk products. *J. Nutr.*, **53**, 249.

368. Hastings, W. H. and Spencer, C. F. (1952). Determinations of free and bound ascorbic acid in fishery products. *J. Mar. Res.*, **11**, 241.

369. Hathaway, I. L. and Davis, H. P. (1945). Studies on the riboflavin content of cheese. *Bull. Neb. Exp. agric. Sta.*, No. 137.

370. Hathaway, I. L. and Davis, H. P. (1947). The vitamin A and carotene content of Nebraska butter. *Bull. Neb. Exp. agric. Sta.*, No. 149.

371. Hauge, S. M., Zscheile, F. P., Carrick, C. W. and Bohren, B. B. (1944). Homogenized liquid and dried eggs. Stability of vitamin A and carotenoids during dehydration and storage. *Industr. Engng. Chem. (Industr.)*, **36**, 1065.

372. Haydak, M. H., Palmer, L. S., Tanquary, M. C. and Vivino, A. E. (1942). Vitamin content of honeys. *J. Nutr.*, **23**, 581.

373. Haydak, M. H., Palmer, L. S., Tanquary, M. C. and Vivino, A. E. (1943). The effect of commercial clarification on the vitamin content of honey. *J. Nutr.*, **26**, 319.

374. Heller, C. A., McCay, C. M. and Lyon, C. B. (1943). Losses of vitamins in large-scale cookery. *J. Nutr.*, **26**, 377.

375. Hellström, V. (1952–53). Die Haltbarkeit des Vitamins C bei der Zerkleinerung von rohen Vegetabilien. *Z. Vitam.-Horm.-u. Fermentforsch.*, **5**, 98.

376. Henderson, L. M., Waisman, H. A. and Elvehjem, C. A. (1941). The distribution of pyridoxine (vitamin B_6) in meat and meat products. *J. Nutr.*, **21**, 589.

377. Hennessy, D. J. and Cerecedo, L. R. (1939). The determination of free and phosphorylated thiamin by a modified thiochrome assay. *J. Amer. chem. Soc.*, **61**, 179.

378. Henry, K. M., Houston, J. and Kon, S. K. (1938). A comparison of biological and fluorimetric measurements of the vitamin B_1 content of raw and processed milks. *Chem. & Ind. (Rev.)*, **57**, 974.

379. Henry, K. M., Houston, J., Kon, S. K. and Osborne, L. W. (1939). The effect of commercial drying and evaporation on the nutritive properties of milk. *J. Dairy Res.*, **10**, 272.

380. Henry, K. M., Houston, J., Kon, S. K. and Thompson, S. Y. (1944). The effects of commercial processing and of storage on some nutritive properties of milk. Comparison of full-cream sweetened condensed milk and evaporated milk with the original raw milk. *J. Dairy Res.*, **13**, 329.

381. Henry, K. M., Houston, J., Kon, S. K. and White, P. (1940). The vitamin B_1 and riboflavin of milk. 4. Comparison of chemical and biological methods of estimation of vitamin B_1. *J. Dairy Res.*, **11**, 167.

382. Henry, K. M. and Kon, S. K. (1938a). The effect of commercial sterilization on the nutritive value of milk. 4. Effect on the vitamin B complex, on vitamin B_1 and on vitamin B_2 (flavin) of milk. *J. Dairy Res.*, **9**, 22.

383. Henry, K. M. and Kon, S. K. (1938b). The effect of commercial sterilization on the nutritive value of milk. 5. The effect of commercial sterilization on the vitamin C of milk. *J. Dairy Res.*, **9**, 185.

384. Henry, K. M. and Kon, S. K. (1942). The vitamin D content of English butterfat throughout the year. *Biochem. J.*, **36**, 456.

385. Hewston, E. M., Dawson, E. H., Alexander, L. M. and Orent-Keilles, E. (1948). Vitamin and mineral content of certain foods as affected by home preparation. *Misc. Publ. U.S. Dep. Agric.*, No. 628.

386. Hewston, E. M., Fisher, M. and Orent-Keiles, E. (1951). Comparison of the 2, 6-dichlorophenolindophenol and 2, 4-dinitrophenylhydrazine methods with the Crampton bioassay for determining vitamin C values in foods. *Tech. Bull. U.S. Dep. Agric.*, No. 1023.

387. Higgins, B. B., Holley, K. T., Pickett, T. A. and Wheeler, C. D. (1941). 2. Thiamine chloride and nicotinic acid content of peanuts and peanut products. *Bull. Ga. Exp. agric. Sta.*, No. 213.

388. Higuchi, K. and Peterson, W. H. (1946). The carotene and vitamin A contents of Wisconsin cheese. *J. Dairy Sci.*, **29**, 789.

389. Higuchi, K., Price, W. V. and Peterson, W. H. (1946). Relation of corn and alfalfa silage to the quality of cheese and its carotene and vitamin A content. *J. Dairy Sci.* **29**, 157.

390. Highman, S. E. (1943). The vitamin A content of some South African dairy products. *S. Afr. J. med. Sci.*, **8**, 28.

391. Hinman, W. F., Brush, M. K. and Halliday, E. G. (1944). The nutritive value of canned foods. 6. Effect of large-scale preparation for serving on the ascorbic acid, thiamin, and riboflavin content of commercially-canned vegetables. *J. Amer. diet. Ass.*, **20**, 752.

392. Hinman, W. F., Brush, M. K. and Halliday, E. G. (1945). The nutritive value of canned foods. 7. Effect of small-scale preparation on the ascorbic acid, thiamin, and riboflavin content of commercially-canned vegetables. *J. Amer. diet. Ass.*, **21**, 7.

393. Hinman, W. F., Higgins, M. M. and Halliday, E. G. (1947). The nutritive value of canned foods. 18. Further studies on carotene, ascorbic acid, and thiamine. *J. Amer. diet. Ass.*, **23**, 226.

394. Hirst, F. and Adam, W. B. (1945). The processing and laboratory examination of canned potatoes. *Chem. & Ind. (Rev.)* No. 12, 91.

395. Hoar, W. S. and Barberie, M. (1945). Distribution of riboflavin in fresh and processed fish. *Canad. J. Res. (E)*, **23**, 8.

396. Hodson, A. Z. (1940a). Riboflavin content of some common vegetables and fruits. *Food Res.*, **5**, 395.

397. Hodson, A. Z. (1940b). The influence of dietary riboflavin on the content of this vitamin in chicken tissue. *J. Nutr.*, **20**, 377.

398. Hodson, A. Z. (1941). Effect of cooking on riboflavin content of chicken meat. *Food Res.*, **6**, 175.

399. Hodson, A. Z. (1944). The pyridoxine content of fresh, pasturized, evaporated and dried milk. *J. Nutr.*, **27**, 415.

400. Hodson, A. Z. (1945). The nicotinic acid, pantothenic acid, choline and biotin content of fresh, irradiated evaporated and dry milk. *J. Nutr.*, **29**, 137.

401. Hodson, A. Z. (1950). Terminal heating of infant formula. 4. Retention of ascorbic acid in orange juice. *J. Amer. diet. Ass.*, **26**, 177.

402. Hoeflake, H. (1951). Een onderzoek naar de variatie van het lactoflavine-, nicotinezuur-, pantotheenzuur- en biotine gehalte in Nederlandse consumptiemelk met behulp van microbiologische bepalingsmethoden. *Thesis, Univ. Amsterdam. (Nutr. Abstr. Rev.,* 1952, **21**, *Abstr.* 3291).

403. Hoeflake, H. (1953). An investigation into the riboflavin, nicotinic acid, pantothenic acid and biotin contents of Dutch market milks, determined by the microbiological method. *Ned. melk- en Zuiveltijdschr.*, **7**, 227. (*Nutr. Abstr. Rev.*, 1954, **24**, *Abstr.* 2998).

404. Hoekstra, W. G., Pope, A. L. and Phillips, P. H. (1952). Synthesis of certain B-vitamins in the cobalt deficient sheep, with special reference to vitamin B_{12}. *J. Nutr.*, **48**, 421.

405. Hoff-Jörgensen, E., Moustgaard, J. and Möller, P. (1952). The content of B-vitamins in some ordinary Danish feedstuffs. (The application of an improved medium for vitamin determinations with *L. casei*). *Acta. agric. Scand.*, **2**, 305.

406. Hoffman, C., Schweitzer, T. R. and Dalby, G. (1940a). The thiamin content of whole-wheat and clear flours. *Cereal Chem.*, **17**, 733.

407. Hoffman, C., Schweitzer, T. R. and Dalby, G. (1940b). The loss of thiamin in bread on baking and toasting. *Cereal Chem.*, **17**, 737.

408. Holman, W. I. M., in Widdowson and McCance (1954), q.v.

409. Holman, W. I. M. (1956). The distribution of vitamins within the tissues of common foodstuffs. *Nutr. Abstr. Rev.*, **26**, 277.

410. Holman, W. I. M. and Godden, W. (1947). The aneurin (vitamin B_1) content of oats. 1. The influence of variety and locality. 2. Possible losses in milling. *J. agric. Sci.*, **37**, 51.

411. Holmes, A. D. (1944a). Riboflavin content of immature Massachusetts lettuce. *Food Res.*, **9**, 121.

412. Holmes, A. D. (1944b). Effect of pasteurization on the riboflavin content of milk. *J. Amer. diet. Ass.*, **20**, 226

413. Holmes, A. D. (1949). Comparison of the stability of reduced ascorbic acid in raw and pasteurized milk. *Amer. J. Dis. Child.*, **78**, 899.

414. Holmes, A. D. (1951). Store vs. delivered milk as a source of reduced ascorbic acid. *J. Amer. diet. Ass.*, **27**, 578.

415. Holmes, A. D. (1952). Stability of ascorbic acid in milk at different stages of processing *J. Pediat.*, **40**, 91.

416. Holmes, A. D. and Holmes, J. O. (1943). Uniformity of riboflavin content of milk produced under standardized conditions. *Amer. J. Dis. Child.*, **66**, 607.

417. Holmes, A. D. and Jones, C. P. (1945). Effect of sunshine upon the ascorbic acid and riboflavin content of milk. *J. Nutr.*, **29**, 201.

418. Holmes, A. D., Jones, C. P. and Ritchie, W. S. (1943). The ascorbic acid content of late-winter tomatoes. *New Engl. J. Med.*, **229**, 461.

419. Holmes, A. D., Jones, C. P. and Wertz, A. W. (1944). Ascorbic acid, riboflavin and thiamine content of cow's milk. Influence of the ration. *Amer. J. Dis. Child.*, **67**, 376.

420. Holmes, A. D., Jones, C. P., Wertz, A. W., Esselen, K. and McKey, B. V. (1944). The ratio of ascorbic, nicotinic and pantothenic acids, riboflavin and thiamin in late summer milk. *J. Dairy Sci.*, **27**, 849.

421. Holmes, A. D., Jones, C. P., Wertz, A. W. and Kuzmeski, J. W. (1943). The ratio of ascorbic acid, riboflavin and thiamine in raw and pasteurized milk. *J. Nutr.*, **26**, 337.

422. Holmes, A. D., Lindquist, H. G., Jones, C. P. and Wertz, A. W. (1945). Effect of high-temperature-short-time-pasteurization on the ascorbic acid, riboflavin and thiamin content of milk. *J. Dairy Sci.*, **28**, 29.

423. Holmes, A. D., Patch, J. A. and Tripp, F. (1943). The relation of season, weight and price to the vitamin C content of oranges. *New Engl. J. Med.*, **228**, 8.

424. Holmes, A. D., Pigott, M. G. and Tripp, F. (1941). Comparative costs of vitamin C in fresh and commercially canned fruit and vegetable juices. *New Engl. J. Med.*, **225**, 68.

425. Holmes, A. D., Tripp, F., Woelffer, E. A. and Satterfield, G. H. (1939a). The influence of pasteurization on the ascorbic acid (vitamin C) content of certified milk. *J. Amer. diet. Ass.*, **15**, 363.

426. Holmes, A. D., Tripp, F., Woelffer, E. A. and Satterfield, G. H. (1939b). A study of breed and seasonal variations in the ascorbic acid content of certified milk from Guernseys and Holsteins. *J. Nutr.*, **17**, 187.

427. Holmes, A. D., Tripp, F., Woelffer, E. A. and Satterfield, G. H. (1940a). Ascorbic acid content of cow's milk at various stages of lactation. *Amer. J. Dis. Child.*, **60**, 1025.

428. Holmes, A. D., Tripp, F., Woelffer, E. A. and Satterfield, G. H. (1940b). Influence of age of cow on ascorbic acid content of certified milk. *Food Res.*, **5**, 263.

429. Holmes, A. D., Tripp,, F. Woelffer, E. A. and Satterfield, G. H. (1941). The ascorbic acid content of cow's milk during pregnancy. *J. Nutr.*, **22**, 267.

430. Holmes, A. D., Tripp, F., Woelffer, E. A. and Satterfield, G. H. (1942a). Relation of volume of daily milk production to ascorbic acid content of cow's milk. *Food Res.*, 7, 111.

431. Holmes, A. D. Tripp, F., Woelffer, E. A. and Satterfield, G. H. (1942b). Ascorbic acid content of cow's milk after five years of continuous lactation. *Food Res.*, 7, 370.

432. Holmes, A. D., Tripp, F., Woelffer, E. A. and Satterfield, G. H. (1943). Ascorbic acid content of cow's milk during four successive lactation periods. *Food Res.*, 8, 237.

433. Hoogland, P. L. (1953). The B-vitamins of cod and haddock. *Fish Res. Bd. Can.*, *Progr. Rep. Atlantic Coast Sta.*, No. 55, 11.

434. Hopkins, R. H. (1943). Riboflavin and vitamin B_1 in war-time beers. *Nature, Lond.*, 152, 274.

435. Hopkins, R. H. and Pennington, R. J. (1947a). The assay of vitamin B_6 complex. *Biochem. J.*, 41, 110.

436. Hopkins, R. H. and Pennington, R. J. (1947b). Vitamin B_6 in brewing. *J. Inst. Brew.*, 53, 251.

437. Hopkins, R. H. and Wiener, S. (1944). Vitamin B_1 and riboflavin in brewing. *J. Inst. Brew.*, 50, 124.

438. Hopkins, R. H. and Wiener, S. (1945a). Riboflavin in beer. *J. Inst. Brew.*, 51, 34.

439. Hopkins, R. H. and Wiener, S. (1945b). Riboflavin in beer. *J. Inst. Brew.*, 51, 133.

440. Horwitt, M. K. (1954) in *The vitamins: chemistry, physiology, pathology*, edited by W. H. Sebrell (Jr.) and R. S. Harris, Vol. III, p. 374. Academic Press Inc., New York.

441. Houston, J., Kon, S. K. and Thompson, S. Y. (1939). The effect of light on the vitamin C of milk in different containers. *J. Dairy Res.*, 10, 471.

442. Houston, J., Kon, S. K. and Thompson, S. Y. (1940a). The effect of commercial pasteurization and sterilization on the vitamin B_1 and riboflavin content of milk as measured by chemical methods. *J. Dairy Res.*, 11, 67.

443. Houston, J., Kon, S. K. and Thompson, S. Y. (1940b). The vitamin B_1 and riboflavin of milk. 1. The application of Jansen's thiochrome test to the estimation of vitamin B_1 in milk. *J. Dairy Res.*, 11, 145.

444. Houston, J., Kon, S. K. and Thompson, S. Y. (1940c). The vitamin B_1 and riboflavin of milk. 2. The different forms of vitamin B_1 in milk. *J. Dairy Res.*, 11, 151.

445. Houston, J., Kon, S. K. and Thompson, S. Y. (1940d). The vitamin B_1 and riboflavin of milk. 3. Effect of stage of lactation and of season on the vitamin B_1 and riboflavin content of milk. *J. Dairy Res.*, 11, 155.

446. Hove, E. L. and Hove, Z. (1944). The chemical estimation of a-tocopherol and total tocopherol in mixtures of the a, β and γ forms. *J. biol. Chem.*, 156, 601.

447. Høygaard, A. and Rasmussen, H. W. (1939). Vitamin C sources in Eskimo foods. *Nature, Lond.*, 143, 943.

448. Hrubetz, M. C., Deuel, H. J. (Jr.) and Hanley, B. J. (1945). The effect of a high vitamin A intake on the composition of human milk. *J. Nutr.*, 29, 245.

449. Hughes, E. B. and Parkinson, T. L. (1945). The nicotinic acid content of tea. *Analyst*, 70, 86.

450. Hughes, E. B. and Smith, R. F. (1946). The nicotinic acid content of coffee. *J. Soc. chem. Ind., Lond.*, 65, 284.

451. Hundley, J. M. (1954). In *The vitamins: chemistry, physiology, pathology*, edited by W. H. Sebrell, (Jr.) and R. S. Harris, Vol. II, p. 541. Academic Press Inc., New York.

452. Hunt, C. H., Rodriguez, L. D. and Bethke, R. M. (1950). The environmental and agronomical factors influencing the thiamine, riboflavin, niacin, and pantothenic acid content of wheat, corn, and oats. *Cereal Chem.*, 27, 79.

453. Ihde, A. J. and Schuette, H. A. (1941). Thiamine, nicotinic acid, riboflavin and pantothenic acid in rye and its milled products. *J. Nutr.*, 22, 527.

454. Inhoffen, H. H. and Pommer, H. (1954). In *The vitamins: chemistry, physiology, pathology*, edited by W. H. Sebrell, (Jr.) and R. S. Harris, Vol. I, p. 100. Academic Press Inc., New York.

455. Ittner, N. R. and Hughes, E. H. (1941).   Riboflavin content of pork muscle.   *Food Res.*, **6**, 239.

456. Ives, M., Pollard, A. E., Elvehjem, C. A. and Strong, F. M. (1946).   The nutritive value of canned foods.   17. Pyridoxine, biotin and "folic acid".   *J. Nutr.*, **31**, 347.

457. Ives, M., Wagner, J. R., Elvehjem, C. A. and Strong, F. M. (1944).   The nutritive value of canned foods.   3. Thiamine and niacin.   *J. Nutr.*, **28**, 117.

458. Ives, M., Zepplin, M., Ames, S. R., Strong, F. M. and Elvehjem, C. A. (1945).   The nutritive value of canned foods.   10. Further studies on riboflavin, niacin and pantothenic acid.   *J. Amer. diet. Ass.*, **21**, 357.

459. Jackson, S. H., Crook, A., Malone, V. and Drake, T. G. H. (1945).   The retention of thiamine, riboflavin and niacin in cooking pork and in processing bacon.   *J. Nutr.*, **29**, 391.

460. Jackson, S. H., Doherty, A. and Malone, V. (1943).   The recovery of the B vitamins in the milling of wheat.   *Cereal Chem.*, **20**, 551.

461. Jackson, S. H., Drake, T. G. H., Slinger, S. J., Evans, E. V. and Pocock, R. (1946).   The influence of riboflavin consumption on its concentration in hen's eggs.   *J. Nutr.*, **32**, 567.

462. James, D. P. (1944).   Riboflavin in fresh fruits.   *Rep. agric. hort. Res. Sta. Bristol*, p. 166.

463. James, D. P. (1947).   Some vitamins of the B group in cider.   *Rep. agric. hort. Res. Sta. Bristol*, p. 192.

464. James, D. P. (1952).   Nicotinic acid, pantothenic acid and biotin in fruit, vegetables and nuts.   *Brit. J. Nutr.*, **6**, 341.

465. Jansen, B. C. P. (1954).   In *The vitamins: chemistry, physiology, pathology*, edited by W. H. Sebrell, (Jr.) and R. S. Harris, Vol. III, p. 454.   Academic Press Inc., New York.

466. Jenkins, G. N. (1943).   Ascorbic acid in mashed potatoes.   *Nature, Lond.*, **151**, 473.

467. Jenkins, G. N. (1946).   Vitamin C content of home-cooked vegetables.   *Brit. med. J.*, **i**, 233.

468. Jenness, R. and Palmer, L. S. (1945).   The vitamin A potency of creamery butter produced in Minnesota.   *J. Dairy Sci.*, **28**, 473.

469. Jentsch, M. S. and Morgan, A. F. (1949).   Thiamin, riboflavin, and niacin content of walnuts.   *Food Res.*, **14**, 40.

470. Johnson, M. L., Scoular, F. I. and Burt, D. F. (1944).   The ascorbic acid content of freshly prepared and of stored orange marmalade.   *J. Amer. diet. Ass.*, **20**, 668.

471. Johnston, C. H., Schauer, L., Rapaport, S. and Deuel, H. J. (Jr.) (1943).   The effect of cooking with and without sodium bicarbonate on the thiamine, riboflavin, and ascorbic acid content of peas.   *J. Nutr.*, **26**, 227.

472. Jones, J. B., Wood, M. A., Phillips, M. G., Fenton, F. and Harris, K. W. (1944).   Ascorbic acid, thiamin, and riboflavin retention in quick-frozen broccoli in institution food service.   *J. Amer. diet. Ass.*, **20**, 369.

473. Josephson, D. V. and Doan, F. J. (1945).   Ascorbic acid in evaporated milk.   *Bull. Pa. agric. Exp. Sta. Bull.*, No. 473.

474. Jukes, T. H. (1941).   The distribution of pantothenic acid in certain products of natural origin.   *J. Nutr.*, **21**, 193.

475. Jukes, T. H. and Williams, W. L. (1954).   In *The vitamins: chemistry, physiology, pathology*, edited by W. H. Sebrell, (Jr.) and R. S. Harris, Vol. I, p. 476.   Academic Press Inc., New York.

476. Kahn, R. M. and Halliday, E. G. (1944).   Ascorbic acid content of white potatoes as affected by cooking and standing on steam-table.   *J. Amer. diet. Ass.*, **20**, 220.

477. Karikka, K. J., Dudgeon, L. T. and Hauck, H. M. (1944).   Influence of variety, location, fertilizer, and storage on the ascorbic acid content of potatoes grown in New York State.   *J. agric. Res.*, **68**, 49.

478. Kárlin, R. (1954).   La vitamine B_{12} dans le lait humain et bovin.   *C.R. Soc. Biol., Paris*, **148**, 371.

479. Karrick, N. L. (1955).   Vitamin content of fishery by-products Part 2—Vitamin B_{12} in Pacific sardine (*Sardinops caeruela*).   *Comm. Fish. Rev.*, **17**, No. 2, 8.

480. Kaski, I. J., Webster, G. L. and Kirch, E. R. (1944). Ascorbic acid content of tomatoes. *Food Res.*, **9**, 386.

481. Kawerau, E. (1944). Ascorbic acid. 3. The ascorbic acid content of fruits and vegetables grown in Eire. *Sci. Proc. R. Dublin Soc.*, **23**, 181.

482. Kay, H. D. (1941). Cheese: some recent chemical and physico-chemical findings. *Chem. & Ind. (Rev.)*, **60**, 411.

483. Kelly, W. C. and Somers, G. F. (1949). The effect of time of harvest, variety, and storage on the ascorbic acid content of potato tubers. *Amer. Potato J.*, **26**, 47.

484. Kemmerer, A. R. and Fraps, G. S. (1943a). Constituents of carotene extracts of plants. *Industr. Engng. Chem. (Anal.)* **15**, 714.

485. Kemmerer, A. R. and Fraps, G. S. (1943b). The vitamin A content of commercial butters sold in Texas. *Bull. Tex. agric. Exp. Sta.*, No. 629.

486. Kemmerer, A. R. and Fraps, G. S. (1945a). Relative value of carotene in vegetables for growth of the white rat. *Arch. Biochem.*, **8**, 197.

487. Kemmerer, A. R. and Fraps, G. S. (1945b). The vitamin A activity of neo-β-carotene U and its steric rearrangement in the digestive tract of rats. *J. biol. Chem.*, **161**, 305.

488. Kemmerer, A. R., Fraps, G. S. and Meinke, W. W. (1945). Constituents of the crude carotene of certain human foods. *Food Res.*, **10**, 66.

489. Kendall, N. (1942). Thiamin content of various milks. *J. Pediat.*, **20**, 65.

490. Kent-Jones, D. W. (1958). The case for fortified flour. *Proc. Nutr. Soc.*, **17**, 38.

491. Kent-Jones, D. W. and Bacharach, A. L. (1941). The Nation's food. IV. Cereals as food. 2. The nutritive value of bread. *Chem. & Ind. (Rev.)*, No. 47, 823.

492. Keys, O. H. (1941). A note on the stability of vitamin C (ascorbic acid) in citrous juices. *N.Z. med. J.*, **40**, 379. (*Nutr. Abstr. Rev.*, 1942, **12**, *Abstr.* 326).

493. Keys, O. H. (1943). Vitamin C in apples and other materials. *N.Z. J. Sci. Tech. (B)*, **24**, 146.

494. Kidson, E. B. (1943). The vitamin C content of Nelson apples. *N.Z. J. Sci. Tech. (B))*, **25**, 134.

495. Kieser, M. E. and Pollard, A. (1946). The apple as a source of vitamin C. Tests in 1946. *Rep. agric. hort. Res. Sta.*, *Bristol*, p. 132.

496. Kieser, M. E. and Pollard, A. (1947). Vitamin C in English apples. *Nature, Lond.*, **159**, 65.

497. Kieser, M. E., Pollard, A. and Stone, A. M. (1949). The effect of manurial treatment on the composition of blackcurrants and their products. *Rep. agric. hort. Res. Sta.*, *Bristol*, p. 159.

498. Kieser, M. E., Pollard, A. and Timberlake, C. F. (1952). Factors affecting the quality and chemical constituents of strawberries: effects of manurial treatments. *Rep. agric. hort. Res. Sta.*, *Bristol*, p. 163.

499. Kik, M. C. (1945). Effect of milling, processing, washing, cooking and storage on thiamine, riboflavin and niacin in rice. *Bull. Ark. agric. Exp. Sta.*, No. 458.

500. Kik, M. C. (1951). Nutritive studies of rice. *Bull. Ark. agric. Exp. Sta.*, No. 508.

501. Kik, M. C. and Van Landingham, F. B. (1943). Riboflavin in products of commercial rice milling and thiamin and riboflavin in rice varieties. *Cereal Chem.*, **20**, 563.

502. Kik, M. C. and Williams, R. R. (1945). The nutritional improvement of white rice. *Bull. nat. Res. Coun., Wash.*, No. 112.

503. Kirk, M. M. and Tressler, D. K. (1941). Ascorbic acid content of pigmented fruits, vegetables and their juices. *Food Res.*, **6**, 395.

504. Kitzes, G., Schuette, H. A. and Elvehjem, C. A. (1943). The B vitamins in honey. *J. Nutr.*, **26**, 241.

505. Klatzkin, C., Norris, F. W. and Wokes, F. (1948). Nicotinic acid in cereals. 1. The effect of germination. *Biochem. J.*, **42**, 414.

506. Klose, A. A., Jones, G. I. and Fevold, H. L. (1943). Vitamin content of spray-dried whole egg. *Industr. Engng. Chem. (Industr.)*, **35**, 1203.

507. Knaut, T. (1955). Zawartość tiaminy i ryboflawiny w mleku surowym i gotowanym. *Roczn. Nauk rol. (B)*, **70**, 197.

508. Knott, E. M., Kleiger, S. C. and Bracamonte-Torres, F. (1943). Factors affecting the thiamine content of breast milk. *J. Nutr.*, **25**, 49.

509. Kodicek, E. (1940a). Estimation of nicotinic acid in animal tissues, blood and certain foodstuffs. 1. Method. *Biochem. J.*, **34**, 712.

510. Kodicek, E. (1940b). Estimation of nicotinic acid in animal tissues, blood and certain foodstuffs. 2. Applications. *Biochem. J.*, **34**, 724.

511. Kodicek, E. (1946). Factors affecting the nutritive value of bread as human food. Discussion. *Proc. Nutr. Soc.*, **4**, 22.

512. Kodicek, E. and Wang, Y. L. (1949). The fluorimetric estimation of riboflavin in foodstuffs and other biological material. *Biochem. J.*, **44**, 340.

513. Kon, S. K. (1940). Biennial reviews on the progress of dairy science. Section D. The nutritional value of milk and milk products. *J. Dairy Res.*, **11**, 196.

514. Kon, S. K. (1944). The chemical composition and nutritive value of milk and milk products. *Proc. Nutr. Soc.*, **2**, 149.

515. Kon, S. K. (1951). Teneur en vitamines du lait. Les variations et leurs causes. *Ann. Nutr., Paris*, **5**, 211.

516. Kon, S. K. (1958). Influence of heat treatment and light on the composition and quality of milk. *Dairy Sci. Abstr.*, **20**, 888.

517. Kon, S. K. (1959). Milk and milk products in human nutrition. *F.A.O. Nutritional Studies*, No. 17. United Nation's Food and Agriculture Organization, Rome.

518. Kon, S. K. and Henry, K. M. (1949). Reviews of the progress of dairy science. D. Nutritive value of milk and milk products. *J. Dairy Res.*, **16**, 68.

519. Kon, S. K. and Henry, K. M. (1951). Reviews of the progress of dairy science. D. Nutritive value of milk and milk products. *J. Dairy Res.*, **18**, 317.

520. Kon, S. K. and Mawson, E. H. (1950). Human milk. Wartime studies of certain vitamins and other constituents. *Spec. Rep. Ser. med. Res. Coun., Lond.*, No. 269. H.M. Stationery Office.

521. Kon, S. K. and Thompson, S. Y. (1949a). Preformed vitamin A in crustacea. *Arch. Biochem.*, **24**, 233.

522. Kon, S. K. and Thompson, S. Y. (1949b). Preformed vitamin A in Northern krill. *Biochem. J.*, **45**, XXXI.

523. Kothavalla, Z. R. and Singh Gill, H. (1943). Studies on the effect of various factors on the vitamin C content of the milk of cows and buffaloes. *Indian J. vet. Sci.*, **13**, 35. (*Nutr. Abstr. Rev.*, 1943, **13**, *Abstr.* 2180).

524. Kramer, M. M., Dickman, R. M., Hildreth, M. D., Kunerth, B. L. and Riddell, W. H. (1939). The riboflavin value of milk. *J. Dairy Sci.*, **22**, 753.

525. Kramer, M. and Satterfield, G. H. (1942). Ascorbic acid content of four varieties of raw wines. *Food Res.*, **7**, 127.

526. Krehl, W. A. and Cowgill, G. R. (1950). Vitamin content of citrus products. *Food Res.*, **15**, 179.

527. Krehl, W. A., De La Huerga, J., Elvehjem, C. A. and Hart, E. B. (1946). The distribution of niacinamide and niacin in natural materials. *J. biol. Chem.*, **166**, 53.

528. Krehl, W. A. and Winters, R. W. (1950). Effect of cooking methods on retention of vitamins and minerals in vegetables. *J. Amer. diet. Ass.*, **26**, 966.

529. Kringstad, H. and Aschehoug, V. (1948). Vitamin A-innholdet i fersk og hermetisk brisling. Sammenliknende biologiske og fysikalsk-kjemiske bestemmelser. *Tidsskr. Hermetikind.*, **34**, 85.

530. Kringstad, H. and Folkvord, S. (1949). The nutritive value of cod roe and cod liver. *J. Nutr.*, **38**, 489.

531. Kringstad, H. and Naess, T. (1939). Eine colorimetrische Methode zur Bestimmung von Nicotinsäure und Nicotinsäureamid in Nahrungsmitteln. *Hoppe-Seylers Z. physiol. Chem.*, **260**, 108.

532. Kringstad, H. and Thoresen, F. (1940). Om forekomsten av antipellagravitaminet, nikotinsyre (-amid) i en del naeringsmidler. *Nord. med.*, **8**, 2248. (*Nutr. Abstr. Rev.*, 1941, **11**, *Abstr.* 1087).

533. Kruisheer, C. I. and Den Herder, P. C. (1952). The vitamin A and carotene contents of Dutch butter. *Ned. melk- en Zuiveltijdschr.*, **6**, 109. (*Nutr. Abstr. Rev.*, 1953, **23**, *Abstr.* 275).

534. Kruisheer, C. I. and Den Herder, P. C. (1953). Regionale variaties in het caroteen—en vitamine A—gehalte van de nederlandse boter. *Ned. melk-en Zuiveltiidschr.*, **7**, 59. (*Nutr. Abstr. Rev.*, 1953, **23**, *Abstr.* 4151).

535. Krukovsky, V. N., Whiting, F. and Loosli, J. K. (1950). Tocopherol, carotenoid and vitamin A content of the milk fat and the resistance of milk to the development of oxidized flavours as influenced by breed and season. *J. Dairy Sci.*, **33**, 791.

536. Kühnau, J. (1956). Tabellen der chemischen Zusammensetzung von Fischen. 1. Teil: Vitamine. *Arch. FischWiss.*, **7**, Suppl. 1, 1.

537. Lamb, F. C. (1946). Nutritive value of canned foods. Factors affecting ascorbic acid content of canned grapefruit and orange juices. *Industr. Engng. Chem.* (*Industr.*), **38**, 860.

538. Lamb, F. C., Pressley, A. and Zuch, T. (1947). Nutritive value of canned foods. 21. Retention of nutrients during commercial production of various canned fruits and vegetables. *Food Res.*, **12**, 273.

539. Lampen, J. O., Bahler, G. P. and Peterson, W. H. (1942). The occurrence of free and bound biotin. *J. Nutr.*, **23**, 11.

540. Lampitt, L. H. and Baker, L. C. (1942). Ascorbic acid in oranges. *Nature, Lond.*, **149**, 271.

541. Lampitt, L. H., Baker, L. C. and Parkinson, T. L. (1942). Disappearance of the ascorbic acid in raw cabbage after mincing or chopping. *Nature, Lond.*, **149**, 697.

542. Lampitt, L. H., Baker, L. C. and Parkinson, T. L. (1943). The vitamin-C content of raw and cooked vegetables. *J. Soc. chem. Ind., Lond.*, **62**, 61.

543. Lampitt, L. H., Baker, L. C. and Parkinson, T. L. (1945a). Vitamin-C content of potatoes. 1. Distribution in the potato plant. *J. Soc. chem. Ind., Lond.*, **64**, 18.

544. Lampitt, L. H., Baker, L. C. and Parkinson, T. L. (1945b). Vitamin-C content of potatoes. 2. The effect of variety, soil, and storage. *J. Soc. chem. Ind., Lond.*, **64**, 22.

545. Lampitt, L. H., Baker, L. C. and Parkinson, T. L. (1945c). Vitamin-C content of vegetables. 2. Effect of storage on raw vegetables. *J. Soc. chem. Ind., Lond.*, **64**, 200.

546. Lampitt, L. H., Baker, L. C. and Parkinson, T. L. (1945d). Vitamin-C content of vegetables. 3. Average figures for raw vegetables. *J. Soc. chem. Ind., Lond.*, **64**, 202.

547. Lampitt, L. H., Baker, L. C. and Parkinson, T. L. (1945e). Vitamin-C content of vegetables. 4. Effect of cooking on cabbage. *J. Soc. chem. Ind., Lond.*, **64**, 260.

548. Lampitt, L. H., Baker, L. C. and Parkinson, T. L. (1945f). The vitamin-C content of vegetables. 5. The influence of variety. *J. Soc. chem. Ind., Lond.*, **64**, 262.

549. Lampitt, L. H., Clayson, D. H. F. and Barnes, E. M. (1945). The destruction of ascorbic acid during the cooking of green vegetables. Observations on the mechanisms involved. *J. Soc. chem. Ind., Lond.*, **63**, 193.

550. Lampitt, L. H., Ginsburg, L. and Baker, L. C. (1950). The vitamin-C content of English and South African cabbages. *J. Sci. Food Agric.*, **1**, 12.

551. Lane, R. L., Johnson, E. and Williams, R. R. (1942). Studies of the average American diet. 1. Thiamine content. *J. Nutr.*, **23**, 613.

552. Lanford, C. S., Finkelstein, B. and Sherman, H. C. (1941). Riboflavin contents of some typical fruits. *J. Nutr.*, **21**, 175.

553. Lantz, E. M. (1951). Ascorbic acid in peaches from Southern New Mexico. *Food Res.*, **16**, 77.

554. Lardinois, C. C., Elvehjem, C. A. and Hart, E. B. (1944). The effect of storage on the retention of certain members of the vitamin B complex. *J. Dairy Sci.*, **27**, 875.

555. Lassen, S., Bacon, K. and Hinderer, E. (1944). Vitamin B complex studies on the California avocado. *J. Amer. diet. Ass.*, **20**, 688.

556. Lassen, S., Bacon, K. and Sutherland, J. (1945).   Vitamin D and pro-vitamin D content of the avocado.   *Food Res.,* **10,** 1.

557. Laufer, S., Schwarz, R. and Laufer L. (1942).   Vitamin B complex content of beers, ales, and malt tonics.   *Food Res.,* **7,** 306.

558. Lawrence, J. M., Herrington, B. L. and Maynard, L. A. (1945).   Human milk studies. XXVII. Comparative values of bovine and human milks in infant feeding.   *Amer. J. Dis. Child.,* **70,** 193.

559. Lawrence, J. M., Herrington, B. L. and Maynard, L. A. (1946).   The nicotinic acid, biotin, and pantothenic acid content of cow's milk.   *J. Nutr.,* **32,** 73.

560. Lee, F. A., Brooks, R. F., Pearson, A. M., Miller, J. I. and Volz, F. (1950).   Effect of freezing rate on meat.   Appearance, palatability, and vitamin content of beef.   *Food Res.,* **15,** 8.

561. Lee, F. A., Brooks, R. F., Pearson, A. M., Miller, J. I. and Wanderstock, J. J. (1954).   Effect of rate of freezing on pork quality.   Appearance, palatability and vitamin content.   *J. Amer. diet. Ass.,* **30,** 351.

562. Lehrer, W. P. (Jr.), Wiese, A. C., Harvey, W. R. and Moore, P. R. (1951).   Effect of frozen storage and subsequent cooking on the thiamine, riboflavin, and nicotinic acid content of pork chops.   *Food Res.,* **16,** 485.

563. Lehrer, W. P. (Jr.), Wiese, A. C., Harvey, W. R. and Moore, P. R. (1952).   The stability of thiamine, riboflavin, and nicotinic acid of lamb chops during frozen storage and subsequent cooking.   *Food Res.,* **17,** 24.

564. Leichsenring, J. M., Morris, L. M., Salmon, W. D., Flanagan, C., Woods, E., Bolin, D. W., Van Duyne, F. O., Wolfe, J. C., Simpson, J. I., Murphy, E. F., Sheets, O. A., Werner, H. O., Leverton, R. M., Schlaphoff, D. M., Peterson, W. J., Kelly, E., Knowles D., Christensen, F. W., Mattson, H., Wegner, M. I., Reder, R. E., Dodds, M. L., Reed, H. M., Orent-Keiles, E., Hewston, E. M., Greenwood, J. B., Latimer, M. and Levy, D. (1951).   Factors influencing the nutritive value of potatoes.   *Tech. Bull. Minn. agric. Exp. Sta.,* No. 196.

565. Le Riche, F. J. H. (1945).   Ascorbic acid content of tomato varieties.   *Fmg. in S. Afr.,* **20,** 105.

566. Le Riche, F. J. H. (1946–7a).   Studies on the processing of vegetables.   3. The chemical composition and nutritional value of lettuce varieties (*Lactuca cativa L.*).   (*Fruit Res. Tech. Ser. No.* 10).   *Sci. Bull. Dep. Agric. S. Afr.,* No. 260.

567. Le Riche, F. J. H. (1946–7b).   Studies on the processing of vegetables.   4. Studies on the ascorbic acid content of cabbage varieties.   (*Fruit Res. Tech. Ser. No.* 11).   *Sci. Bull. Dep. Agric. S. Afr.,* No. 261.

568. Le Riche, F. J. H. and Burger, I. J. (1946).   Studies on the processing of vegetables.   2. The composition and processing of tomato varieties.   (*Fruit Res. Tech. Ser. No.* 9).   *Sci. Bull. Dep. Agric. S. Afr.,* No. 258.

569. Le Riche, F. J. H. and Burger, I. J. (1948).   Studies on the processing of vegetables.   6. ii. Ascorbic acid losses in green peas during canning.   (*Fruit Res. Tech. Ser. No.* 22).   *Sci. Bull. Dep. Agric. S. Afr.,* No. 287.

570. Le Riche, F. J. H. and Mouton, J. A. (1948).   Studies on the processing of vegetables.   6. i. The chemical composition of some Western Cape Province carrot varieties.   (*Fruit Res. Tech. Ser. No.* 22).   *Sci. Bull. Dep. Agric. S. Afr.,* No. 287.

571. Lesher, M., Brody, J. K., Williams, H. H. and Macy, I. G. (1945).   Human milk studies. 26. Vitamin A and carotenoid contents of colostrum and mature human milk.   *Amer. J. Dis. Child.,* **70,** 182.

572. Leverton, R. M. and Odell, G. V. (1958).   The nutritive value of cooked meats.   *Misc. Publ. Okla. agric. Exp. Sta.,* MP-49.

573. Lewis, H. and Fieger, E. A. (1946).   A two-year study of the vitamin A potency of Louisiana milk and butter.   *Bull. La. agric. Exp. Sta.,* No. 405.

574. Lewis, U. J., Register, U. D., Thompson, H. T. and Elvehjem, C. A. (1949).   Distribution of vitamin B_{12} in natural materials.   *Proc. Soc. exp. Biol., N. Y.,* **72,** 479.

575. Lie, J. and Lunde, G. (1940).   Vitamin B_1 i en del norske naeringsmidler.   *Nord. Med.,* **8,** 2250.

576. Lieck, H. and Søndergaard, H. (1958). The content of vitamin B_6 in Danish foods. *Int. Z. Vitaminforsch.*, **29**, 68.

577. Lillie, R. J., Bird, H. R., Sizemore, J. R., Kellog, W. L. and Denton, C. A. (1954). Assay of feedstuffs and concentrates for vitamin B_{12} potency. *Poult. Sci.*, **33**, 686.

578. Lineberry, R. A. and Burkhart, L. (1942). The vitamin C content of small fruits. *Proc. Amer. Soc. hort. Sci.*, **41**, 198.

579. Lineberry, R. A. and Burkhart, L. (1943). The stability of vitamin C in small fruits. *Fruit Prod. J.*, **22**, 164.

580. Lodi, M. (1943). Untersuchungen über den Gehalt von Carotin, Vitamin B_1, B_2 und C bei der alkoholischen Gärung der Weinbeeren. *Vitam. u. Horm.*, **4**, 443. (*Nutr. Abstr. Rev.*, 1948, **18**, *Abstr.* 318).

581. Loeffler, H. J. (1946a). Retention of ascorbic acid in strawberries during processing, frozen storage, and manufacture of Velva fruits. *Food Res.*, **11**, 69.

582. Loeffler, H. J. (1946b). Retention of ascorbic acid in raspberries during freezing, frozen storage, puréeing, and manufacture into Velva fruit. *Food Res.*, **11**, 507.

583. Loosli, J. K., Krukovsky, V. N., Lofgreen, G. P. and Musgrave, R. B. (1950). The comparative value of Ladino clover, birdsfoot trefoil, timothy and alfalfa hays for yield and quality of milk. *J. Dairy Sci.*, **33**, 228.

584. Lord, J. W. (1945). Seasonal variation of carotene and vitamin A in butterfat and in serum. *Biochem. J.*, **39**, 372.

585. Love, R. M., Lovern, J. A. and Jones, N. R. (1959). The chemical composition of fish tissues. *Department of Scientific and Industrial Research. Food Investigation Spec. Rep.* No. 69. H.M. Stationery Office.

586. Lovern, J. A. (1943). The nation's food. 6. Fish as food. 3. The vitamin and mineral content of fish. *Chem. & Ind.* (*Rev.*), **62**, 328.

587. Lovern, J. A. (1944). Effect of processing and handling on the composition, vitamin content, keeping quality and culinary properties of fish. *Proc. Nutr. Soc.*, **2**, 100.

588. Luckey, T. D., Briggs, G. M. (Jr.), Moore, P. R., Elvehjem, C. A. and Hart, E. B. (1945). Studies on the liberation of compounds in the folic acid group. *J. biol. Chem.*, **161**, 395.

589. Lunde, G. (1939). Neuere Forschungen über die Vitamine in Fischen und Fischprodukten. *Angew. Chem.*, **52**, 521.

590. Lunde, G., Aschehoug, V. and Kringstad, H. (1937). Fish as a source of vitamins A and D. Herring, Brisling and their products. *Industr. Engng. Chem.* (*Industr.*), **29**, 1171.

591. Lunde, G., Kringstad, H. and Olsen, A. (1938). *Avh. norske VidenskAkad.* 1. *Mat.-Naturv. Klasse No.* 7 (quoted by Fixsen and Roscoe, 1939–40, q.v.).

592. Lynes, K. J. and Norris, F. W. (1948a). Biotin in the materials and process of brewing. *J. Inst. Brew.*, **54**, 150.

593. Lynes, K. J. and Norris, F. W. (1948b). Biotin in the materials and process of brewing. *J. Inst. Brew.*, **54**, 207.

594. McCance, R. A. (1944). The chemistry of growth and the food value of the common eel. *Biochem. J.*, **38**, 474.

595. McCance, R. A., Widdowson, E. M., Moran, T., Pringle, W. J. S. and Macrae, T. F. (1945). The chemical composition of wheat and rye and of flours derived therefrom. *Biochem. J.*, **39**, 213.

596. McCay, C. M., Pijoan, M. and Taubken, H. R. (1944). Ascorbic acid losses in mincing fresh vegetables. *Science*, **99**, 454.

597. McCollum, J. P. (1955). Distribution of carotenoids in the tomato. *Food Res.*, **20**, 55.

598. McDowall, F. H., Bathurst, N. O. and Campbell, I. L. (1947). The thiamin, riboflavin, and niacin content of some New Zealand milks. *N.Z. J. Sci. Tech.*, (*A*), **28**, 316.

599. McDowall, A. K. R. (1956). Variations in the carotene and vitamin A contents of herd butterfats throughout lactation. *J. Dairy Res.*, **23**, 111.

600. McDowall, A. K. R. and McDowall, F. H. (1953). The vitamin A potency of New Zealand butter. *J. Dairy Res.*, **20**, 76.

601. McElroy, O. E., Munsell, H. E. and Stienbarger, M. C. (1939). Ascorbic acid content of tomatoes as affected by home canning and subsequent storage, and of tomato juice and fresh orange juice as affected by refrigeration. *J. Home Econ.*, **31**, 325.

602. McFee, J. W. and Watts, J. H. (1958). Effect of non-antiscorbutic reducing substances upon the ascorbic acid content of baked potatoes. *Food Res.*, **23**, 114.

603. McGillivray, W. A. (1949a). Vitamin content of New Zealand meats. 1. Methods of assay for the B group vitamins. *N.Z. J. Sci. Tech. (A),.* **31**, 23.

604. McGillivray, W. A. (1949b). Vitamin content of New Zealand meats. 2. Lamb and mutton. *N.Z. J. Sci. Tech. (A).*, **31**, 30.

605. McGillivray, W. A. (1952). The effect of tocopherol and carotene supplements on the vitamin A potency of New Zealand butterfat. *J. Dairy Res.*, **19**, 119.

606. McGillivray, W. A. and Thompson, S. Y. (1957). The influence of pasture on the vitamin A and carotene in the milk of cows. *Proc. Nutr. Soc.*, **16**, 30.

607. McGucken, F. C. and Goddard, V. R. (1948). Thiamine and riboflavin content of raw and cooked dried apricots. *J. Amer. diet. Ass.*, **24**, 510.

608. McIntire, J. M., Schweigert, B. S. and Elvehjem, C. A. (1943). The retention of vitamins in veal and lamb during cooking. *J. Nutr.*, **26**, 621.

609. McIntire, J. M., Schweigert, B. S. and Elvehjem, C. A. (1944). The choline and pyridoxine content of meats. *J. Nutr.*, **28**, 219.

610. McIntire, J. M., Schweigert, B. S., Henderson, L. M. and Elvehjem, C. A. (1943). The retention of vitamins in meat during cooking. *J. Nutr.*, **25**, 143.

611. McIntire, J. M., Schweigert, B. S., Herbst, E. J. and Elvehjem, C. A. (1944). Vitamin content of variety meats. *J. Nutr.*, **28**, 35.

612. McIntire, J. M., Waisman, H. A., Henderson, L. M. and Elvehjem, C. A. (1941). Nicotinic acid content of meat products. *J. Nutr.*, **22**, 535.

613. McIntosh, J. A., Tressler, D. K. and Fenton, F. (1942). Ascorbic acid content of five quick-frozen vegetables as affected by composition of cooking utensil and volume of cooking water. *J. Home Econ.*, **34**, 314.

614. McKillican, M. E. (1948). The stability of carotene in carrots during storage. *Sci. Agric.*, **28**, 183.

615. MacKinney, G. and Sugihara, J. M. (1942). Riboflavin estimation in fruits and vegetables. *J. Amer. chem. Soc.*, **64**, 1980.

616. MacLinn, W. A. and Fellers, C. R. (1938). Ascorbic acid (vitamin C) in tomatoes and tomato products. *Bull. Mass. agric. Exp. Sta.*, No. 354.

617. McVicar, R. W. and Berryman, G. H. (1942). Nicotinic acid in foods. *J. Nutr.*, **24**, 235.

618. Macy, I. G. (1949). The composition of human colostrum and milk. *Amer. J. Dis. Child.*, **78**, 589.

619. Macy, I. G., Kelley, H. and Sloan, R. (1950). The composition of milks. A compilation of the comparative composition and properties of human, cow and goat milk, colostrum, and transitional milk. *Bull. nat. Res. Coun.*, No. 119.

620. Mapson, L. W. (1942). Vitamin methods. 5. A note on the determination of ascorbic acid in fruits and vegetables in the presence of SO_2. *Biochem. J.*, **36**, 155.

621. Mapson, L. W. (1943). Vitamin methods. 6. The estimation of ascorbic acid in the presence of reductones and allied substances. *J. Soc. chem. Ind., Lond.*, **62**, 223.

622. Mapson, L. W. (1952). Factors in distribution affecting the quality and nutritive value of foodstuffs. Loss of nutrients during the transport and distribution of fruits and vegetables. *Chem. & Ind. (Rev.)*, No. 2, 25.

623. Mapson, L. W. (1956). Recent research on vitamins. Effect of processing on the vitamin content of foods. *Brit. med. Bull.*, **12**, 73.

624. Martin, G. W. (1941). Vitamin B_1 content of crust and crumb of white bread. *Chem. & Ind. (Rev.)*, **60**, 342.

625. Mathews, D. M. and Bacharach, A. L. (1941). Root vegetables as anti-scorbutics in infant feeding. *Brit. med. J.*, **ii**, 226.

626. Mattick, A. T. R., Hiscox, E. R., Crossley, E. L., Lea, C. H., Findlay, J. D., Smith, J. A. B., Thompson, S. Y., Kon, S. K. and Egdell, J. W. (1945). The effect of temperature of pre-heating, of clarification and of bacteriological quality of the raw milk on the keeping properties of whole-milk powder dried by the Kestner Spray process. *J. Dairy Res.*, **14**, 116.

627. Mattill, H. A. (1954). In *The vitamins: chemistry, physiology, pathology*, edited by W. H. Sebrell (Jr.) and R. S. Harris, Vol. III, p. 512. Academic Press Inc., New York.

628. Mawson, E. H. and Kon, S. K. (1945). Vitamin C content of milk as consumed. *Lancet*, **249**, 14.

629. Maxa, V. (1949). The decreases of vitamin C during some treatments of milk. *Int. Dairy Congr. XII, Stockholm*, **2**, 208.

630. Mayfield, H. L. and Hedrick, M. T. (1949). Thiamine and riboflavin retention in beef during roasting, canning, and corning. *J. Amer. diet. Ass.*, **25**, 1024.

631. Mayfield, H. L. and Richardson, J. E. (1940a). Ascorbic acid content of parsnips. *Food Res.*, **5**, 361.

632. Mayfield, H. L. and Richardson, J. E. (1940b). The effect of winter storage on the vitamin content of cabbage and onions. *Bull. Mont. agric. Exp. Sta.*, No. 379.

633. Mayfield, H. L. and Richardson, J. E. (1943). Ascorbic acid content of strawberries and their products. *Bull. Mont. agric. Exp. Sta.*, No. 412.

634. Mayfield, H. L., Roehm, R. R. and Beeckler, A. F. (1955). Riboflavin and thiamine content of eggs from New Hampshire and White Leghorn hens fed diets containing condensed fish or dried whole solubles. *Poult. Sci.*, **34**, 1106.

635. Meiklejohn, J. (1943). Loss of thiamin from cooked potato. *Nature, Lond.*, **151**, 81.

636. Melnick, D. (1942). Collaborative study of the applicability of microbiological and chemical methods to the determination of niacin (nicotinic acid) in cereal products. *Cereal Chem.*, **19**, 553.

637. Melville, R. (1947). The nutritive value of nuts. *Chem. & Ind. (Rev.)*, No. **22**, 304.

638. Metcalfe, E., Rehm, P. and Winters, J. (1940). Variations in ascorbic acid content of grapefruit and oranges from the Rio Grande Valley of Texas. *Food Res.*, **5**, 233.

639. Meyer, B. H., Hinman, W. F. and Halliday, E. G. (1947). Retention of some vitamins of the B complex in beef during cooking. *Food Res.*, **12**, 203.

640. Mickelsen, O., Waisman, H. A. and Elvehjem, C. A. (1939a). The distribution of vitamin B_1 (thiamin) in meat and meat products. *J. Nutr.*, **17**, 269.

641. Mickelsen, O., Waisman, H. A. and Elvehjem, C. A. (1939b). The distribution of riboflavin in meat and meat products. *J. Nutr.*, **18**, 517.

642. Millares, R. and Fellers, C. R. (1949). Vitamin and amino acid content of processed chicken meat products. *Food Res.*, **14**, 131.

643. Miller, C. D. and Linden, S. (1947). Vitamin D and C values of milk. *Rep. Hawaii agric. Exp. Sta.*, 1944–46, p. 89.

644. Miller, E. V. and Schaal. E. E. (1951). Individual variation of the fruits of the pineapple (*Ananas comosus L. Merr.*) in regard to certain constituents of the juice. *Food Res.*, **16**, 252.

645. Miller, M. C. (1947). Reductone interference in estimation of vitamin C. *Food Res.*, **12**, 343.

646. Miller, R. C., Pence, J. W., Dutcher, R. A., Ziegler, P. T. and McCarty, M. A. (1943). The influence of the thiamine intake of the pig on the thiamine content of pork with observations on the riboflavin content of pork. *J. Nutr.*, **26**, 261.

647. Mills, M. B., Damron, C. M. and Roe, J. H. (1949). Ascorbic acid, dehydroascorbic acid and diketogulonic acid in fresh and processed foods. *Analyt. Chem.*, **21**, 707.

648. Ministry of Agriculture, Fisheries and Food (1957). Specification for cod liver oil. (Unpublished).

649. Mitchell, J. H., Van Blaricom, L. O. and Roderick, D. B. (1948). The effect of canning and freezing on the carotenoids and ascorbic acid content of peaches. *Bull. S.C. agric. Exp. Sta.*, No. 372.

R

650. Moore, P. R., Lepp, A., Luckey, T. D., Elvehjem, C. A. and Hart, E. B. (1947). Storage, retention and distribution of folic acid in the chick. *Proc. Soc. exp. Biol., N. Y.*, **64**, 316.

651. Moore, T. (1957). *Vitamin A*, ch. 30. Elsevier Publishing Co., London.

652. Moore, T. and Payne, J. E. (1942). The vitamin A contents of the livers of sheep, cattle and pigs. *Biochem. J.*, **36**, 34.

653. Moran, T. (1958). Personal communication.

654. Moran, T. (1959). Nutritional significance of recent work on wheat flour and bread. *Nutr. Abstr. Rev.*, **29**, 1.

655. Morgan, A. F., Bentley, L. S. and Groody, M. (1944). Vitamin content of prunes as affected by storage and other factors. *Food Res.*, **9**, 132.

656. Morgan, A. F. and Haynes, E. G. (1939). Vitamin B_1 content of human milk as affected by ingestion of thiamin chloride. *J. Nutr.*, **18**, 105.

657. Morgan, A. F., Kidder, L. E., Hunner, M., Sharokh, B. K. and Chesbro, R. M. (1949). Thiamine, riboflavin, and niacin content of chicken tissues as affected by cooking and frozen storage. *Food Res.*, **14**, 439.

658. Morgan, A. F., MacKinney, G. and Cailleau, A. (1945). Losses of ascorbic acid and four B vitamins in vegetables as a result of dehydration, storage and cooking. *Food Res.*, **10**, 5.

659. Morgan, E. J. (1942). Parsley as a rich source of vitamin C. *Nature, Lond.*, **150**, 92.

660. Morse, E. H., Potgieter, M. and Walker, G. R. (1958). Published vs analysed values for ascorbic acid. *J. Amer. diet. Ass.*, **34**, 265.

661. Morton, R. A., Lord, J. W. and Goodwin, T. W. (1941). Milk fats from cows fed on fresh pasture and ensiled green fodder. 2. Estimation of vitamin A activity. *J. Soc. chem. Ind., Lond.*, **60**, 310.

662. Moschette, D. S., Hinman, W. F. and Halliday, E. G. (1947). Nutritive value of canned foods. Effect of time and temperature of storage on vitamin content of commercially canned fruits and fruit juices (stored 12 months). *Industr. Engng. Chem. (Industr.)*, **39**, 994.

663. Moseley, M. A. (Jr.) and Satterfield, G. H. (1940). The ascorbic acid (vitamin C) content of six varieties of cantaloupes. *J. Home Econ.*, **32**, 104.

664. Moyer, J. C. and Tressler, D. K. (1943). Thiamin content of fresh and frozen vegetables. *Food Res.*, **8**, 58.

665. Munks, B., Robinson, A. Williams, H. H. and Macy, I. G. (1945). Human milk studies. XXV. Ascorbic acid and dehydroascorbic acid in colostrum and mature human milk. *Amer. J. Dis. Child.*, **70**, 176.

666. Munsell, H. E. (1940). Vitamins and their occurrence in foods. *Milbank mem. Fd. quart. Bull.*, **18**, 311.

667. Munsell, H. E. (1942). Riboflavin content of some common foods. *Food Res.*, **7**, 85.

668. Munsell, H. E. (1943). The vitamin A, vitamin B_1 (thiamin), vitamin C (ascorbic acid) and riboflavin content of common foods. A summary of "representative" values. *Milbank mem. Fd. quart. Bull.*, **21**, 102.

669. Munsell, H. E. (1945). Ascorbic acid content of fruits of Puerto Rico with data on miscellaneous products. *Food Res.*, **10**, 42.

670. Munsell, H. E., Streightoff, F., Bendor, B., Orr, M. L., Ezekiel, S. R., Leonard, M. H., Richardson, M. E. and Koch, F. G. (1949). Effect of large-scale methods of preparation on the vitamin content of food. 3. Cabbage. *J. Amer. diet. Ass.*, **25**, 420.

671. Murai, M., Pen, F. and Miller, C. D. (1958). *Some tropical and South Pacific Island foods—description, history, use, composition and nutritive value.* Univ. Hawaii Press, Honolulu, Hawaii.

672. Murneek, A. E., Maharg, L. and Wittwer, S. H. (1954). Ascorbic acid (vitamin C) content of tomatoes and apples. *Bull. Mo. agric. Exp. Sta.*, No. 568.

673. Murphy, E. (1946). Storage conditions which affect the vitamin C content of Maine-grown potatoes. *Amer. Potato J.*, **23**, 197.

674. Murphy, E. F. (1941). Ascorbic acid content of onions and observations on its distribution. *Food Res.*, **6**, 581.

675. Murphy, E. F. (1942). The ascorbic acid content of different varieties of Maine-grown tomatoes and cabbages as influenced by locality, season, and stage of maturity. *J. agric. Res.*, **64**, 483.

676. Murphy, E. F. (1944). The vitamin C content of Maine foods. *Bull. Me. agric. Exp. Sta.*, No. 426.

677. Murphy, E. F., Dove, W. F. and Akeley, R. V. (1945). Observations on genetic, physiological and environmental factors affecting the vitamin C content of Maine-grown potatoes. *Amer. Potato J.*, **22**, 62.

678. Murray, H. C. (1948). Vitamin content of field-pea products: retention of thiamin and riboflavin on cooking. *Food Res.*, **13**, 397.

679. Nagel, A. H. and Harris, R. S. (1943). Effect of restaurant cooking and service on vitamin content of foods. *J. Amer. diet. Ass.*, **19**, 23.

680. Navia, J. M., López, H., Cimadevilla, M. and Fernández, E. (1955) Nutrient composition of Cuban foods. 1. Foods of vegetable origin. *Food Res.*, **20**, 97.

681. Navia, J. M., López, H. Cimadevilla, M. and Fernández, E. (1957). Nutrient composition of Cuban foods. 2. Foods of vegetable origin. *Food Res.*, **22**, 131.

682. Neff, A. W., Parrish, D. B., Hughes, J. S. and Payne, L. F. (1949). The state of vitamin A in eggs. *Arch. Biochem.*, **21**, 315.

683. Neilands, J. B. and Strong, F. M. (1948). The enzymatic liberation of pantothenic acid. *Arch. Biochem.*, **19**, 287.

684. Neilands, J. B., Strong, F. M. and Elvehjem, C. A. (1947). The nutritive value of canned foods. 25. Vitamin content of canned fish products. *J. Nutr.*, **34**, 633.

685. Neuwelier, W. (1944). Der Nikotinsäuregëhalt der Frauenmilch und seine Abhängigkeit von der Zufuhr,. *Z. Vitaminforsch.*, **15**, 193.

686. Neuweiler, W. (1948). Über das Vitamin E der Frauenmilch. *Int. Z. Vitaminforsch.*, **20**, 108.

687. Neuweiler, W. and Fischer, H. (1954). Über das Vitamin B_6 in der Frauenmilch. *Int. Z. Vitaminforsch.*, **25**, 205.

688. Newman, K. R. and Fellers, C. R. (1940). Vitamin C in packaged foods purchased in retail markets. *J. Amer. diet. Ass.*, **16**, 695.

689. Noble, I. (1951). Color and ascorbic acid variations in cabbage cooked by various methods. *Food Res.*, **16**, 71.

690. Noble, I. and Gomez, L. (1951). Thiamine and riboflavin retention in beef and veal heart. *J. Amer. diet. Ass.*, **27**, 752.

691. Noble, I. and Gordon, J. (1949). Thiamine and riboflavin retention in bacon. *J. Amer. diet. Ass.*, **25**, 130.

692. Noble, I. and Gordon, J. (1956). Ascorbic acid and color retention in green beans cooked by different methods. *J. Amer. diet. Ass.*, **32**, 119.

693. Noble, I., Gordon, J. and Catterson, L. (1948). Thiamine and riboflavin retention in beef tongue. *J. Amer. diet. Ass.*, **24**, 1068.

694. Noble, I. and Hanig, M. M. D. (1948). Ascorbic acid and dehydroascorbic acid content of raw and cooked vegetables. *Food Res.*, **13**, 461.

695. Noble, I. and Waddell, E. (1945). Effects of different methods of cooking on the ascorbic acid content of cabbage. *Food Res.*, **10**, 246.

696. Noll, C. I. and Jensen, O. G. (1941). The chemical determination of nicotinic acid in milk and milk derivatives. *J. biol. Chem.*, **140**, 755.

697. Noonan, J. C., Webb, R. E., Attaya, R. B. and Miller, J. C. (1951). Influence of location on the ascorbic acid content of the Irish potato. *Amer. Potato J.*, **28**, 521.

698. Norris, F. W. (1945a). Nicotinic acid in brewing materials. *J. Inst. Brew.*, **51**, 38.

699. Norris, F. W. (1945b). Nicotinic acid in the materials and process of brewing. *J. Inst. Brew.*, **51**, 177.

700. Norris, L. C. and Bauernfeind, J. C. (1940).   Effect of level of dietary riboflavin upon quantity stored in eggs and rate of storage.   *Food Res.*, **5**, 521.

701. Nurmikko, V. and Virtanen, A. I. (1956).   Der Vitamin-B_{12} (Cobalamin) Gehalt der Kuhmilch.   *Milchwissenschaft*, **11**, 192.

702. Nutritive values of wartime foods (1945).   *M.R.C. (War) Memor., No.* 14. H.M. Stationery Office, London.

703. Olliver, M. (1936).   The ascorbic acid content of fruits and vegetables with special reference to the effect of cooking and canning.   *J. Soc. chem. Ind., Lond.*, **55**, 153.

704. Olliver, M. (1938).   The ascorbic acid content of fruits and vegetables.   *Analyst*, **63**, 2.

705. Olliver, M. (1940).   Antiscorbutic values of fruits and vegetables.   *Lancet*, **239**, 190.

706. Olliver, M. (1941).   The effect of cooking on the nutritive value of vegetables.   *Chem. & Ind. (Rev.)*, **60**, 586.

707. Olliver, M. (1943).   Ascorbic acid values of fruits and vegetables for dietary surveys.   *Chem. & Ind. (Rev.)*, **62**, 146.

708. Olliver, M. (1947).   The cabbage as a source of ascorbic acid in human diet.   *Chem. & Ind. (Rev.)*, No. 18, 235.

709. Olliver, M. (1954).   In *The vitamins: chemistry, physiology, pathology*, edited by W. H. Sebrell (Jr.) and R. S. Harris, Vol. I, p. 261.   Academic Press Inc., New York.

710. Olson, O. E., Burris, R. H. and Elvehjem, C. A. (1947).   A preliminary report of the "folic acid" content of certain foods.   *J. Amer. diet. Ass.*, **23**, 200.

711. Olsson, N., Akerberg, E. and Blixt, B. (1955).   Investigations concerning formation, preservation and utilization of carotene.   *Acta agric. Scand.*, **5**, 113.

712. Orent-Keiles, E., Hewston, E. M. and Butler, L. I. (1947).   Vitamin and mineral values of vegetables as served in an army mess.   *Misc. Publ. U.S. Dep. Agric.*, No. 632.

713. Oser, B. L. and Melnick, D. (1945).   Physiological availability to the rat of crude carotene in vegetables.   *J. Nutr.*, **30**, 385.

714. Oser, B. L., Melnick, D. and Oser, M. (1943).   Influence of cooking procedure upon retention of vitamins and minerals in vegetables.   *Food Res.*, **8**, 115.

715. Osmond, A. (1946).   Tables of composition of Australian foods.   *National Health and Medical Research Council Nutrition Committee Spec. Rep. Ser., Canberra*, No. 2.

716. Parkinson, T. L. (1952).   The determination of ascorbic acid in canned foods containing ferrous iron.   *J. Sci. Food Agric.*, **3**, 555.

717. Parrish, D. B., Martin, W. H., Atkeson, F. W. and Hughes, J. S. (1946).   The vitamin A and carotene content of market butter produced in Kansas.   *J. Dairy Sci.*, **29**, 91.

718. Parrish, D. B., Wise, G. H. and Hughes, J. S. (1947).   Properties of the colostrum of the dairy cow.   1. Tocopherol levels in the colostrum and in the early milk.   *J. Dairy Sci.*, **30**, 849.

719. Patton, M. B. and Green, M. E. (1954).   Factors affecting vitamin values and palatability. 1. Compilation of national co-operative research findings on cabbage.   *Bull. Ohio agric. Exp. Sta.*, No. 742.

720. Patton, M. B. and Miller, L. H. (1947).   Effect of crushed ice refrigeration on conservation of vitamin C content and on retention of weight of Ohio-grown vegetables.   *Food Res.*, **12**, 222.

721. Pearson, P. B. and Darnell, A. L. (with Weir, J.) (1946).   The thiamine, riboflavin, nicotinic acid and pantothenic acid content of colostrum and milk of the cow and ewe.   *J. Nutr.*, **31**, 51.

722. Pearson, P. B., Melass, V. H. and Sherwood, R. M. (1946).   The pantothenic acid content of the blood and tissues of the chicken as influenced by the level in the diet.   *J. Nutr.*, **32**, 187.

723. Perlman, L. and Morgan, A. F. (1945).   Stability of B vitamins in grape juices and wines.   *Food Res.*, **10**, 334.

724. Perroteau, A. (1951).   Influence de différents procédés de conservation et de cruisson sur la valeur vitaminique des aliments.   *Bull. Soc. sci. Hyg. aliment, Paris*, **39**, 46.

725. Petersen, C. F., Lampman, C. E. and Stamberg, O. E. (1947). Effect of riboflavin intake on egg production and riboflavin content of eggs. *Poult. Sci.*, **26**, 180.

726. Petersen, W. H., Skinner, J. T. and Strong, F. M. (1943). *Elements of Food Biochemistry*, p. 272. Prentice-Hall, New York.

727. Peterson, W. J., Brady, D. E. and Shaw, A. O. (1943). Fluorometric determination of riboflavin in pork products. *Industr. Engng. Chem. (Anal.)*, **15**, 634.

728. Pian, M. L. and Paul, P. (1949). The effect of method of processing on eating quality and vitamin C retention of peas. *Quart. Bull. Mich. agric. Exp. Sta.*, **31**, 416.

729. Platenius, H. and Jones, J. B. (1944). Effect of modified atmosphere storage on ascorbic acid content of some vegetables. *Food Res.*, **9**, 378.

730. Platt, B. S. (1945). Tables of representative values of foods commonly used in tropical countries. *Spec. Rep. Ser. med. Res. Coun., Lond.*, No. 253.

731. Pollard, A., Kieser, M. E. and Bryan, J. D. (1944). Factors influencing the vitamin C content of tomatoes. *Rep. agric. hort. Res. Sta., Bristol*, p. 171.

732. Pollard, A., Kieser, M. E. and Bryan, J. D. (1945a). The apple as a source of vitamin C. *Rep. agric. hort. Res. Sta., Bristol*, p. 200.

733. Pollard, A., Kieser, M. E. and Bryan, J. D. (1945b). Factors influencing the composition of the tomato. A comparison of varieties and of indoor and outdoor culture. *Rep. agric. hort. Res. Sta., Bristol*, p. 203.

734. Pollard, A., Kieser, M. E. and Bryan, J. (1946). The stability of ascorbic acid in black-currant syrup. *Chem. & Ind. (Rev.)*, No. 45, 402.

735. Polskin, L. J., Kramer, B. and Sobel, A. E. (1945). Secretion of vitamin D in milks of women fed fish liver oil. *J. Nutr.*, **30**, 451.

736. Poole, C. F., Grimball, P. C. and Kanapaux, M. S. (1944). Factors affecting the ascorbic acid content of cabbage lines. *J. agric. Res.*, **68**, 325.

737. Porter, T., Wharton, M. A. and Bennett, B. B. (1947). Evaluation of carotene content of fresh and cooked spinach. *Food Res.*, **12**, 133.

738. Potgieter, M. and Greenwood, M. L. (1950). Influence of cooking method on ascorbic acid and thiamine contents of four varieties of kale (*Brassica oleracea v. acephala*). *Food Res.*, **15**, 223.

739. Pressley, A., Ridder, C., Smith, M. C. and Caldwell, E. (1944). The nutritive value of canned foods. 2. Ascorbic acid and carotene or vitamin A content. *J. Nutr.*, **28**, 107.

740. Price, S. A. (1946). The vitamin B-complex content of the commercial milling products of Egyptian rice. *Cereal Chem.*, **23**, 318.

741. Puffer, M. E., Hinman, W. F., Charley, H. and Halliday, E. G. (1942). Vitamin C, carotene, calcium, and phosphorus in expressed vegetable juice. *Food Res.*, **7**, 140.

742. Pugsley, L. I., Wills, G. and D'Aoust, T. (1947). The vitamin A activity and carotene content of tomato juice. *Canad. J. Res. (E)*, **25**, 162.

743. Pyke, M. (1939). The distribution of vitamin-B_1 in foods as determined by chemical analysis. *J. Soc. chem. Ind., Lond.*, **58**, 338.

744. Pyke, M. (1940). Observations on the distribution of vitamin B_1 in some plant families. *Biochem. J.*, **34**, 330.

745. Pyke, M. (1942a). The vitamin content of vegetables. *J. Soc. chem. Ind., Lond.*, **61**, 149.

746. Pyke, M. (1942b). Effect of shredding and grating on the vitamin C content of raw vegetables. *Nature, Lond.*, **149**, 499.

747. Pyke, M. A. (1937). The chemical measurement of vitamin B_1 in foodstuffs and biological material by means of the thiochrome reaction. *Biochem. J.*, **31**, 1958.

748. Pyke, M., Melville, R. and Sarson, H. (1942). Vitamin C in walnuts. *Nature, Lond.*, **150**, 267.

749. Pyke, M. and Wright, M. D. (1941). Vitamin content of salmon. *Nature, Lond.*, **147**, 267.

750. Quaife, M. L. (1947). Tocopherols (vitamin E) in milk: their chemical determination and occurrence in human milk. *J. biol. Chem.*, **169**, 513.

751. Quinn, V. P., Scoular, F. I. and Johnson, M. L. (1946).   Ascorbic acid content of cabbage salads.   *Food Res.*, **11**, 163.

752. Quinones, V. L., Guerrant, N. B. and Dutcher, R. A. (1944).   Vitamin content of some tropical fruits, their juices and nectars.   *Food Res.*, **9**, 415.

753. Rabinowitz, J. C., Mondy, N. I. and Snell, E. E. (1948).   The vitamin B_6 group.   13. An improved procedure for determination of pyridoxal with *Lactobacillus casei*.   *J. biol. Chem.*, **175**, 147

754. Rabinowitz, J. C. and Snell, E. E. (1947).   Vitamin B_6 group. Extraction procedures for the microbiological determination of vitamin B_6.   *Analyt.. Chem.*, **19**, 277.

755. Rabinowitz, J. C. and Snell, E. E. (1948).   The vitamin B_6 group.   14. Distribution of pyridoxal, pyridoxamine and pyridoxine in some natural products.   *J. biol. Chem.*, **176**, 1157.

756. Rakieten, M. L., Newman, B., Falk, K. B. and Miller, I. (1951).   Comparison of some constituents in fresh-frozen and freshly squeezed orange juice.   *J. Amer. diet. Ass.*, **27**, 864.

757. Rakieten, M. L., Newman, B., Falk, K. G. and Miller, I. (1952).   Comparison of some constituents in fresh-frozen and freshly squeezed orange juice,   2. *J. Amer. diet. Ass.*, **28**, 1050.

758. Randoin, L. (1947).   Au nom de la Commission des Vitamines.   *Bull. Acad. nat. Med., Paris*, **131**, 422.

759. Reder, R. (1938).   The vitamin D content of certain egg and egg oil products.   *Poult. Sci.*, **17**, 521.

760. Reedman, E. J. and Buckby, L. (1943).   The vitamin B_1 content of canned pork.   *Canad. J. Res.*, (*D*), **21**, 261.

761. Reestman, A. J., Van Eekelen, M., Fontein, H. and Hendriks, T. F. (1943).   Het ascorbinezuurgehalte van de Nederlandsche aardappelrassen.   *Landbouwk. Tijdschr., 's-Grav.*, **55**, 574.

762. Register, U. D., Lewis, U. J., Thompson, H. T. and Elvehjem, C. A. (1949).   Variations in the vitamin B_{12} content of selected samples of pork and beef muscle.   *Proc. Soc. exp. Biol., N.Y.*, **70**, 167.

763. Reid, M. E. (1942).   Protection of ascorbic acid during its extraction from plant tissues.   *Food Res.*, **7**, 288.

764. Reig Feliu, A. (1952).   Retencion de vitamina C en el jugo de naranja, desaireado y pasteurizado, durante el almacenaje a varias temperaturas.   *Bol. Inst. Invest. agron., Madr.*, **12**, 151.

765. Reinart, A. (1949).   Über die antioxydative Wirkung des E-Vitamins (α-tocopherol), des synthetischen α-tocopherols und des di-α-tocopherol-acetates in Milchfett.   *Int. Dairy Congr. XII, Stockholm*, **2**, 405.

766. *Report of the Government Chemist upon the work of his department for the year ending* 31*st March*, 1958.   H. M. Stationery Office, London.

767. Retzer, J. L., Van Duyne, F. O., Chase, J. T. and Simpson, J. I. (1945).   Effect of steam and hot-water blanching on ascorbic acid content of snap beans and cauliflower.   *Food Res.*, **10**, 518.

768. Rice, E. E., Beuk, J. F. and Fried, J. F. (1947).   Effect of commercial curing, smoking, storage, and cooking operations upon vitamin content of pork hams.   *Food Res.*, **12**, 239.

769. Rice, E. E., Daly, M. E., Beuk, J. F. and Robinson, H. E. (1945).   The distribution and comparative content of certain B-complex vitamins in pork muscular tissues.   *Arch. Biochem.*, **7**, 239.

770. Rice, E. E., Fried, J. F. and Hess, W. R. (1946).   Storage and microbial action upon vitamins of the B-complex in pork.   *Food Res.*, **11**, 305.

771. Rice, E. E. and Robinson, H. E. (1944).   Vitamin B-complex studies on dehydrated meats.   *Food Res.*, **9**, 92.

772. Rice, E. E., Squires, E. M. and Fried, J. F. (1948).   Effect of storage and microbial action on vitamin content of pork.   *Food Res.*, **13**, 195.

773. Rice, E. E., Strandine, E. J., Squires, E. M. and Lyddon, B. (1946). The distribution and comparative content of certain B-complex vitamins in chicken muscles. *Arch. Biochem.*, **10**, 251.

774. Richardson, J. E. and Mayfield, H. L. (1940). The quality and vitamin content of green peas when cooked or home-canned. *Bull. Mont. agric. Exp. Sta.*, No. 381.

775. Richardson, J. E. and Mayfield, H. L. (1941). Vitamin C content of winter fruits and vegetables. *Bull. Mont. agric. Exp. Sta.*, No. 390.

776. Richardson, J. E. and Mayfield, H. L. (1943). Conserving vitamin C in potato cookery. *War Circ. Mont. agric. Exp. Sta.*, No. 1.

777. Roberts, E. C., and Snell, E. E. (1946). An improved medium for microbiological assays with *Lactobacillus casei*. *J. biol. Chem.*, **163**, 499.

778. Robinson, W. B. (1949). The effect of sunlight on the ascorbic acid content of strawberries. *J. agric. Res.*, **78**, 257.

779. Robinson, W. B., Stotz, E. and Kertesz, Z. I. (1945). The effect of manufacturing methods on the ascorbic acid content and consistency characteristics of tomato juice. *J. Nutr.*, **30**, 435.

780. Roderuck, C. E., Coryell, M. N., Williams, H. H. and Macy, I. G. (1945). Human milk studies. 24. Free and total riboflavin contents of colostrum and mature human milk. *Amer. J. Dis. Child.*, **70**, 171.

781. Roderuck, C. E., Williams, H. H. and Macy, I. G. (1945). Human milk studies. 23. Free and total thiamine contents of colostrum and mature human milk. *Amer. J. Dis. Child.*, **70**, 162.

782. Rohrer, V. and Treadwell, C. R. (1944). The content and stability of ascorbic acid in orange juice under home conditions. *Texas Rep. Biol. Med.*, **2**, 175.

783. Roine, P., Wichmann, K. and Vihavainen, L. (1955). Askorbiinihapon määristä ja säilyvydestä eri perunalajikkeissa. *Suom. Maataloust. Seur. Julk.*, **83**, 71.

784. Rolf, L. A. (1940). The effect of cooking and storage on the ascorbic acid content of potatoes. *J. agric. Res.*, **61**, 381.

785. Rose, D. and Peterson, R. (1948). Canadian Wiltshire bacon. 30. Effects of curing and cooking on the thiamine, riboflavin and niacin contents of longissimus dorsi muscles. *Canad. J. Res.*, (F), **26**, 66.

786. Ross, E. (1944). Effect of time and temperature of storage on vitamin C retention in canned citrus juices. *Food Res.*, **9**, 27.

787. Rubino, F. (1954). Sul contenuto in acido ascorbico del succo di limone sotto posto alla "flash pasteurisation". *Boll. Soc. ital. Biol. sper.*, **30**, 244.

788. Russell, W. C., Taylor, M. W. and Beuk, J. F. (1943). The nicotinic acid content of common fruits and vegetables as prepared for human consumption. *J. Nutr.*, **25**, 275.

789. Sale, J. W. (with Osborn, R. A.) (1946). Ascorbic acid in tomatoes and tomato juice, 1942–43 seasons. *J. Ass. off. agric. Chem., Wash.*, **29**, 69.

790. Sale, J. W. and Osborn, R. A. (1947). Ascorbic acid in grapefruit juice, orange juice, and their blends: 1943. *J. Ass. off. agric. Chem., Wash.*, **30**, 673.

791. Sarma, P. S., Snell, E. E. and Elvehjem, C. A. (1947). The bioassay of vitamin B_6 in natural materials. *J. Nutr.*, **33**, 121.

792. Sarett, H. P., Bennett, M. J., Riggs, T. R. and Cheldelin, V. H. (1946). Thiamine, riboflavin, nicotinic acid, pantothenic acid and ascorbic acid content of restaurant foods. *J. Nutr.*, **31**, 755.

793. Sarett, H. P. and Cheldelin, V. H. (1945). Thiamine, riboflavin and nicotinic acid retention in preparation of overseas hams and bacons. *J. Nutr.*, **30**, 25.

794. Satterfield, G. H., Bell, T. A., Cook, F. W. and Holmes, A. D. (1947). Ascorbic acid content of hen's eggs. *J. Amer. diet. Ass.*, **23**, 1052.

795. Satterfield, G. H. and Yarbrough, M. (1940). Varietal differences in ascorbic acid (vitamin C) content of strawberries. *Food Res.*, **5**, 241.

796. Sautier, P. M. (1946a). Thiamine assays of fishery products. *Comm. Fish. Rev.*, **8**, No. 2, 17.

797. Sautier, P. M. (1946b).   Riboflavin assays of fishery products.   *Comm. Fish. Rev.*, **8**, No. 3, 19.

798. Saviano, M. (1942).   Ricerche sul contenuto in vitamina A di piesci mediterranei.   1. *Anguilla vulgaris.   Boll. Soc. ital. Biol. sper.*, **17**, 135.

799. Schätzlein, C. and Fox-Timmling, E. (1940).   Untersuchungen über den Vitamin C-Gehalt von Gemüse und Obst.   *Z. Untersuch. Lebensmitt.*, **79**, 157.

800. Scheid, H. E., Andrews, M. M. and Schweigert, B. S. (1952).   Comparison of methods for determination of the vitamin B_{12} potency of meats.   *J. Nutr.*, **47**, 601.

801. Scheid, H. E., Bennett, B. A. and Schweigert, B. S. (1953).   Thiamine, riboflavin, and niacin content of organ meats.   *Food Res.*, **18**, 109.

802. Scheid, H. E. and Schweigert, B. S. (1951).   Liberation and microbiological assay of vitamin B_{12} in animal tissues.   *J. biol. Chem.*, **193**, 299.

803. Scheid, H. E. and Schweigert, B. S. (1954).   Vitamin B_{12} content of organ meats.   *J. Nutr.*, **53**, 419.

804. Schroder, G. M., Satterfield, G. H. and Holmes, A. D. (1943).   The influence of variety, size, and degree of ripeness upon the ascorbic acid content of peaches.   *J. Nutr.*, **25**, 503

805. Schultz, F. W. and Knott, E. M. (1939).   Factors affecting the vitamin B_1 content of evaporated milk.   *Proc. Soc. exp. Biol., N.Y.*, **40**, 532.

806. Schweigert, B. S., Bennett, B. A., Marquette, M., Scheid, H. E. and McBride, B. H. (1952). Thiamine, riboflavin and niacin content of processed meats.   *Food Res.*, **17**, 56.

807. Schweigert, B. S. and Guthneck, B. T. (1953).   Liberation and measurement of pantothenic acid in animal tissues.   *J. Nutr.*, **51**, 283.

808. Schweigert, B. S., McIntire, J. M. and Elvehjem, C. A. (1943).   The retention of vitamins in meats during storage, curing and cooking.   *J. Nutr.*, **26**, 73.

809. Schweigert, B. S., McIntire, J. M. and Elvehjem, C. A. (1944).   The retention of vitamins in pork hams during curing.   *J. Nutr.*, **27**, 419.

810. Schweigert, B. S., Nielsen, E., McIntire, J. M. and Elvehjem, C. A. (1943).   Biotin content of meat and meat products.   *J. Nutr.*, **26**, 65.

811. Schweigert, B. S. and Payne, B. J. (1956).   A summary of the nutrient content of meat. *American Meat Institute Foundation Bulletin*, No. 30.

812. Schweigert, B. S., Pollard, A. E. and Elvehjem, C. A. (1946).   The folic acid content of meats and the retention of this vitamin during cooking.   *Arch. Biochem.*, **10**, 107.

813. Scott, M. L., Hill, F. W., Norris, L. C. and Heuser, G. F. (1946).   Chemical determination of riboflavin. *J. biol. Chem.*, **165**,65.

814. Scott, M. L., Randall, F. E. and Hessel, F. H. (1941).   A modification of the Snell and Strong microbiological method for determining riboflavin.   *J. biol. Chem.*, **141**, 325.

815. Scott, W. G. and Taylor, R. J. (1956).   The vitamin A and carotene potency of national (household) butter determined by a chromatographic ultra-violet spectrophotometric method of assay.   *Analyst*, **81**, 117.

816. Scoular, F. I. and Kelsay, J. (1947).   Ascorbic acid, carotene, and vitamin A content of Residence Hall food.   *J. Amer. diet. Ass.*, **23**, 862.

817. Scoular, F. I. and Willard, H. (1944).   Effect of refrigeration on ascorbic acid content of canned fruit juices after opening.   *J. Amer. diet. Ass.*, **20**, 223.

818. Scrimshaw, N. S., Hutt, F. B. and Scrimshaw, M. W. (1945).   The effect of genetic variation in the fowl on the thiamine content of the egg.   *J. Nutr.*, **30**, 375.

819. Sharp, P. F., Shields, J. B. and Stewart, A. P. (Jr.) (1945).   Nutritive quality of spray-dried whole milk in relation to manufacture and storage.   *Proc. Inst. Fd. Tech.*, p. 54.

820. Shenoy, K. G. and Ramasarma, G. B. (1954).   Extraction procedure and determination of the vitamin B_{12} content of some animal livers.   *Arch. Biochem.*, **51**, 371.

821. Sherwood, R. C., Nordgren, R. and Andrews, J. S. (1941).   Thiamin in the products of wheat milling and in bread.   *Cereal Chem.*, **18**, 811.

822. Shimer, S. R. and Purinton, H. J. (1948).   The ascorbic acid and carotene content of fresh and frozen New Hampshire berries.   *Tech. Bull. N.H. agric. Exp. Sta.*, No. 92.

823. Shrimpton, D. H. (1956).   The estimation of vitamin B_{12} activity in feeding stuffs with *Lactobacillus leichmannii* and *Ochromonas malhamensis*.   *Analyst*, **81**, 94.

824. Shull, G. M., Hutchings, B. L. and Peterson, W. H. (1942).   A microbiological assay for biotin.   *J. biol. Chem.*, **142**, 913.

825. Siegel, L., Melnick, D. and Oser, B. L. (1943). Bound pyridoxine (vitamin B_6) in biological materials. *J. biol. Chem.*, **149**, 361.

826. Sinclair, H. M. (1958). Nutritional aspects of high-extraction flour. *Proc. Nutr. Soc.*, **17**, 28.

827. Slater, E. C. and Morell, D. B. (1946). A modification of the fluorimetric method of determining riboflavin in biological materials. *Biochem. J.*, **40**, 644.

828. Slater, E. C. and Rial, J. (1942). The thiamin (vitamin B_1) content of some Australian biscuits and breakfast foods. *Med. J. Aust.*, **ii**, 231.

829. Smith, M. C. and Caldwell, E. (1943). The effect of maceration of foods upon their ascorbic acid values. *Science*, **101**, 308.

830. Smith, A. M. and Gillies, J. (1940). The distribution and concentration of ascorbic acid in the potato (*Solanum tuberosum*). *Biochem. J*, **34**, 1312.

831. Smith, E. B., Hiltz, M. C. and Robinson, A. D. (1948). Variability of ascorbic acid within and between cabbages. *Food Res.*, **13**, 236.

832. Snell, E. E., Aline, E., Couch, J. R. and Pearson, P. B. (1941). The effect of diet on the pantothenic acid content of eggs. *J. Nutr.*, **21**, 201.

833. Snell, E. E. and Keevil, C. S. (Jr.) (1954). In *The vitamins: chemistry, physiology, pathology*, edited by W. H. Sebrell (Jr.) and R. S. Harris, Vol. I, p. 255. Academic Press Inc., New York.

834. Snell, E. E. and Strong, F. M. (1939). A microbiological assay for riboflavin. *Industr. Engng. Chem. (Anal.)*, **11**, 346.

835. Snell, E. E. and Wright, L. D. (1941). A microbiological method for the determination of nicotinic acid. *J. biol. Chem.*, **139**, 675.

836. Society of Public Analysts, Analytical Methods Committee (1950). Bibliography on carotene estimation, with special reference to green-leaf material. *Analyst*, **75**, 574.

837. Somers, G. F., Hamner, K. C. and Kelly, W. C. (1950). Further studies in the relationship between illumination and the ascorbic acid content of tomato fruits. *J. Nutr.*, **40**, 133.

838. Somers, G. F., Hamner, K. C. and Nelson, W. L. (1945). Field illumination and commercial handling as factors in determining the ascorbic acid content of tomatoes received at the cannery. *J. Nutr.*, **30**, 425.

839. Somers, G. F., Kelly, W. C., Thacker, E. J. and Redder, A. M. (1951). The occurrence of substances which interfere with the determination of ascorbic acid in anthocyanin-containing plant products. *Food Res.*, **16**, 62.

840. *Southern Co-op. Ser. Bull.* (1951). No. 10. Studies of sampling techniques and chemical analyses of vegetables.

841. Stamberg, O. E. and Lehrer, W. P. (Jr.) (1947). Composition, including thiamine and riboflavin, of edible dry legumes. *Food Res.*, **12**, 270.

842. Stamberg, O. E. and Petersen, C. F. (1946). Riboflavin and thiamin loss in cooking eggs. *J. Amer. diet. Ass.*, **22**, 315.

843. Stamberg, O. E., Petersen, C. F. and Lampman, C. E. (1946a). Effect of riboflavin intake on the content of egg whites and yolks from individual hens. *Poult. Sci.*, **25**, 329.

844. Stamberg, O. E., Petersen, C. F. and Lampman, C. E. (1946b). Ratio of riboflavin in yolks and whites of eggs. *Poult. Sci.*, **25**, 327.

845. Stamberg, O. E. and Theophilus, D. R. (1945). Photolysis of riboflavin in milk. *J. Dairy Sci.*, **28**, 269.

846. *Statutory Instrument Emergency Laws.* (1951). No. 668. Food standards (cream) order, 1951. H.M. Stationery Office, London.

847. Stefaniak, J. J. and Petersen, W. H. (1946). The pantothenic acid, niacin, and biotin content of commercial and experimental milks. *J. Dairy Sci.*, **29**, 783.

848. Stevens, H. B. and Fenton, F. (1951). Dielectric vs. stewpan cookery. Comparison of palatability and vitamin retention in frozen peas. *J. Amer. diet. Ass.*, **27**, 32.

849. Stewart, A. P. (Jr.) and Sharp, P. F. (1946). Vitamin C content of market milk, evaporated milk, and powdered whole milk. *J. Nutr.*, **31**, 161.

850. Stewart, C. P. (1946). Losses of nutrients in the preparation of foodstuffs. Loss of nutrients in cooking. *Proc. Nutr. Soc.*, **4**, 164.

851. Stokes, J. L., Larsen, A., Woodward, C. R. (Jr.) and Foster, J. W. (1943). A Neurospora assay for pyridoxine. *J. biol. Chem.*, **150**, 17.

852. Stokstad, E. L. R. (1954). In *The vitamins: chemistry, physiology, pathology*, edited by W. H. Sebrell (Jr.) and R. S. Harris, Vol. III, p. 168. Academic Press Inc., New York.

853. Storvick, C. A., Davey, B. L., Nitchals, R. M. and Coffey, R. E. (1950). Reduced ascorbic acid content of foods served in institutional quantities. *Food Res.*, **15**, 373.

854. Strachen, C. C. (1942). Factors influencing ascorbic acid retention in apple juice. *Publ. Dep. Agric. Can.* 732 (*Tech. Bull.* 40).

855. Strachen, C. C. and Atkinson, F. E. (1946). Ascorbic acid content of tomato varieties and its retention in processed products. *Sci. Agric.*, **26**, 83.

856. Streightoff, F., Bendor, B., Munsell, H. E., Orr, M. L., Ezekiel, S. R., Leonard, M. H., Richardson, M. E. and Koch, F. G. (1949). Effect of large scale methods of preparation on the vitamin content of food: 5. Spinach. *J. Amer. diet. Ass.*, **25**, 770.

857. Streightoff, F., Munsell, H. E., Bendor, B., Orr, M. L., Cailleau, R., Leonard, M. H., Ezekiel, S. R., Kornblum, R. and Koch, F. G. (1946). Effect of large-scale methods of preparation on vitamin content of food: 1. Potatoes. *J. Amer. diet. Ass.*, **22**, 117.

858. Streightoff, F., Munsell, H. E., Bendor, B., Orr, M. L., Leonard, M. H., Ezekiel, S. R. and Koch, F. G. (1946). Effect of large-scale methods of preparation on the vitamin content of food: 2. Carrots. *J. Amer. diet. Ass.*, **22**, 511.

859. Sullivan, R. A., Bloom, E. and Jarmol, J. (1943). The value of dairy products in nutrition 3. The riboflavin, pantothenic acid, nicotinic acid and biotin content of several varieties of cheese. *J. Nutr.*, **25**, 463.

860. Sutherland, C. K., Halliday, E. G. and Hinman, W. F. (1947). Vitamin retention and acceptability of fresh vegetables cooked by four household methods and by an institutional method. *Food Res.*, **12**, 496.

861. Sutton, T. S., Warner, R. G. and Kaeser, H. E. (1947). The concentration and output of carotenoid pigments, vitamin A, and riboflavin in the colostrum and milk of dairy cows. *J. Dairy Sci.*, **30**, 927.

862. Sydenstricker, V. P., Singal, S. A., Briggs, A. P., DeVaughn, N. M. and Isbell, H. (1942). Observations on the "egg white injury" in man, and its cure with a biotin concentrate. *J. Amer. med. Ass.*, **118**, 1199.

863. Tarr, H. L. A. (1952). Chromatographic separation and microbiological assay of indigenous and added cobalamins in crude animal protein materials. *Canad. J. Technology*, **30**, 265.

864. Taylor, A. M. (1943). The application of the Spekker photoelectric absorptiometer to the determination of vitamin C. *Biochem. J.*, **37**, 54.

865. Technical Committee in Charge of the Nation-wide Survey (1947). Butter as a source of vitamin A in the diet of the people of the United States. *Misc. Publ. U.S. Dep. Agric.*, No. 636.

866. Teeri, A. E., Loughlin, M. E. and Josselyn, D. (1957). Nutritive value of fish. 1. Nicotinic acid, riboflavin, vitamin B_{12} and amino acids of various salt-water species. *Food Res.*, **22**, 145.

867. Teply, L. J., Derse, P. H., Krieger, C. H. and Elvehjem, C. A. (1953). Nutritive value of canned foods.—Vitamin B_6, folic acid, beta-carotene, ascorbic acid, thiamine, riboflavin and niacin content and proximate composition. *J. agric. Food Chem.*, **1**, 1204.

868. Teply, L. J., Krehl, W. A. and Elvehjem, C. A. (1945). Studies on the nicotinic acid content of coffee. *Arch. Biochem.*, **6**, 139.

869. Teply, L. J., Strong, F. M. and Elvehjem, C. A. (1942a). The distribution of nicotinic acid in foods. *J. Nutr.*, **23**, 417.

870. Teply, L. J., Strong, F. M. and Elvehjem, C. A. (1942b). Nicotinic acid, pantothenic acid and pyridoxine in wheat and wheat products. *J. Nutr.*, **24**, 167.

871. Theophilus, D. R. and Stamberg, O. E. (1945). The influence of breed, feed, and processing on the riboflavin content of milk. *J. Dairy Sci.*, **28**, 259.

872. Thiessen, E. J. (1949). Conserving vitamin C by varying canning procedures in snap beans, tomatoes, peaches and pears. *Food Res.*, **14**, 481.

873. Thomas, J. M., Bina, A. F. and Brown, E. B. (1942). The nicotinic acid content of cereal products. *Cereal Chem.*, **19**, 173.

874. Thompson, H. T., Dietrich, L. S. and Elvehjem, C. A. (1950). The use of *Lactobacillus leichmannii* in the estimation of vitamin B_{12} activity. *J. biol. Chem.*, **184**, 175.

875. Thompson, J. C. (1946). Losses of nutrients in the preparation of foodstuffs. Discussion. *Proc. Nutr. Soc.*, **4**, 171.

876. Thompson, M. L., Cunningham, E. and Snell, E. E. (1944). The nutritive value of canned foods. 4. Riboflavin and pantothenic acid. *J. Nutr.*, **28**, 123.

877. Thornton, N. C. (1943). Carbon dioxide storage. 14. The influence of carbon dioxide, oxygen and ethylene on the vitamin C content of ripening bananas. *Contr. Boyce Thompson, Inst.* **13**, 201.

878. Todhunter, E. N. (1939). Further studies on the vitamin A and C content of Washington grown apples. *Bull. Wash. St. agric. Exp. Sta.*, No. 375. (*Nutr. Abstr. Rev.*, 1939–40, **9**, *Abstr.* 2840).

879. Todhunter, E. N. (1942). The ascorbic acid (vitamin C) content of rhubarb. *Proc. Amer. Soc. hort. Sci.*, **40**, 437.

880. Todhunter, E. N. and Robbins, R. C. (1941a). Ascorbic acid (vitamin C) content of red raspberries preserved by the frozen-pack method. *Food Res.*, **6**, 435.

881. Todhunter, E. N. and Robbins, R. C. (1941b). Ascorbic acid (vitamin C) content of garden-type peas preserved by the frozen pack method. *Bull. Wash. St. agric. Exp. Sta.*, No. 408. (*Nutr. Abstr. Rev.*, 1943, **12**, *Abstr.* 2235).

882. Toepfer, E. W., Zook, E. G., Orr, M. L. and Richardson, L. R. (1951). Folic acid content of foods. Microbiological assay by standardized methods and compilation of data from the literature. *U.S. Dep. Agric. Handbk.* No. 29.

883. Toepfer, E. W., Zook, E. G. and Richardson, L. R. (1954). Microbiological procedure for the assay of pantothenic acid in foods: results compared with those by bioassay. *J. Ass. off. agric. Chem., Wash.*, **37**, 182.

884. Tomarelli, R. M., Spence, E. R. and Bernhart, F. W. (1955). Biological availability of vitamin B_6 of heated milk. *J. agric. Food Chem.*, **3**, 338.

885. Trefethen, I., Causey, K. and Fenton, F. (1951). Effects of four cooking pressures on locally grown broccoli: cooking time, palatability, ascorbic acid, thiamine, and riboflavin. *Food Res.*, **16**, 409.

886. Trefethen, I. and Fenton, F. (1951). Effects of four cooking pressures on commercially frozen peas: cooking time, palatability, ascorbic acid, folic acid, thiamine, and riboflavin. *Food Res.*, **16**, 342.

887. Tressler, D. K. (1942a). The vitamin C content of New York State vegetables. *Circ. N.Y. St. agric. Exp. Sta.*, No. 196.

888. Tressler, D. K. (1942b). Nutritive value of dried and dehydrated fruits and vegetables. *Tech. Bull. N.Y. agric. Exp. Sta.*, No. 262.

889. Tressler, D. K. and Moyer, J. C. (1941). Changes in vitamin C content of Bartlett pears in cold and gas storage. *Food Res.*, **6**, 373.

890. Tucker, R. E., Hinman, W. F. and Halliday, E. G. (1946). The retention of thiamin and riboflavin in beef cuts during braising, frying, and broiling. *J. Amer. diet. Ass.*, **22**, 877.

891. Tullo, J. W. and Stringer, W. J. (1945). Riboflavin in beer and in the brewing process. *J. Inst. Brew.*, **51**, 86.

892. Vail, G. E. (1942). The effect of processing upon the nutritive value of food. *J. Amer. diet. Ass.*, **18**, 569.

893. Vail, G. E. and Westerman, B. D. (1946). B-Complex vitamins in meat. 1. Thiamin and riboflavin content of raw and cooked pork. *Food Res.*, **11**, 425.

894. Van Der Mijll Dekker, L. P. and Engel, C. (1952). The vitamin A, B_1, B_2 and C contents of bottled sterilized milk during storage under various conditions. *Ned. melk en Zuiveltijdschr.*, **6**, 104.

895. Van Duyne, F. O., Bruckart, S. M., Chase, J. T. and Simpson, J. I. (1945). Ascorbic acid content of freshly harvested vegetables. *J. Amer. diet. Ass.*, **21**, 153.

896. Van Duyne, F. O., Chase, J. T., Fanska, J. R. and Simpson, J. I. (1947). Effect of certain home practices on reduced ascorbic acid content of peas, rhubarb, snap beans, soybeans and spinach. *Food Res.*, **12**, 439.

897. Van Duyne, F. O., Chase, J. T., Owen, R. F. and Fanska, J. R. (1948). Effect of certain home practices on riboflavin content of cabbage, peas, snapbeans, and spinach. *Food Res.*, **13**, 162.

898. Van Duyne, F. O., Chase, J. T. and Simpson, J. I. (1944). Effect of various home practices on ascorbic acid content of cabbage. *Food Res.*, **9**, 164.

899. Van Duyne, F. O., Chase, J. T. and Simpson, J. I. (1945). Effect of various home practices on ascorbic acid content of potatoes. *Food Res.*, **10**, 72.

900. Van Duyne, F. O., Owen, R. F., Wolfe, J. C. and Charles, V. R. (1951). Effect of cooking vegetables in tightly covered and pressure saucepans. Retention of reduced ascorbic acid and palatability. *J. Amer. diet. Ass.*, **27**, 1059.

901. Van Duyne, F. O., Wolfe, J. C. and Owen, R. F. (1950). Retention of riboflavin in vegetables preserved by freezing. *Food Res.*, **15**, 53.

902. Van Eekelen, M. (1953). The occurrence of vitamin C in foods. *Proc. Nutr. Soc.*, **12**, 228.

903. Van Koetsveld, E. E. (1953). Differences in the vitamin B_{12} content of cow's milk during the last month indoors and the first week at pasture. *Nature, Lond.*, **171**, 483.

904. Vavich, M. G. and Kemmerer, A. R. (1950). The carotenes of cantaloupes. *Food Res.*, **15**, 494.

905. Vavich, M. G., Stern, R. M. and Guerrant, N. B. (1945). Nutritive value of canned foods. Determination of ascorbic acid of fresh green peas. *Industr. Engng. Chem. (Anal.)*, **17**, 531.

906. Vinacke, W. R., Hartzler, E. and Tanada, Y. (1950). Processed rice in Hawaii. Nutritive value, susceptibility to insect infestation and consumer acceptance as compared with white and brown rice. *Tech. Bull. Hawaii agric. Exp. Sta.*, No. 10.

907. *Vitamin C requirements of human adults.* (1953). *Spec. Rep. Ser. med. Res. Coun., Lond.*, No. 280. H.M. Stationery Office.

908. Wagner, J. R., Ives, M., Strong, F. M. and Elvehjem, C. A. (1945). Nutritive value of canned foods. 7. Effect of commercial canning and short-time storage on ascorbic acid content of grapefruit juice. *Food Res*, **10**, 469.

909. Waibel, P. E., Sunde, M. L. and Cravens, W. W. (1952). Effect of addition of pencillin to the hen's ration on biotin and folic acid content of eggs. *Poult. Sci.*, **31**, 621.

910. Waisman, H. A. and Elvehjem, C. A. (1941a). Chemical estimation of nicotinic acid and vitamin B_6. *Industr. Engng. Chem. (Anal.)*, **13**, 221.

911. Waisman, H. A. and Elvehjem, C. A. (1941b). *The vitamin content of meat.* Burgess Publishing Co., Minneapolis, Minn.

912. Waisman, H. A., Henderson, L. M., McIntire, J. M. and Elvehjem, C. A. (1942). The effect of enzymatic digestion on the pantothenic acid content of meats determined by the microbiological method. *J. Nutr.*, **23**, 239.

913. Waisman, H. A., Mickelsen, O., McKibbin, J. M. and Elvehjem, C. A. (1940). Nicotinic acid potency of food materials and certain chemical compounds. *J. Nutr.*, **19**, 483.

914. Walker, A. R. P. and Arvidsson, U. B. (1952). The vitamin C content of braised cabbage cooked under pressure and prepared on a very large scale. *S. Afr. J. med. Sci.* **17**, 143.

915. Wallis, G. C. (1944). A breed comparison in the vitamin D content of milk with notes on a modified technique for the vitamin D assay of low-potency fats and oils. *J. Dairy Sci.* **27**, 733.

916. Warne, L. G. G. (1942). Kohlrabi as a source of vitamin C. *Brit. med. J.*, **i**, 387.

917. Watt, B. K. and Merrill, A. L. (1950). Composition of foods—raw, processed, prepared. *U.S. Dep. Agric., Handbk.* No. 8.

918. Watts, J. H. and Griswold, R. M. (1953). Enzyme and ascorbic acid content of fresh and frozen pineapple. *Food Res.*, **18**, 162.

919. Welch, B. E., Perrett, R. W., Clements, J. H. and Couch, J. R. (1954). The relation of vitamin B_{12} to egg yolk storage of folic acid. *J. Nutr.*, **54**, 601.

920. Wentworth, J. and Lewis, H. (1958). Riboflavin, niacin and thiamin in Apalachicola Bay oysters. *Food Res.*, **23**, 194.

921. Werner, H. O. and Leverton, R. M. (1946). The ascorbic acid content of Nebraska-grown potatoes as influenced by variety, environment, maturity, and storage. *Amer. Potato J.*, **23**, 265.

922. Werner, H. O., Leverton, R. M. and Gram, M. R. (1951). Reduced ascorbic acid content of potatoes grown with and without straw mulching and irrigation in Eastern Nebraska. *Bull. Neb. agric. Exp. Sta.*, No. 170.

923. Wertz, A. W. and Weir, C. E. (1944).   The effect of institutional cooking methods on the vitamin content of foods.   1. The thiamine content of potatoes.   *J. Nutr.*, **28**, 255

924 Wertz, A. W. and Weir, C. E. (1946).   Effect of institutional cooking methods on vitamin content of foods.   2. Ascorbic acid content of potatoes.   *Food Res.*, **11**, 319.

925. West, C. and Zilva, S. S. (1944).   Synthesis of vitamin C in stored apples.   *Biochem. J.*, **38**, 105.

926. Westerman, B. D., Vail, G. E., Kalen, J., Stone, M. and Mackintosh, D. L. (1952a)·   B-Complex vitamins in meat.   3. Influence of storage temperature and time on the vitamins in pork muscle.   *J. Amer. diet. Ass.*, **28**, 49.

927. Westerman, B. D., Vail, G. E., Kalen, J., Stone, M. and Mackintosh, D. L. (1952b).   B-Complex vitamins in meat.   4. Influence of storage time and temperature on the vitamins in pork roasts.   *J. Amer. diet. Ass.*, **28**. 331.

928. Wharton, M. A. and Ohlson, M. A. (1949).   The availability to the rat of certain carotenes in raw and cooked vegetables.   *Quart. Bull. Mich. agric. Exp. Sta.*, **32**, 130.

929. Wheeldon, L. W. and Myers, W. M. (1952).   Riboflavin and calorie content of some samples of New South Wales beer.   *Aust. J. Sci.*, **14**, 126, (*Nutr. Abstr. Rev.*, 1953, **23**, *Abstr.* 1602).

930. Wheeler, K., Tressler, D. K. and King, C. G. (1939).   Vitamin C content of vegetables.   12. Broccoli, cauliflower, endive, cantaloup, parsnips, New Zealand spinach, kohlrabi, lettuce, and kale.   *Food Res.*, **4**, 593.

931. Whipple, D. V. (1935).   Vitamins A, D, and B in oysters—effect of cooking upon vitamins A and B_1.   *J. Nutr.*, **9**, 163.

932. Whitford, C., Pickering, C., Summers, K., Weis, A. and Bisbey, B. (1951).   The vitamin content of eggs as affected by dehydration and storage.   *Bull. Mo. agric. Exp. Sta.*, No. 483.

933. Widdowson, E. M. and McCance, R. A. (1954).   Studies on the nutritive value of bread and on the effect of variations in the extraction rate of flour on the growth of undernourished children.   *Spec. Rep. Ser. med. Res. Coun., Lond.*, No. 287, H.M. Stationery Office.

934. Wilcox, E. B. and Galloway, L. S. (1951).   Ascorbic acid and carotene in fresh and stored celery.   *J. Amer. diet. Ass.*, **27**, 965.

935. Wilcox, E. B. and Galloway, L. S. (1952a).   The B vitamins in raw and cooked lamb.   1. Thiamine.   *Food Res.*, **17**, 67.

936. Wilcox, E. B. and Galloway, L. S. (1952b).   The B vitamins in raw and cooked lamb.   2. Riboflavin and niacin.   *Food Res.*, **17**, 144.

937. Wilcox, E. B. and Morrell, K. E. (year not stated).   The vitamin content of peas as influenced by maturity, fertilizers, and variety.   *Bull. Utah agric. Exp. Sta.*, No. 337.

938. Wilcox, E. B. and Neilson, A. M. (1947).   Effect of quantity preparation on the ascorbic acid content of cabbage salad.   *J. Amer. diet. Ass.*, **23**, 223.

939. Wilkinson, H. (1939).   The vitamin A and vitamin D contents of butter.   2. Seasonal variation.   *Analyst*, **64**, 17.

940. Williams, R. J., Cheldelin, V. H. and Mitchell, H. K. (1942).   The B vitamin content of milk from animals of different species.   *Univ. Texas Publ.*, No. 4237, p. 97.

941. Williams, V. R. and Fieger, E. A. (1944).   A study of some of the vitamin B-complex factors in rice and its milled products.   2. *Cereal Chem.*, **21**, 540.

942. Williams, V. R., Knox, W. C. and Fieger, E. A. (1943).   A study of some of the vitamin B-complex factors in rice and its milled products.   *Cereal Chem.*, **20**, 560.

943. Wilson, H. E. C. and Roy, G. K. (1938).   The flavine and vitamin B_6 (anti-dermatitis) content of Indian foodstuffs.   *Indian J. med. Res.*, **25**, 879. (*Nutr. Abstr. Rev.* 1938, **8**, *Abstr.* 1822).

944. Wilson, R. H., Ambrose, A. M., Deeds, F., Dutton, H. J. and Bailey, G. F. (1946).   The content and biological availability of carotene in raw and dehydrated carrots and other vegetables.   *Arch. Biochem.*, **10**, 131.

945. Winikoff, D. (1946).   Ascorbic acid in the milk of Melbourne women.   *Med. J. Aust.*, **33**, 205.

946. Winston, J. R. and Miller, E. V. (1948).   Vitamin C content and juice quality of exposed and shaded citrus fruits.   *Food Res.*, **13**, 456.

947. Wishart, J. W. (1954). Ascorbic acid (vitamin C) content of varieties of blackcurrants. *Tasm. J. Agric.*, **25**, 164.

948. Woessner, W. W., Elvehjem, C. A. and Schuette, H. A. (1939). The determination of ascorbic acid in commercial milks. *J. Nutr.*, **18**, 619.

949. Woessner, W. W., Elvehjem, C. A. and Schuette, H. A. (1940). The determination of ascorbic acid in evaporated milk, powdered milk and powdered milk products. *J. Nutr.*, **20**, 327.

950. Woessner, W. W., Weckel, K. G. and Schuette, H. A. (1940). The effect of commercial practices on ascorbic acid and dehydroascorbic acid (vitamin C) in milk. *J. Dairy Sci.*, **23**, 1131.

951. Wojna-Nowicka, L. (1954). Straty kwasu askorbinowego w surówkach powstale na skutek przyrzadzania. *Roczn. Zakl. Hig. Warsz.*, **5**, 195.

952. Wokes, F., Barr, J. R., Brunskill, L. and Shaw, A. C. (1947). Seasonal variations in vitamin C content of tomatoes grown in Great Britain. *Nature, Lond.*, **159**, 171.

953. Wokes, F., Barr, J. R., Brunskill, L. and Shaw, A. C. (1948). Vitamin C in English tomatoes. *J. Soc. chem. Ind., Lond.*, **67**, 262.

954. Wokes, F. and Melville, R. (1948). Vitamin C in the walnut (*Juglans regia*). *Biochem. J.*, **43**, 585.

955. Wokes, F. and Melville, R. (1949). Apparent vitamin C in the walnut (*Juglans regia*) *Biochem. J.*, **45**, 343.

956. Wokes, F. and Nunn, G. (1948). Vitamin C in potatoes. *Nature, Lond.*, **162**, 900.

957. Wokes, F. and Organ, J. G. (1942). Vitamin C from green tomatoes. *Nature, Lond.*, **150**, 523.

958. Wokes, F. and Organ, J. G. (1943). Oxidising enzymes and vitamin C in tomatoes. *Biochem. J.*, **37**, 259.

959. Wokes, F. and Organ, J. G. (1944). The stability of vitamin C in blackcurrant syrup. *Quart. J. Pharm.*, **17**, 188.

960. Wokes, F., Organ, J. G., Duncan, J. and Jacoby, F. C. (1943a). Apparent vitamin C in foods. *Biochem. J.*, **37**, 695.

961. Wokes, F., Organ, J. G., Duncan, J. and Jacoby, F. C. (1943b). Apparent vitamin C in certain foodstuffs. *Nature, Lond.*, **152**, 14.

962. Wolfe, J. C., Owen, R. F., Charles, V. R. and Van Duyne, F. O. (1949). Effect of freezing and freezer storage on the ascorbic acid content of musk melon, grapefruit sections, and strawberry purée. *Food Res.*, **14**, 243.

963. Wolff, L. K. (1938). Methoden zur Bestimmung von Vitamin A, bezw. Karotin in Nahrungsmitteln. *Z. Vitaminforsch.*, **7**, 227.

964. Wood, M. A., Collings, A. R., Stodola, V., Burgoin, A. M. and Fenton, F. (1946). Effect of large-scale food preparation on vitamin retention: cabbage. *J. Amer. diet. Ass.*, **22**, 677

965. Yacowitz, H., Miller, R. F., Norris, L. C. and Heuser, G. F. (1952). Vitamin B_{12} studies with the hen. *Poult. Sci.*, **31**, 89.

966. Zepplin, M. and Elvehjem, C. A. (1944). Effect of refrigeration on retention of ascorbic acid in vegetables. *Food Res.*, **9**, 100.

967. Zimmerman, W. I., Tressler, D. K. and Maynard, L. A. (1941). Determination of carotene in fresh and frozen vegetables by an improved method. 2. Carotene content of asparagus and green lima beans. *Food Res.*, **6**, 57..

968. Zook, E. G., MacArthur, M. J. and Toepfer, E. W. (1956). Pantothenic acid in foods. *U.S. Dep. Agric. Handbk.* No. 97.

969. Zscheile, F. P., Beadle, B. W. and Kraybill, H. R. (1943). Carotene content of fresh and frozen green vegetables. *Food Res.*, **8**, 299.

970. Zweede, A. K. (1956). De Voedingswaarde van Zwarte bessen. *Voeding*, **17**, 125.

971. Coppock, J. B. M., Carpenter, B. R. and Knight, R. A. (1956). Cereal products fortification: the B vitamins, with special reference to thiamine losses in baked products. *J. Sci. Food Agric.*, **7**, 457.

972. Coppock, J. B. M., Carpenter, B. R. and Knight, R. A. (1957). Thiamine losses in bread baking. *Chem. & Ind.*, p. 735.

Part III Amino-Acids

B. P. HUGHES

Introduction

This part of the report deals with the amino-acid composition of foods. The tables are considerably shorter than those of the preceding sections because it has been possible to condense the information they give. There are two reasons for this:

First, the amino-acid composition of the proteins in many foods of similar type is for all practical purposes the same. By expressing the values in terms of nitrogen rather than in terms of food it has been possible to eliminate variations due to non-protein components, particularly fat and moisture, and to give single series of values for all meat, all fish and all milk products. It has also been possible to condense the cereal section in a similar way. Where an amino-acid in a particular food differs significantly from the average for the type of food the appropriate value is given.

Second, in the average diet in the United Kingdom about 55 per cent. of the protein is derived from meat, milk products, fish, and eggs, 35 per cent. from cereals (mainly wheat), and of the remaining 10 per cent. the potato contributes half (Annual Report of the Nutritional Food Survey Committee, 1957). Individual diets do, of course, differ considerably, but since in the average diet the main sources of dietary protein are meat, fish, milk products and eggs, and cereals, and since it is within these groups that the greatest uniformity in amino-acid content is found, it has been possible to present the amino-acid composition of 90 per cent. of the main dietary sources of protein in a few short tables. The composition of the foods providing the remaining 10 per cent., including the potato and other vegetables, differs much more widely; individual values are given for those varieties of these foods which have been analysed, and also for nuts, for which a considerable amount of data is available.

This simplification of the tables appears to be justified by the fact that when calculated from these tables the amino-acid composition of two diets, one characteristic of an English child and the other of an English adult, was found to agree closely with the amino-acid composition found by direct analysis by a chromatographic method (Hughes 1959).

ARRANGEMENT OF THE TABLES

The information in this section is contained in five tables giving the amino-acid composition of cereals, milk products and eggs, meat and fish, nuts, and vegetables. No values for fruits are given as there is little information available, but in any case fruits contribute an insignificant amount to the normal person's amino-acid intake.

The composition of each food or group of foods has been expressed as grams of amino-acid per gram of nitrogen. The amount of the various amino-acids in 100 grams of a particular food can be calculated by multiplying the amount of nitrogen in 100 grams of the food (as given in Part I) by the value for the amino-acid given in these tables.

Each amino-acid is referred to in the tables by its recognised abbreviation, first suggested by Brand and Edsall (1947) and adopted by the Biochemical Journal (1953) and the British Journal of Nutrition (1953). The amino-acids are arranged alphabetically in two groups. The first group consists of the following:—Arginine (Arg); Cystine (Cy_2S_2); Histidine (Hist); Isoleucine (Ileu); Leucine (Leu); Lysine (Lys); Methionine (Met); Phenylalanine (Phe); Threonine (Thr); Tryptophane (Try); Tyrosine (Tyr) and Valine (Val). These are the acids for which most information is available; they include the "essential amino-acids" (Rose, Oesterling and Wormack, 1948), which are those required in the diet for normal growth of the weanling rat; with the exception of histidine and arginine they are also required to maintain nitrogen balance in the human adult. Cystine and tyrosine are also included because, when they are present in a diet, the requirements of methionine and phenylalanine respectively are reduced.

The second group consists of Alanine (Ala); Aspartic acid (Asp); Glutamic acid (Glu); Glycine (Gly); Proline (Pro); and Serine (Ser). These are acids which appear to be synthesised in the human body in amounts adequate for normal requirements, and which need not be present in a diet provided there is an adequate supply of dietary nitrogen for their synthesis.

SELECTION OF THE VALUES

The values given in these tables are all derived from the literature. Original reports of analyses published in the last 15 years were extensively surveyed, and the values reported by different workers were compared. The values given are based on analytical figures obtained mainly by the use of microbiological and chromatographic techniques, and are averages of the values thought to be the most accurate and to cover representative samples of the food.

In selecting these values, differences between values reported by different workers for the same food presented a problem. These differences may be due to natural variation between samples: they can arise from variations both in the proportions of the individual proteins in the food, and also in the proportion and composition of the non-protein nitrogen fraction, which contains amino-acids and peptides. Alternatively, they may be due to analytical error. When differences are reported by workers using different techniques it is often particularly difficult to decide whether they are real or analytical in origin.

Results in marked disagreement with the values reported by several independent workers have been disregarded. Where the only data available were based on results from microbiological analyses, and were limited and conflicting, preference was given to the results of those workers whose values for other foods agreed with values obtained by the more recently developed chromatographic methods.

Selection of data for the sulphur-containing amino-acids in foods was difficult because of the possibility that these acids may be partially destroyed or modified during the hydrolysis of the protein prior to the analysis, and for this reason a number of low values have been discarded in computing some of the means.

Methionine is partially converted to methionine sulphoxide during hydrolysis; the extent of conversion can be estimated separately using chromatographic techniques, but the exact effect on microbiological assays is not known, and some reported values for methionine obtained by microbiological assay appear to be too low. The destruction of cystine and csyteine during hydrolysis has been appreciated by many workers, and they have modified their methods accordingly (Schram, Moore and Bigwood, 1954; Horn and Blum, 1956), but in other cases no special precautions were recorded and some very low values were reported. These have been discarded where more reliable values were available.

EFFECTS OF COOKING

The values given in the tables are mainly for raw foods, and not much is known about the effects of cooking and of heat processing generally on the amino-acids in foods. Reduction in the biological availability of certain amino-acids can be caused, although actual destruction seldom occurs. Reduction in availability is probably small in foods such as meat, fish and eggs, which contain little carbohydrate. Kuiken and Lyman (1948) have shown that appreciable destruction or reduction in availability does not occur during the cooking of meat. On the other hand, baking may lower the nutritive value of the wheat flour proteins (Sabiston and Kennedy, 1957), although little or no destruction occurs except in the crust (McDermott and Pace, 1957). Similarly the biological availability of the amino-acids in dried milk may be impaired (Henry, Kon, Lea and White, 1948).

In the case of green vegetables there is a considerable loss of nitrogen on cooking, so that the composition of the cooked food may be rather different from the raw. However, no amino-acid analyses of cooked green vegetables are available. Since such a small proportion of the dietary protein is derived from green vegetables, the lack of information here is of little practical importance.

Tables to Part III

AMINO-ACIDS

GRAMS PER GRAM NITROGEN

Cereals and Cereal Foods

Food	Arg	Cy_2S_2	Hist	Ileu	Leu	Lys	Met	Phe	Thr	Try	Tyr	Val	Ala	Asp	Glu	Gly	Pro	Ser
Barley (whole grain) ..	0·31	0·13	0·12	0·24	0·43	0·21 0·14*	0·09	0·31	0·23	0·09	0·22	0·31	0·28	0·37	1·28	0·27	0·58	0·23
Bread, white (60% extraction)	0·21	0·14	0·13	0·23	0·46	0·12	0·12	0·31	0·18	—	0·20	0·26	0·19	0·26	2·06	0·21	0·72	0·28
Bread, white (crust) ..	0·21	—	0·13	0·23	0·44	0·11	0·11	0·28	0·18	—	0·18	0·25	0·19	0·24	1·98	—	0·69	0·27
Flour (100% extraction)	0·27	0·13	0·13	0·24	0·40	0·17	0·10	0·29	0·18	0·08	0·20	0·27	0·21	0·31	1·73	0·24	0·63	0·30
Flour (70 – 75 % extraction)	0·23	0·13	0·13	0·24	0·43	0·13	0·10	0·32	0·18	0·06	0·20	0·29	0·17	0·26	2·10	0·21	0·72	0·30
Flour (65 – 66 % extraction)	0·21	0·14	0·13	0·23	0·44	0·12	0·10	0·34	0·18	0·08	0·21	0·26	0·20	0·26	2·09	0·21	0·73	0·29
Maize (whole grain) ::	0·31	0·13	0·15	0·25	0·75	0·19	0·13	0·31	0·26	0·05	0·24	0·35	0·62	0·77	0·96	0·19	0·52	0·26
Oats (whole grain) ::	0·41	0·11	0·12	0·29	0·44	0·23	0·09	0·31	0·21	0·08	0·24	0·34	0·32	0·26	1·15	0·26	0·36	0·21
Rice, brown (whole grain, no hulls)	0·53	0·11	0·14	0·30	0·51	0·26	0·13	0·29	0·22	0·09	0·36	0·39	—	—	—	—	—	—
Rice, white ::	0·50	0·10	0·14	0·29	0·53	0·19	0·13	0·30	0·24	0·09	0·31	0·41	0·35	0·28	0·67	0·41	0·28	0·31
Rye (whole grain) ::	0·31	0·11	0·13	0·24	0·38	0·23	0·10	0·29	0·21	0·08	0·26	0·31	—	—	1·23	—	—	0·24
Wheat, bran :: ::	0·47	0·09	0·19	0·23	0·39	0·26	0·08	0·24	0·19	0·14	—	0·29	—	—	—	—	—	—
Wheat, germ :: ::	0·43	0·09	0·17	0·22	0·37	0·38	0·09	0·23	0·28	0·06	—	0·29	—	—	—	—	—	—

* Processed, i.e. pearl-barley.

Milk Products and Eggs

Food	Arg	Cy₂S₂	Hist	Ileu	Leu	Lys	Met	Phe	Thr	Try	Tyr	Val	Ala	Asp	Glu	Gly	Pro	Ser
Egg white	0·39	0·14	0·15	0·36	0·56	0·41	0·25	0·37	0·31	0·12	0·26	0·49	—	0·69	0·79	0·26	0·26	0·43
Egg, whole	0·40	0·13	0·16	0·36	0·56	0·42	0·19	0·33	0·33	0·11	0·27	0·45	—	0·67	0·77	0·24	0·27	0·48
Egg yolk	0·44	0·11	0·16	0·36	0·53	0·42	0·14	0·29	0·36	0·11	0·29	0·42	—	—	0·75	0·21	0·27	0·55
Milk, cow's, and cheese	0·23	0·05 / 0·03*	0·17	0·39	0·62	0·49	0·15	0·32	0·29	·0·09	0·35	0·44	0·23	0·51	1·39	0·12	0·61	0·36
Milk, human	0·21	0·12	0·14	0·35	0·59	0·39	0·13	0·25	0·28	0·10	0·30	0·39	0·24	0·58	1·24	0·14	0·54	0·30
Colostrum, human ..	0·36	0·16	0·14	0·27	0·48	0·39	0·11	0·30	0·41	0·14	0·34	0·42	—	—	—	—	—	—

* Cheese.

Meat and Fish

Food	Arg	Cy₂S₂	Hist	Ileu	Leu	Lys	Met	Phe	Thr	Try	Tyr	Val	Ala	Asp	Glu	Gly	Pro	Ser
Meat and meat products	0·41 / 0·38*	0·08	0·20	0·32	0·49 / 0·56†	0·51	0·15	0·26 / 0·32‡	0·28	0·08	0·21	0·33 / 0·38‡	0·39	0·57	0·96	0·28	0·26	0·26
Fish	0·36§ / 0·59§	0·07	0·13∥ / 0·23∥ / 0·36¶	0·32	0·47	0·56	0·18	0·23	0·28	0·06	0·19	0·33	0·38	0·59	0·88	0·38	0·37	0·33
Gelatin	0·49	Tr.	0·43	0·09	0·18	0·25	0·05	0·13	0·12	—	0·22	0·14	0·61	0·37	0·63	1·51	1·67**	0·23

* Liver, Kidney, Brain, Rabbit muscle.
† Liver, Kidney, Brain, Heart, Tongue.
‡ Liver, Kidney, Brain.
§ Prawn and Shrimp.
∥ Mackerel.
¶ Tuna.
** Proline and Hydroxyproline.

Nuts

Food	Arg	Cy_2S_2	Hist	Ileu	Leu	Lys	Met	Phe	Thr	Try	Tyr	Val	Ala	Asp	Glu	Gly	Pro	Ser
Almond ..	0·63	0·11	0·14	0·24	0·41	0·16	0·08	0·32	0·17	0·05	—	0·31	—	—	—	—	—	—
Brazil ..	0·83	0·19	0·13	0·23	0·43	0·16	0·32	0·21	0·16	0·07	—	0·30	—	—	—	—	—	—
Cashew ..	0·60	0·15	0·12	0·35	0·44	0·23	0·10	0·27	0·21	0·14	—	0·46	—	—	—	—	—	—
Coconut ..	0·78	0·11	0·13	0·28	0·45	0·22	0·11	0·26	0·19	0·13	—	0·35	—	—	—	—	—	—
Filbert ..	0·91	0·16	0·12	0·36	0·39	0·18	0·06	0·23	0·18	0·09	0·23	0·39	—	0·44	1·28	0·59	0·35	0·60
Peanut ..	0·66	0·10	0·15	0·26	0·39	0·22	0·06	0·31	0·18	0·07	0·19	0·31	0·18	0·88	1·25	0·34	0·32	0·41
Walnut ..	0·81	0·11	0·14	0·27	0·43	0·16	0·11	0·27	0·21	0·06	—	0·34	—	—	—	—	—	—

Vegetables

Food	Arg	Cy_2S_2	Hist	Ileu	Leu	Lys	Met	Phe	Thr	Try	Tyr	Val	Ala	Asp	Glu	Gly	Pro	Ser
Beans, broad ..	0·37	0·07	0·18	0·34	0·48	0·34	0·03	0·21	0·16	0·06	0·19	0·32	0·16	0·41	0·86	0·23	0·28	0·36
Beans, haricot, etc.*	0·36	0·06	0·20	0·38	0·51	0·44	0·08	0·39	0·29	0·08	—	0·41	—	—	—	—	—	—
Beet ..	0·11	—	0·09	0·20	0·21	0·21	0·03	0·09	0·15	0·06	—	0·19	—	—	—	—	—	—
Brussels sprouts†	0·39	0·10	0·14	0·26	0·27	0·27	0·06	0·21	0·21	0·06	0·13	0·27	—	—	—	—	—	—
Cabbage†	0·47	—	0·11	0·18	0·26	0·23	0·06	0·16	0·17	0·05	—	0·21	—	—	—	—	—	—
Carrots ..	0·22	—	0·09	0·27	0·36	0·28	0·07	0·23	0·24	0·05	—	0·34	—	—	—	—	—	—
Cauliflower†	0·26	0·04	0·12	0·27	0·39	0·34	0·13	0·21	0·26	0·08	—	0·36	—	—	—	—	—	—
Lentils ..	0·52	0·06	0·14	0·33	0·44	0·39	0·04	0·26	0·23	0·05	—	0·35	—	—	—	—	—	—
Peas‡ ..	0·54	0·08	0·11	0·31	0·43	0·33	0·06	0·25	0·25	0·06	0·26	0·29	(0·24)	(0·54)	(1·98)	(0·38)	—	—
Potatoes†	0·33	0·12	0·09	0·28	0·29	0·31	0·10	0·26	0·23	0·08	0·18	0·32	0·26	1·07§	1·49§	0·12	0·16	0·17
Soya ..	0·46	—	0·16	0·33	0·48	0·40	0·08	0·31	0·25	0·09	0·23	0·33	0·31	0·82	1·19	0·28	0·33	0·36
Spinach†	0·28	—	0·09	0·25	0·40	0·32	0·11	0·28	0·25	0·11	—	0·32	—	—	—	—	—	—
Sprouting broccoli†	0·36	—	0·11	0·24	0·33	0·34	0·11	0·19	0·21	0·08	—	0·26	—	—	—	—	—	—
Turnip tops† ..	0·38	0·09	0·12	0·20	0·39	0·22	0·15	0·31	0·26	0·09	0·28	0·32	—	—	—	—	—	—

* Mature seeds.   † Composition appears to vary considerably.
‡ Average of immature and mature (dry) peas.   Peas appear to be very variable, figures in parenthesis are based on isolated crude protein.
§ High proportion present as glutamine and asparagine. || Includes various products, flour, meal, etc.

References to Part III

1. Ågren, G. (1949). Microbiological determinations of amino acids in foodstuffs. *Acta chem. scand.*, **3**, 931.

2. Ågren, G. (1951). Microbiological determinations of amino acids in foodstuffs. *Acta chem. scand.*, **5**, 766.

3. Albanese, A. A. (1950). *Protein and Amino Acid Requirements of Mammals.* Academic Press Inc., New York.

4. Alexander, J. C., Beckner, C. W. and Elvehjem, C. A. (1953). The alanine, cystine, glycine and serine contents of meat. *J. Nutr.*, **51**, 319.

5. *Annual Report of the National Food Survey Committee* (1957). Domestic Food Consumption and Expenditure: 1955. H.M. Stationery Office, London.

6. Bachstez, M. and Bustamente, M. S. (1955). Beiträge zur Kenntnis Mexikanischer Drogen, Pflanzen und Nahrungsmittel. XVI Mitteilung. Verteilung der Amino-säuren in essbaren Anteil der Krahbe (*Peneus setiferus, L.*), *Z. Lebensmitt Untersuch.*, **100**, 266.

7. Balasubramanian, S. C., Ramachandran, M., Viswanatha, T. and De, S. S. (1952a). Amino-acid composition of Indian foodstuffs. 1. Tryptophane, leucine, isoleucine and valine contents of some cereals. *Indian J. med. Res.*, **40**, 73.

8. Balasubramanian, S. C., Ramachandran, M., Viswanatha, T. and De, S. S. (1952b). Amino-acid composition of Indian foodstuffs. 2. Lysine, methionine, phenylalanine and histidine contents of some cereals. *Indian J. med. Res.*, **40**, 219.

9. Baptist, N. G. (1954). Essential amino-acids of some common tropical legumes and cereals. *Brit. J. Nutr.*, **8**, 218.

10. Barton-Wright, E. C. and Moran, T. (1946). The microbiological assay of amino-acids. II. The distribution of amino-acids in the wheat grain. *Analyst*, **71**, 278.

11. Baumgarten, W., Mather, A. W. and Stone, L. (1945). Glutamic acid content of feed materials. *Cereal Chem.*, **22**, 514.

12. Baumgarten, W., Mather, A. W. and Stone, L. (1946). Essential amino acid composition of feed materials. *Cereal Chem.*, **23**, 135.

13. Bergh, H. (1952). Determination of the amino acids, cystine, methionine, tyrosine and tryptophane in animal and vegetable materials. *Acta agric. Scand.*, **2**, 158.

14. Bigwood, E. J. (1953). *Present problems in nutritional research.* Verlag Birkhauser, Basle.

15. Bigwood, E. J., Crockaert, R. and Bilinski, E. (1953). Acides aminés du tissu musculaire (boeuf et veau). *Bull. Acad. roy. Med. Belg.*, **18**, 82.

16. Block, R. J. and Bolling, D. (1946). The amino acid composition of cow and human milk proteins. *Arch. Biochem.*, **10**, 359.

17. Block, R. J. and Bolling, D. (1951). *The Amino Acid Composition of Proteins and Foods.* C. C. Thomas. Springfield, Ill.

18. Block, R. J. and Bolling, D. (Unpublished). See Block, R. J. and Bolling, D. (1951).

19. Block, R. J. and Mitchell, H. H. (1946). The correlation of the amino acid composition of proteins with their nutritional value. *Nutr. Abstr. Rev.*, **16**, 249.

20. Brand, E. and Edsall, J. T. (1947). The chemistry of the proteins and amino acids. *Ann. Rev. Biochem.*, **16**, 223.

21. Bruno, D. and Carpenter, K. J. (1957). A modified procedure for the estimation of "available lysine" in food proteins. *Biochem. J.*, 67, 13P.

22. Bureau of Biological Research, Rutgers University, New Brunswick (1951). *Co-operative determination of the amino acid content, and of the nutritive value of six selected protein food sources* 1946-1950.

23. Chattergee, K. P., Ray, A. and Banerjee, S. (1956). Essential amino acid composition of pulses and rice. *Food Res.*, **21**, 569.

24. Chang, I. C. L. and Murray, H. C. (1949). Biological value of the protein and mineral, vitamin and amino acid content of soymilk and curd. *Cereal Chem.*, **26**, 297.

25. Cheung, M. W., Pratt, E. L. and Fowler, D. I. (1953). Total amino acid composition of mature human milk. *Pediatrics.*, **12**, 353.

26. Chitre, R. G., Williams, J. N. (Jr.) and Elvehjem, C. A. (1950). Nutritive value of canned foods. XLIII. A study of the protein value of young and mature peas. *J. Nutr.*, **42**, 207.

27. Deas, C. P. and Tarr, H. L. A. (1949). Amino acid composition of fishery products. *J. Fish. Res. Bd. Can.*, **7**, 513.

28. De Man, T. J. and De Heus, J. G. (1948). Het arginine en tryptophaangehalte van aardappelen en van een aantal voeder middelen. *Voeding*, **9**, 62.

29. Duncan, C. W., Watson, G. I., Dunn, K. M. and Eley, R. E. (1952). Nutritive values of crops and cow's milk as affected by soil fertility. II. The essential amino acids in colostrum and milk proteins. *J. Dairy Sci.*, **35**, 128.

30. Dunn, M. S. (1948). Unpublished, see Block, R. J. and Bolling, D. (1951).

31. Dunn, M. S., Camien, M. N., Eiduson, S. and Malin, R. B. (1949). The nutritive value of canned foods, *J. Nutr.*, **39**, 177.

32. Dunn, M. S., Camien, M. N., Malin, R. B., Murphy, E. A. and Reiner, P. J. (1949). Percentages of twelve amino acids in blood, carcass, heart, kidney, liver, muscle and skin of eight animals. *Univ. Calif. Publ. Physiol.*, **8**, 293.

33. Dunn, M. S., Camien, M. N., Shankman, S. and Block, H. (1948). Amino acids in lupine and soybean seeds and sprouts. *Arch. Biochem.*, **18**, 195.

34. Dustin, J. P., Schram, E., Moore, S. and Bigwood, E. J. (1953). Dosage chromatographique des acides aminés d'une graine de céréale (orge), d'un foin, et d'un tourteau de lin. *Bull. Soc. Chim. biol., Paris*, **35**, 1137.

35. Eastoe, J. E. (1955). The amino acid composition of mammalian collagen and gelatin. *Biochem. J.*, **61**, 589.

36. Edwards, C. H., Carter, L. P. and Outland, C. E. (1955). Cystine, tyrosine and essential amino acid contents of selected foods. *J. agric. Food Chem.*, **3**, 952.

37. Edwards, L. E., Sealock, R. R., O'Donnell, W. W., Bartlett, G. R., Barclay, M. B., Tully, R., Tybout, R. H., Box, J. and Murlin, J. R. (1946). Biological value of proteins in relation to the essential amino acids which they contain. *J. Nutr.*, **32**, 597.

38. Evans, R. J., Butts, H. A., Davidson, J. A. and Bandemer, S. L. (1949). The amino acid content of fresh and stored shell eggs. I. Leucine, isoleucine, valine, glycine, serine, threonine, aspartic acid and glutamic acid. *Poult. Sci.*, **28**, 691.

39. Evans, R. J., Davidson, J. A., Bandemer, S. L. and Butts, H. A. (1949). The amino acid content of fresh and stored shell eggs. II. Arginine, histidine, lysine, methionine, cystine, tyrosine, tryptophan, phenylalanine and proline. *Poult. Sci.*, **28**, 697.

40. Fang, S. C., Bullis, D. E. and Butts, J. S. (1953). Investigation of barcelona and du chilly filbert nuts. III. Amino acids and B-vitamin contents of oil-free filbert nut meal. *Food Res.*, **18**, 555.

41. Flynn, L. M., Zuber, M. S., Leweke, D. H., Grainger, R. B. and Hogan, A. G. (1954). Relation between protein content of corn and concentration of amino acids and nicotinic acid. *Cereal Chem.*, **31**, 217.

42. Frey, K. J. (1952). Variations in the protein and amino acid contents of different oat varieties. *Cereal Chem.*, **29**, 77.

43. Greenhut, I. T., Potter, R. L. and Elvehjem, C. A. (1947). The phenylalanine and tryptophan content of meat. *Arch. Biochem.*, **15**, 549.

44. Greenhut, I. T., Sirny, R. J. and Elvehjem, C. A. (1948). The lysine, methionine and threonine contents of meats. *J. Nutr.*, **35**, 689.

45. Greenwood, D. A., Kraybill, H. R. and Schweigert, B. S. (1951). Amino acid composition of fresh and cooked beef cuts. *J. biol. Chem.*, **193**, 23.

46. Gunness, M., Dwyer, I. M. and Stokes, J. L. (1946). Microbiological methods for the determination of amino acids. *J. biol. Chem.*, **163**, 159.

47. Harvey, D. (1956). Tables of the amino acids in foods and feeding stuffs. *Tech. Commun. Bur. Anim. Nutr., Aberd.*, No. 19.

48. Heathcote, J. G. (1950). The protein quality of oats. *Brit. J. Nutr.*, **4**, 145.

49. Henry, K. M., Kon, S. K., Lea, C. H. and White, J. C. D. (1948). Deterioration on storage of dried skim milk. *J. Dairy Res.*, **15**, 292.

50. Hepburn, F. N., Lewis, E. W. (Jr.) and Elvehjem, C. A. (1957). The amino acid content of wheat flour and bread. *Cereal Chem.*, **34**, 312.

51. Hirsch, J. S., Niles, A. D. and Kemmerer, A. R. (1952). The essential amino acid content of several vegetables. *Food Res.*, **17**, 442.

52. Hodson, A. Z. and Kreuger, G. M. (1946). Essential amino acid content of casein and fresh and processed cow's milk as determined microbiologically on hydrolysates. *Arch. Biochem.*, **10**, 55.

53. Holmes, P. (1953). The amino acid composition of certain seed proteins. *Aust. J. exp. Biol. med. Sci.*, **31**, 595.

54. Horn, M. J. and Blum, A. E. (1956). A microbiological method for determination of cystine in foods. *Cereal Chem.*, **33**, 18.

55. Horn, M. J., Blum, A. E., Gersdorff, E. F. and Warren, H. W. (1953). Sources of error in microbiological determinations of amino-acids on acid hydrolysates. *J. biol. Chem.*, **203**, 907.

56. Horn, M. J., Jones, D. B. and Blum, A. E. (1946). Microbiological determination of methionine in proteins and foods. *J. biol. Chem.*, **166**, 321.

57. Horn, M. J., Jones, D. B. and Blum, A. E. (1947a). Microbiological determination of lysine in proteins and foods. *J. biol. Chem.*, **169**, 71.

58. Horn, M. J., Jones, D. B. and Blum, A. E. (1947b). Microbiological determination of threonine in proteins and foods. *J. biol. Chem.*, **169**, 739.

59. Horn, M. J., Jones, D. B. and Blum, A. E. (1947c). Microbiological determination of valine in proteins and foods. *J. biol. Chem.*, **170**, 719.

60. Horn, M. J., Jones, D. B. and Blum, A. E. (1948a). Microbiological determination of histidine in proteins and foods. *J. biol. Chem.*, **172**, 149.

61. Horn, M. J., Jones, D. B. and Blum, A. E. (1948b). Microbiological determination of arginine in proteins and foods. *J. biol. Chem.*, **176**, 59.

62. Horn, M. J., Jones, D. B. and Blum, A. E. (1949). Microbiological determination of isoleucine in proteins and foods. *J. biol. Chem.*, **180**, 695.

63. Horn, M. J., Jones, D. B. and Blum, A. E. (1950). Methods for microbiological and chemical determinations of essential amino acids in proteins and foods. *Misc. Publ. U.S. Dep. Agric.*, No. 696.

64. Hughes, B. P. (1958). The amino-acid composition of potato protein and of cooked potato. *Brit. J. Nutr.*, **12**, 188.

65. Hughes, B. P. (1959). The amino-acid composition of three mixed diets. *Brit. J. Nutr.*, **13**, 330.

66. Jeliffe, D. B., Arroyare, G., Aguirre, F., Aguirre, A. and Scrimshaw, N. S. (1956). The amino acid composition of certain tropical pulses and cereals. *J. Trop. Med. Hyg.*, **59**, 216.

67. Jones, D. B., Caldwell, A. and Widness, K. D. (1948). Comparative growth-promoting values of the proteins of cereal grains. *J. Nutr.*, **35**, 639.

68. Kelley, E. G. and Bawn, R. R. (1953). Protein amino acid contents of vegetable leaf proteins. *J. agric. Food Chem.*, **1**, 680.

69. Kemmerer, A. R. and Acosta, R. (1949). The essential amino acid content of several vegetables. *J. Nutr.*, **38**, 527.

T

70. Kik, M. C. (1955). Influence of processing on nutritive value of milled rice. *J. agric. Food Chem.*, **3**, 606.

71. Kimura, S. (1956). Studies on Japanese foods XXIV. The amino acid composition of cereals and soybean proteins by column chromatographic analysis. *Eiyô to Shokuryô*, **9**, 75 (through *Chem. Abstr.*, 1957, **51**, *Abstr.* no. 15818 b–e).

72. Kuiken, K. A. and Lyman, C. M. (1949). Essential amino acid composition of soybean meals prepared from twenty strains of soybeans. *J. biol. Chem.*, **177**, 29.

73. Kuiken, K. A. and Lyman, C. M. (with Dieterich, S., Bradford, M. and Trant, M.) (1948). Availability of amino acids in some foods. *J. Nutr.*, **36**, 359.

74. Kuiken, K. A., Lyman, C. M. and Hale, F. (1947). The tryptophan content of meat. *J. biol. Chem.*, **171**, 561.

75. Kuiken, K. A. and Pearson, P. B. (1949). The essential amino acid (except tryptophan) content of colostrum and milk of cow and ewe. *J. Nutr.*, **39**, 167.

76. Lahiry, N. L. and Proctor, B. E. (1956). The microbiological determination of the essential amino acids in fish protein. *Food Res.*, **21**, 87.

77. Lopez-Matas, A. and Fellers, C. R. (1948). Composition and nutritive value of fresh, cooked and processed swordfish. *Food Res.*, **13**, 387.

78. Lyman, C. M., Butler, B., Moseley, O., Wood, S. and Hale, F. (1946). The methionine content of meat. *J. biol. Chem.*, **166**, 173.

79. Lyman, C. M. and Kuiken, K. A. (1949). The amino acid composition of meat and some other foods. Arginine, histidine, isoleucine, leucine, lysine, methionine, phenylalanine, threonine, tryptophan and valine. *Bull. Tex. agric. Exp. Sta.*, No. 708.

80. Lyman, C. M., Kuiken, K. A. and Hale, F. (1947a). The histidine content of meat. *J. biol. Chem.*, **171**, 233.

81. Lyman, C. M., Kuiken, K. A. and Hale, F. (1947b). The essential amino acid content of cotton seed, peanut and soybean products. *Bull. Tex. agric. Exp. Sta.*, No. 692.

82. Lyman, C. M., Kuiken, K. A. and Hale, F. (1956). Essential amino acid content of farm feeds. *J. agric. Food Chem.*, **4**, 1008.

83. Massieu, G. H., Guzman, J., Cravioto, R. O. and Calvo, J. (1949). Determination of some essential amino acids in several uncooked and cooked Mexican foodstuffs. *J. Nutr.*, **38**, 293.

84. McCance, R. A., Widdowson, E. M. and Shackleton, L. R. B. (1936). The nutritive value of fruits, vegetables, and nuts. *Spec. Rep. Ser. med. Res. Coun., Lond.*, No. 213. H.M. Stationery Office.

85. McDermott, E. E. and Pace, J. (1957). The content of amino-acids in white flour and bread. *Brit. J. Nutr.*, **11**, 446.

86. McElroy, L. N., Clandinin, D. R., Lobay, W. and Pethybridge, S. I. (1949). Nine essential amino acids in pure varieties of wheat, barley and oats. *J. Nutr.*, **37**, 329.

87. Millares, R. and Fellers, C. R. (1949). Vitamin and amino acid content of processed chicken meat products. *Food Res.*, **14**, 131.

88. Miller, R. C., Aurand, L. W. and Flach, W. R. (1950). Amino acids in high and low protein corn. *Science*, **112**, 57.

89. Miller, S. and Ruttinger, V. (1951). Essential amino acids in mature human milk. *Proc. Soc. exp. Biol., N.Y.*, **77**, 96.

90. Miller, S., Ruttinger, V., Rutledge, M. M., Frahm, R., Maurer, S., Mayer, E. Z., Kaucher, M., Macy, I. G., Pratt, J. P. and Hamil, B. M. (1950). Human milk studies. 27. Essential amino acids in human colostrum and transitional milk. *J. Nutr.*, **40**, 499.

91. Mulder, E. G. and Bakema, K. (1956). The effect of the nitrogen, phosphorus, potassium and magnesium nutrition of potato plants on the content of free amino-acids and on the amino acid composition of the protein of the tuber. *Plant & Soil*, **7**, 135.

92. Murphy, E. A. and Dunn, M. S. (1950). Nutritional value of peanut protein. *Food Res.*, **15**, 498.

93. Murphy, D. M., Kline, B. E., Robbins, R. N., Teply, L. J. and Derse, P. H. (1957). Amino acids in nine frozen vegetables. *J. agric. Food Chem.*, **5**, 608.

94. Neuberger, A. and Sanger, F. (1942). The nitrogen of the potato. *Biochem. J.*, **36**, 662.

95. Nielands, J. B., Sirny, R. J., Sohljell, I., Strong, F. M. and Elvehjem, C. A. (1949). The nutritive value of canned foods. *J. Nutr.*, **39**, 187.

96. Nunnikhoven, R. (1955). De aminozuur-sammenstelling van tarwe-eiwitten in verband met de uitmalingsgraad alsmede de instrumentatie voor kolomchromatografie. *Thesis*, *Univ. Amsterdam*.

97. Orr, M. L. and Watt, B. K. (1957). Amino acid content of foods. *U.S. Dep. Agric.*, *Home Econ. Res. Rep.*, No. 4.

98. Proctor, B. E. and Bahia, D. S. (1950). Effect of high-voltage cathode rays on amino acids in fish meal. *Food Tech.*, **4**, 357.

99. Proctor, B. E. and Lahiry, N. L. (1956). Evaluation of amino acids in fish processed by various methods. *Food Res.*, **21**, 91.

100. Raica, N., Heimann, J. and Kemmerer, A. R. (1956). Amino acid proportions in food proteins compared to proportions utilized in rat growth. *J. agric. Food Chem.*, **4**, 704·

101. Riesen, W. H., Clandinin, D. R., Elvehjem, C. A. and Cravens, W. W. (1947). Liberation of essential amino acids from raw, properly heated and overheated soybean oil meal. *J. biol. Chem.*, **167**, 143.

102. Rose, W. C. (1949). Amino acid requirements of man. *Fed. Proc.*, **8**, 546.

103. Rose, W. C. (1957). The amino acid requirements of adult man. *Nutr. Abstr. Rev.*, **27**, 631.

104. Rose, W. C., Oesterling, M. J. and Womack, M. (1948). Comparative growth on diets containing ten and nineteen amino acids, with further observations upon the role of glutamic and aspartic acids. *J. biol. Chem.*, **176**, 753.

105. Sabiston, A. R. and Kennedy, B. M. (1957). Effect of baking on the nutritive value of proteins in white bread with and without supplements of non–fat dry milk and of lysine. *Cereal Chem.*, **34**, 94.

106. Sarkar, B. C. R., Luecke, R. W., Duncan, C. W. and Eley, R. E. (with Watson, G. I. and Rykala, A. J. J.) (1949). The amino acid composition of bovine colostrum and milk. *J. Dairy Sci.*, **32**, 671.

107. Sauberlich, H. E., Chang, W. Y. and Salmon, W. D. (1953). The amino acid composition and protein content of corn as related to variety and nitrogen fertilization. *J. Nutr.*, **51**, 241.

108. Schram, E., Dustin, J. P., Moore, S. and Bigwood, E. J. (1953). Application de la chromatographie sur échanger d'ions à l'étude de la composition des aliments en acides aminés. *Analytic. chim. acta.*, **9**, 149.

109. Schram, E., Moore, S. and Bigwood, E. J. (1954). Chromatographic determination of cystine as cysteic acid. *Biochem. J.*, **57**, 33.

110. Schweigert, B. S. (1947). Unpublished. See Block, R. J. and Bolling, D. (1951).

111. Schweigert, B. S., Bennett, B. A. and Guthneck, B. T. (1951). Further studies on the amino acid composition of pork and lamb cuts. *J. biol. Chem.*, **190**, 697.

112. Schweigert, B. S., Bennett, B. A. and Guthneck, B. T. (1954). Amino acid composition of organ meats. *Food Res.*, **19**, 219.

113. Schweigert, B. S., Bennett, B. A., Guthneck, B. T., Kraybill, H. R. and Greenwood, D. A. (1949). The amino acid composition of pork and lamb cuts. *J. biol. Chem.*, **180**, 1077.

114. Schweigert, B. S., Bennett, B. A., McBride, B. H. and Guthneck, B. T. (1952). Amino acid content of processed meats. *J. Amer. diet. Ass.*, **28**, 23.

115. Schweigert, B. S., Tatman, I. E. and Elvehjem, C. A. (1945). The leucine, valine and isoleucine content of meats. *Arch. Biochem.*, **6**, 177.

116. Sirny, R. J., Greenhut, I. T. and Elvehjem, C. A. (1950). The arginine and histidine contents of meat. *J. Nutr.*, **41**, 383.

17. Slack, E. B. (1948). Nitrogenous constituents of the potato. *Nature, Lond.*, **161**, 211.

118. Snyderman, S. E., Holt, L. E. (Jr.), Norton, P. M., Smellie, F. and Boyer, A. (1957). Valine and histidine requirement of the normal infant. *Fed. Proc.*, **16**, 399.

119. Soupart, P., Moore, S. and Bigwood, E. J. (1954).   Amino acid composition of human milk.   *J. biol. Chem.*, **206**, 699.

120. Stokes, J. L., Gunnes, M., Dwyer, I. M. and Caswell, M. C. (1945).   Microbiological methods for the determination of amino acids.   *J. biol. Chem.*, **160**, 35.

121. Vijayaraghavan, P. K. and Srinivasan, P. R. (1953).   Essential amino acid composition of some common Indian pulses.   *J. Nutr.*, **51**, 261.

122. Violante, A. M., Sirny, R. J. and Elvehjem, C. A. (1952).   The aspartic acid, glutamic acid, proline and tyrosine content of meat.   *J. Nutr.*, **47**, 307.

123. Williams, H. H. (1955).   "Essential" amino acid content of animal feeds.   *Mem. Cornell agric. Exp. Sta.*, No. 337.

Index of foods

Dd. 505891 K32 5/74

ISBN 0 11 450005 3 *